Student Solutions Manual

for use with

Prepared by JOHANN BAYER
UNIVERSITY OF TORONTO

NELSON EDUCATION

NELSON EDUCATION

Student Solutions Manual
by Johann Bayer

for use with *Physics for the Life Sciences,* Second Edition
by Martin Zinke-Allmang, Ken Sills, Reza Nejat, and Eduardo Galiano-Riveros

Vice President, Editorial Higher Education:
Anne Williams

Publisher:
Paul Fam

Executive Marketing Manager:
Sean Chamberland

Technical Reviewer:
Abdelhaq Hamza

Developmental Editor:
My Editor Inc.

Senior Production Coordinator:
Ferial Suleman

Design Director:
Ken Phipps

Managing Designer:
Franca Amore

Cover Design:
Dianna Little

Cover Images:
Bongarts/Getty Images (speed skater); Eraxion/iStockphoto (brain); Exactostock/Superstock (arm); Medical RF/Superstock (leg); Eraxion/iStockphoto (active neuron)

Printer:
RR Donnelley

Printed and bound in the United Stated of America.
1 2 3 4 15 14 13 12

For more information contact Nelson Education Ltd., 1120 Birchmount Road, Toronto, Ontario, M1K 5G4. Or you can visit our Internet site at http://www.nelson.com

ISBN-13: 978-0-17-660444-8
ISBN-10: 0-17-660444-8

Table of Contents

Preface

The *Student Solutions Manual for use with Physics for the Life Sciences*, Second Edition by Zinke-Allmang/Sills/Nejat/Galiano-Riveros was prepared by Johann Bayer, University of Toronto to assist students in mastering the skills required for an understanding of physics in a life sciences environment. The importance of mastering the "basics" cannot be overemphasized. You will find that the text, *Physics for the Life Sciences*, Second Edition, has a wealth of questions to assist you.

This Student Solutions Manual contains the worked out solutions to all odd-numbered multiple-choice questions, conceptual questions, and analytical problems at the end of each chapter in your book.

Many of the questions contained in your book – and this solutions manual – have multiple parts. Working multiple problems is one very good approach to clarifying and solidifying the fundamental concepts. We suggest that your Student Solutions Manual will provide maximum benefit if you consult it after you have attempted to solve a problem.

We greatly appreciate the technical check by Abdelhaq Hamza, University of New Brunswick, on the Solutions Manual to ensure accuracy. We also appreciate the work of Rick Goulding, Memorial University, on the chapter 3 solutions.

CHAPTER ONE

Physics and the Life Sciences

MULTIPLE CHOICE QUESTIONS

Multiple Choice 1.1

Correct Answer (c). m_{brain} directly proportional to M_{body} means that b = +1 in:

$$m_{brain} = a \cdot M_{body}^{b} \quad \textbf{(1)}$$

Note that the coefficient b is the slope of the curve after the natural logarithm is taken on both sides of Eq. [1].

Multiple Choice 1.3

Correct Answer (e). The precision of each number is represented by the smaller power of ten in the number. Smaller powers of ten indicate more precise numbers. (d) is the least precise number since the smallest power of ten is 10^{11} for the last digit. (a) follows with a precision of 10^{6}, (b) with 10^{-2}, (c) with 10^{-6}, and (e) is the most precise with 10^{-18} being the smallest power of ten in the number.

CONCEPTUAL QUESTIONS

Conceptual Question 1.1

No. We build physical models to describe observations of the world around us. These observations face limitations that are then unavoidably transferred to the physical model. Upon improving on our observations, the model might still be valid, it might need corrections, or might be wrong in a fundamental way. Similarly, to build physical models we are required to make some assumptions as a starting point, these assumptions form the basis for the physical model. However, further observations might confirm or deny the initial assumptions and thus validate or invalidate the physical model. Physical models are therefore under constant revision and continued testing.

Conceptual Question 1.3

This office is roughly 4 m wide by 5 m long by 3 m high. Therefore, in m^3 the volume is 60 m^3. Since 1 m = 10^2 cm = 10^3 mm = 10^{-3} km we can express the volume of the office as 60 m^3 = 6×10^7 cm^3 = 6×10^{10} mm^3 = 6×10^{-8} km^3. Although all these values are correct expressing volumes of this order of magnitude would be simpler in m^3.

Conceptual Question 1.5

We can expect a smaller slope of the graph for the birds as compared to the mammals. A smaller slope on this log-log graph represents a smaller ratio of m_{brain} to M_{body} and thus smaller brain size relative to the size of the subjects in the class. From the data discussed in the chapter, on average and insofar as we can infer the intelligence of non-human subjects, larger brain mass to body mass ratio seems to be correlated to intelligence.

ANALYTICAL PROBLEMS

Problem 1.1

(a) 1.23×10^2

(b) 1.230×10^3

(c) 1.23000 × 104 since the last zero is significant it must be expressed

(d) 1.23×10^{-1}

(e) 1.23×10^{-3} the zeros between the decimal point and the 1 are not significant

(f) 1.23000×10^{-6} the zeros between the decimal point and the 1 are not significant, however the three zeros to the right of the 3 are significant

Problem 1.3

The product must be given to the number of significant figures of the least accurate number, that is the number with the smallest number if significant figures:

(a) 5.61×10^{-1} both numbers have three significant figures since the zeros in 0.00456 after the decimal point and before the 4 are not significant

(b) 5.61×10^2 note that the last zero in 1230 is not significant

(c) $5.6088 \times 10^0 = 5.6088$ both numbers have five significant figures

(d) $5.609 \times 10^0 = 5.609$ note that the zero in 0.01230 after the decimal point and before the 1 is not significant while the last zero is significant

Problem 1.5

Sums and differences must be given with the precision of the least precise number, where the precision is found by the smallest power of ten present in each number:

(a) 5.79×10^2 both numbers are precise to 10^0 so the result must be quoted to that precision as 579 and then expressed in scientific notation

(b) 1.23×10^3 while 0.456 is precise to 10^{-3}, 1230 is only precise to 10^1 as the last zero is not significant and the result includes significant figures up to 10^1

(c) 3.33×10^{-1} both numbers are precise to 10^{-3} so the result is 0.333 which is then written in scientific notation

(d) 3.34×10^{-1} the number 123.123 is the least precise of the two to only 10-3 so the result is 0.334 which is then written in scientific notation

Problem 1.7

My height is 165 cm or 1.65 m, written in scientific notation it is:

(a) $1.65 \text{ m} \times (10^9 \text{ nm} / 1 \text{ m}) = 1.65 \times 10^9 \text{ nm}$

(b) $1.65 \text{ m} \times (10^3 \text{ mm} / 1 \text{ m}) = 1.65 \times 10^3 \text{ mm}$

(c) $1.65 \text{ m} \times (10^2 \text{ cm} / 1 \text{ m}) = 1.65 \times 10^2 \text{ cm}$

(d) $1.65 \times 100 \text{ m} = 1.65 \text{ m}$

(e) $1.65 \text{ m} \times (1 \text{ km} / 10^3 \text{ m}) = 1.65 \times 10^{-3} \text{ km}$

Representing the length in m (d) is best suited for lengths of the order of my height.

Problem 1.9

We start with a total time of 7×10^6 s so that we can calculate:

(a) $7 \times 10^6 \text{ s} \times (1 \text{ min} / 60 \text{ s}) = 10^5 \text{ min}$

(b) $10^5 \text{ min} \times (1 \text{ h} / 60 \text{ min}) = 2 \times 10^3 \text{ h}$

(c) $2 \times 10^3 \text{ h} \times (1 \text{ day} / 24 \text{ h}) = 8 \times 10^1 \text{ day}$

(d) $8 \times 10^1 \text{ day} \times (1 \text{ year} / 365 \text{ day}) = 2 \times 10^{-1}$ year

Representing the total time as 80 days (c) or 0.2 years (d) would be well suited for times of the order of the time spent brushing your teeth.

Problem 1.11

You must be careful when converting units to any power other than one. For example, $1 \text{ s}^2 = 1 \text{ s}^2 \times (10^3 \text{ ms} / 1 \text{ s})^2 = 10^6 \text{ ms}^2$. With this in mind:

(a) $10 \text{ m/s}^2 \times (10^3 \text{ mm} / 1 \text{ m}) = 10^4 \text{ mm/s}^2$

(b) $10 \text{ m/s}^2 \times (1 \text{ s} / 10^3 \text{ ms})^2 = 10^{-5} \text{ m/ms}^2$

(c) $10 \text{ m/s}^2 \times (1 \text{ km} / 10^3 \text{ m}) \times (3600 \text{ s} / 1 \text{ h})^2 = 10^5 \text{ km/h}^2$

(d) $10 \text{ m/s}^2 \times (1 \text{ Mm} / 10^6 \text{ m}) \times [(3600 \text{ s} / 1 \text{ h}) \times (24 \times 365 \text{ h} / 1 \text{ yr})]^2 = 10^{10} \text{ Mm/yr}^2$

(e) $10 \text{ m/s}^2 \times (10^6 \text{ μm} / 1 \text{ m}) \times (1 \text{ s} / 10^3 \text{ ms})^2 = 10^1 \text{ μm/ms}^2 = 10 \text{ μm/ms}^2$

Problem 1.13

For conversion purposes, first note that $1 \text{ km} = 10^3 \text{ m} = 10^4 \text{ dm} = 10^5 \text{ cm}$, and for litres $1 \text{ L} = 10^3 \text{ cm}^3$. Furthermore, although the radius given has four significant figures, we the multiplicative factor for the volume has been approximated to 4 with only one significant figure. With these in mind:

(a) $4 \times (6378 \text{ km})^3 \times (10^5 \text{ cm} / 1 \text{ km})^3 = 1.038 \times 10^{27} \text{ cm}^3 = 10^{27} \text{ cm}^3$

(b) $4 \times (6378 \text{ km})^3 \times (10^3 \text{ m} / 1 \text{ km})^3 = 1.038 \times 10^{21} \text{ m}^3 = 10^{21} \text{ m}^3$

(c) $4 \times (6378 \text{ km})^3 = 1.038 \times 10^{11} \text{ km}^3 = 10^{11} \text{ km}^3$

(d) $4 \times (6378 \text{ km})^3 \times (10^4 \text{ dm} / 1 \text{ km})^3 = 1.038 \times 10^{24} \text{ dm}^3 = 10^{24} \text{ dm}^3$

(e) Using (a) $1.038 \times 10^{27} \text{ cm}^3 \times (1 \text{ L} / 10^3 \text{ cm}^3) = 1.038 \times 10^{24} \text{ L} = 10^{24} \text{ L}$

Problem 1.15

An equation cannot be both dimensionally correct and wrong. It is important to note that the sum or difference of two terms is dimensionally correct only if both terms have the same dimensions.

(a) Wrong. On the left-hand side we have $[A] = [L^2]$, while on the right-hand side we have $[4\pi] \times [R] = 1 \times [L]$ since 4π is a dimensionless quantity. Since $[L^2] \neq [L]$ the equation is dimensionally wrong.

(b) Wrong. On the right-hand side we have $[x_1] = [L]$ being added to $[v_1 t^2] = ([L]/[T]) \times [T^2] = [L] \times [T]$. Since $[L] \neq [L] \times [T]$, the two quantities cannot be added and the formula is dimensionally wrong.

(c) Correct. On the left-hand side we have $[V] = [L^3]$, and on the right-hand side we have $[xyz] = [L] \times [L] \times [L] = [L^3]$. Since both sides match the equation is dimensionally correct.

(d) Wrong. On the right-hand side we have $[m/2] = [T]/[2] = [T]$ being added to $[7] = 1$. Since $[T] \neq 1$, and a quantity with dimensions cannot be added to a dimensionless quantity the formula is dimensionally wrong.

Problem 1.17

From Figure 1.9 we derived the relationship:

$$m_{\text{brain}} \propto M_{\text{body}}^{0.68}$$

We can use one of the data points listed in Table 1.5 alongside the proportionality relationship to find out the mass of the brain for the pygmy sloth. I will use line 12 in the table that lists values for the mainland three-toed sloth with brain mass m_s = 15.1 g and body mass M_s = 3.121 kg. We know that the pygmy sloth has a body mass of M_p = 3 kg and we want to find its brain mass m_p. From the proportionality relationship:

$$m_s \propto M_s^{0.68} \quad \text{and} \quad m_p \propto M_p^{0.68}$$

We can then solve for m_m:

$$m_p = m_s \times \left(\frac{M_p}{M_s}\right)^{0.68}$$

$$= (15.1\,\text{g}) \times \left(\frac{3}{3.121}\right)^{0.68} = 14.7\,\text{g}$$

Thus, a mass of approximately 15 g is what we would expect for the brain of the pigmy three-toed sloth. A brain mass of 200 g would put in question the measurement for the body mass, highlight an experimental error, an anomalous sample of the species (maybe with a severe brain defect), or simply an error in the reported data or calculations (possibly by one order of magnitude).

Problem 1.19

Both the car and the cow produce the same mass, the cow producing methane, the car producing carbon dioxide. The molar mass of methane (CH_4) is 16 g/mol while the molar mass of carbon dioxide (CO_2) is 44 g/mol. This means in one gram of CH_4 you will find 1/16 mol, while in one gram of CO_2 you will find 1/44 mol. Therefore, if you have the same mass of CH_4 and CO_2, there will be 44/16 more moles of CH_4 than of CO_2. Since per mole CH_4 has 3.7 times the global warming potential of CO_2, the cow will have 3.7 × (44/16) = 10 times the global warming potential of the car.

Problem 1.21

To compare and rank the relative magnitudes we need to establish the point of comparison. Regardless of the comparison standard, the relative magnitudes and thus the ranking should come up the same. I will use the force exerted by my mother as the point of comparison and will call that force F_m. We will use the proportionality relationship:

$$F \propto \frac{M}{R^2},$$

where M is the mass of the object exerting the gravitational force, and R is the distance between that object and the baby. My mother's mass was about 70 kg and the moment I was born I was really close to my mother. The distance between our centers was probably around 10 cm.

The mass of the Moon is 7×10^{22} kg and it is at a distance of 4×10^{8} m from Earth.

So the force exerted by the Moon F_M will be related to the force exerted by my mother F_m according to:

$$\frac{F_M}{F_m} = \frac{m_M / R_M^2}{m_m / R_m^2} = \left(\frac{m_M}{m_m}\right) \times \left(\frac{R_m^2}{R_M^2}\right)$$

$$= \left(10^{21}\right) \times \left(6 \times 10^{-20}\right)$$

Thus, $F_M = 60\ F_m$.

The mass of the Sun is 2×10^{30} kg and it is at a distance of 2×10^{11} m from Earth. So the force exerted by the Sun F_S will be related to the force exerted by my mother F_m according to:

$$\frac{F_S}{F_m} = \frac{m_S / R_S^2}{m_m / R_m^2} = \left(\frac{m_S}{m_m}\right) \times \left(\frac{R_m^2}{R_S^2}\right)$$

$$= \left(3 \times 10^{28}\right) \times \left(3 \times 10^{-25}\right)$$

Thus, $F_S = 10^4\ F_m$.

The mass of Jupiter is 2×10^{27} kg and it is on average at a distance of 8×10^{11} m from Earth. So the force exerted by Jupiter F_J will be related to the force exerted by my mother F_m according to:

$$\frac{F_J}{F_m} = \frac{m_J / R_J^2}{m_m / R_m^2} = \left(\frac{m_J}{m_m}\right) \times \left(\frac{R_m^2}{R_J^2}\right).$$

$$= \left(3 \times 10^{25}\right) \times \left(2 \times 10^{-26}\right)$$

Thus, $F_J = 0.6\ F_m$.

The mass of Mars is 6×10^{23} kg and it is on average at a distance of 2×10^{11} m from Earth. So the force exerted by Mars F_{Mars} will be related to the force exerted by my mother F_m according to:

$$\frac{F_{Mars}}{F_m} = \frac{m_{Mars} / R_{Mars}^2}{m_m / R_m^2} = \left(\frac{m_{Mars}}{m_m}\right) \times \left(\frac{R_m^2}{R_{Mars}^2}\right)$$

$$= \left(10^{23}\right) \times \left(3 \times 10^{-25}\right)$$

Thus, $F_{Mars} = 0.03\ F_m$.

The correct ranking from smallest to largest is:

$$F_{Mars} < F_J < F_m < F_M < F_S$$

Problem 1.23

The current life expectancy of a human is about 70 years $\sim 2 \times 10^9$ s. Although the heart rate changes with age and with the level of activity, on average we could use the rest heart rate of an adult, which is around 70 bpm, or 70 beats per minute. Since 70 bpm = 1.2 beats/s, throughout your life your heart will beat:

$$\left(2 \times 10^9\ \text{s}\right) \times \left(1.2\ ^{\text{beats}}\!/\!_{\text{s}}\right) \cong 2 \times 10^9\ \text{beats}$$

In other words, your heart will beat about 2 billion times.

Problem 1.25

The number of grains of sand will be V_b/V_g, where V_b is the volume of the beach, and V_g is the volume of a grain of sand. Since the beach is box-shaped, $V_b = l \times w \times d$, where l is the length, w is the width, and d is the depth.

(a) Since 1 mm^3 = 1 mm^3 × (1 m / 10^3 mm)^3 = 10^{-9} m^3, with h = 4 m we have:

$$\frac{V_b}{V_g} = \frac{100\,\text{m} \times 10\,\text{m} \times 4\,\text{m}}{10^{-9}\,\text{m}^3} = 4 \times 10^{12}\text{ grains}$$

(b) Since the grains have the same volume of 10^{-9} m^3 but h = 2 m we have:

$$\frac{V_b}{V_g} = \frac{100\,\text{m} \times 10\,\text{m} \times 2\,\text{m}}{10^{-9}\,\text{m}^3} = 2 \times 10^{12}\text{ grains}$$

(c) With h = 4 m and the grains with average volume 2 mm^3 = 2 × 10^{-9} m^3 we have:

$$\frac{V_b}{V_g} = \frac{100\,\text{m} \times 10\,\text{m} \times 4\,\text{m}}{2 \times 10^{-9}\,\text{m}^3} = 2 \times 10^{12}\text{ grains}$$

From (b) to (c) we have doubled the depth of the box. Doubling one of the dimensions of the box will only double the total volume of the box. If we had instead doubled each one of the dimensions of the box, the volume would have increased by a factor of 2^3 = 8. We also doubled the total volume of a grain of sand and this therefore compensates exactly the doubling of the depth of the box and the doubling of the volume of the box. This is different from our conversions of cubed units because in the conversions all three dimensions are being converted. Therefore, the final effect is the cube of the conversion in one of the linear dimensions.

Problem 1.27

Earth is roughly a sphere of radius 6400 km. The surface area of a sphere of radius R is given by $4\pi R^2$. However, about ¾ of the surface of the Earth is covered by water. Therefore the dry surface of the Earth is an area of:

$$A_{dry} = \frac{1}{4} \times 4\pi R^2 = \pi\left(6400\,\text{km}\right)^2 \cong 10^{14}\,\text{m}^2$$

An average person is about 1.70 m tall and about 60 cm wide at the shoulders. To simplify the estimate, a coffin would then be 2 m long by 1 m wide so each dead person will take up A_{person} = 2 m^2. There is enough room to bury:

$$\frac{A_{dry}}{A_{person}} = \frac{10^{14}}{2} \cong 5 \times 10^{13}\text{ people}$$

According to an estimate done by the *Population Reference Bureau*, about 100 billion people (10^{11}) have lived and died on Earth. To the significant figures we are estimating, this number is not relevant. The current population on Earth is close to 7 billion (7 × 10^9), and according to the *United Nations* the current death rate is about 8.4 deaths per 1000 people per year. If the population on Earth remains stable at 7 billion, each year about (8.4/1000) × (7 × 10^9) = 6 × 10^7 people die. Therefore to cover the dry surface of Earth with graves we will have to wait:

$$\frac{\left(5 \times 10^{13}\text{ people}\right)}{6 \times 10^{7}\ {}^{\text{people}}\!/_{\text{yr}}} = 8 \times 10^5\text{ yr} \sim 1\,\text{Myr}$$

However, this estimate ignores the changes in birth rate as well as death rate. Both these quantities are quite hard to predict.

CHAPTER TWO

Kinematics

MULTIPLE CHOICE QUESTIONS

Multiple Choice 2.1

Correct Answer (d). The initial and final position vectors are equal so the difference will be zero. That is, the displacement is zero as calculated from Eq. [2.1]. However, the distance travelled is not zero as this takes into account the path used to travel. Using Eq. [2.2] we see that the average velocity will be zero. However, since the distance is not zero, the average speed will be non-zero and positive.

Multiple Choice 2.3

Correct Answer (c). As the child moves in a circle, her acceleration is centripetal and thus directed toward the centre of curvature. In this case, the centre of curvature is the centre of the circle made by the child and is located where the father stands.

CONCEPTUAL QUESTIONS

Conceptual Question 2.1

Yes, when the object is slowing down.

Conceptual Question 2.3

(a) At the moment the object reaches its highest altitude, its velocity is zero and its acceleration is equal to the acceleration due to gravity.

(b) Same as part (a) since the acceleration of the object is constant.

Conceptual Question 2.5

(a) Yes, because the object may change its direction without changing its speed. An example of this is uniform circular motion in.

(b) No.

Conceptual Question 2.7

(a) The same as if thrown on steady ground.

(b) The path is the projectile trajectory in the last equation of Case Study 2.1, where $v_{\text{initial},x}$ is the constant horizontal velocity of the train.

Conceptual Question 2.9

(a) Uniform circular motion

(b) Accelerated motion along a straight line with linear increase (or decrease) in speed.

Conceptual Question 2.11

The gravitational acceleration downward is smaller than the centripetal acceleration required to hold it on a circular path; as a result the bottom of the bucket has to push the water down when it is at the top of the loop. Newton’s third law then states that the water pushes the bottom of the bucket upward. Compare the water to a person on a fast roller coaster, as opposed to a slow Ferris wheel.

ANALYTICAL PROBLEMS

Problem 2.1

(a) We define the vector sum as **r**, so that we can write **r** = **a** + **b**, or, in component notation,

$$r_x = a_x + b_x = 5 + (-14) = -9$$
$$r_y = a_y + b_y = 5 + 5 = 10$$

Thus, **r** = (–9, 10) as shown in Figure 1.

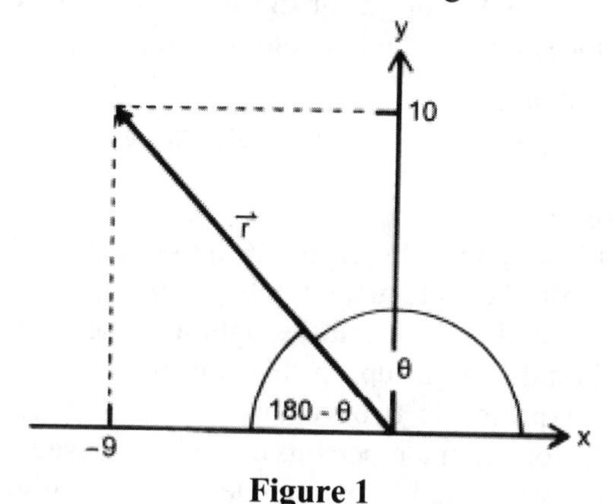

Figure 1

(b) The magnitude of vector **r** is calculated with the Pythagorean theorem:

$$|\mathbf{r}| = \sqrt{r_x^2 + r_y^2} = \sqrt{(-9)^2 + 10^2} = 13.5$$

To characterize the vector **r** in polar coordinates, its angle with the positive x–axis must also be determined. This can be done geometrically, as can be seen from Figure 1:

$$\tan\theta = \frac{r_y}{r_x} = -1.11 \quad \Rightarrow \quad \theta = 132^\circ$$

Your pocket calculator may show θ = – 48°. Take care to always draw the vector to check that your answer makes sense. To your calculator, –a/b cannot be distinguished from

a/(–b). It is the job of the person using the calculator to interpret the physical meaning of the number the calculator returns.

Problem 2.3
Using the x_1-coordinate axis the red dot is located at coordinate 3 so that $\vec{r}_1 = 3$. However, using the x_2-coordinate axis the red dot is at coordinate 1 so that $\vec{r}_2 = 1$. Note that $\vec{r}_2 = \vec{r}_1 - \vec{x}_1$, where $\vec{x}_1 = 2$ is the position vector for the origin of the x_2-coordinate axis as measured on the x_1-coordinate axis.

Problem 2.5
Using Eq. [2.2], $\vec{v}_{av} = 10.1\,\mathrm{m/s} = 36.4\,\mathrm{km/h}$.

Problem 2.7
(a) We choose the origin at the bottom of the feet of the person, with the x–axis pointing horizontal and toward the right and the y–axis pointing straight up. In this coordinate system we express the two vectors shown in Figure 2.32 for the male person, $\mathbf{d}_1$ and $\mathbf{d}_2$. Based on the given lengths (magnitudes) and the given angle we find:

$$\vec{d}_1 = \begin{pmatrix} 0 \\ |d_1| \end{pmatrix} = \begin{pmatrix} 0 \\ 150\ cm \end{pmatrix}$$
$$\vec{d}_2 = \begin{pmatrix} |d_2|\sin\theta \\ -|d_2|\cos\theta \end{pmatrix} = \begin{pmatrix} 45.9\ cm \\ -65.5\ cm \end{pmatrix} \qquad (1)$$

Note the negative sign in the y–component of the second vector! The vector from the bottom of the feet to the hand is the sum of the two vectors in Eq. [1]:

$$\vec{d}_{male} = \vec{d}_1 + \vec{d}_2 = \begin{pmatrix} 45.9\ cm \\ 84.5\ cm \end{pmatrix}$$

(b) The calculations are analogous for the female person and yield:

$$\vec{d}_{female} = \begin{pmatrix} -37.3\,cm \\ 76.8\,cm \end{pmatrix}$$

Problem 2.9
Assume that the bacterium moves along a straight line:

$$t = \frac{d}{v} = \frac{2(8.4\ \text{cm})}{3.5\ \mu\text{m/s}} = 4.8\times10^4\,\text{s} = 13.3\ \text{hr}$$

Actual bacteria move in random fashion; this type of motion is discussed in Chapter 11.

Problem 2.11
We have motion with constant acceleration in both directions. We can write Eq. [2.9] for both the x- and y-directions using the given initial position, initial velocity, and constant acceleration (all quantities in SI units):

$$\begin{aligned} x &= 2 - 3t + t^2/2 \\ y &= 3 + 2t + t^2 \end{aligned} \qquad (1)$$

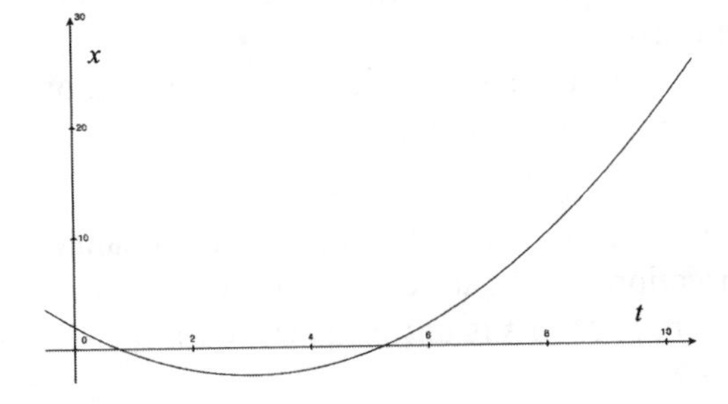

Figure 2

Graphically, both functions in Eq. [1] represent upright parabolas such that at $t = 0$ s both x and y are positive. However, while the y-t graph is increasing and does not pass by $y = 0$ m, the graph of x-t is initially decreasing and crosses $x = 0$ m at $t = 0.19$ s and later at $t = 1.31$ s.

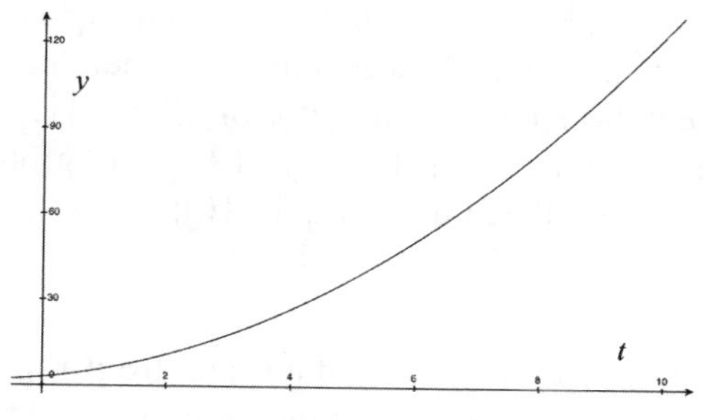

Figure 3

Furthermore, x-t is decreasing for time between $t = 0$ s and $t = 3$ s, and increasing from $t = 3$ s to $t = 10$ s. At $t = 10$ s the positions are $x = 22$ m and $y = 123$ m. In Figure 2 we have the x-t graph, while in Figure 3 we have the y-t graph.

Problem 2.13

We will assume that $t_f = 8$ s. Since there are three different accelerations we split the problem in three parts. From $t_1 = 0$ s to $t_2 = 2$ s the acceleration is $a_1 = 2$ m/s^2. Eq. [2.9] can be used to find the position x_2 at $t_2 = 2$ s after accelerating for $\Delta t = 2$ s:

$$x_2 = x_1 + v_1\Delta t + \frac{1}{2}a_1\Delta t^2 = 10\,\text{m} \quad \textbf{(1)}$$

We also need the velocity v_2 at t_2 calculated from Eq. [2.6] after $\Delta t = 2$ s:

$$v_2 = v_1 + a_1\Delta t = 1\,\text{m/s} \quad \textbf{(2)}$$

From $t_2 = 2$ s to $t_3 = 6$ s we have $a_2 = -1$ m/s^2. Eq. [2.9] gives the position x_3 at $t_3 = 6$ s, with x_2 from Eq. [1] and v_2 from Eq. [2] as the object accelerates for $\Delta t = 4$ s:

$$x_3 = x_2 + v_2\Delta t + \frac{1}{2}a_2\Delta t^2 = 6\,\text{m} \quad \textbf{(3)}$$

We also need the velocity v_3 at t_3 calculated from Eq. [2.6] after $\Delta t = 4$ s:

$$v_3 = v_2 + a_2\Delta t = -3\,\text{m/s} \quad \textbf{(4)}$$

In the last segment, from $t_3 = 6$ s to $t_f = 8$ s we have $a_3 = 2$ m/s^2. We use again Eq. [2.9] to find the position x_f at $t_f = 8$ s. We use x_3 from Eq. [3] and v_3 from Eq. [4] as the object accelerates for $\Delta t = 2$ s:

$$x_f = x_3 + v_3\Delta t + \frac{1}{2}a_3\Delta t^2 = 4\,\text{m}$$

The final x-position of the object is $x_f = 4$ m.

Problem 2.15

The average velocity is given by Eq. [2.1]. Although we do not know the initial position x_i we can find x_f in terms of x_i and calculate the average velocity:

$$\vec{v}_{av} = \frac{\vec{x}_f - \vec{x}_i}{\Delta t}, \quad \textbf{(1)}$$

for $\Delta t = 8$ s. The motion is easily divided into four segments: $\Delta t_1 = 1$ s from $t = 0$ s to $t = 1$ s and $a_1 = 2$ m/s^2, $\Delta t_2 = 2$ s from $t = 1$ s to $t = 3$ s and $a_2 = 0$ m/s^2, $\Delta t_3 = 3$ s from $t = 3$ s to $t = 6$ s and $a_3 = -1$ m/s^2, and the last interval $\Delta t_4 = 2$ s from $t = 6$ s to $t = 8$ s where $a_4 = 0$ m/s^2. From the graph we also know the initial velocities at each segment given by $v_1 = 0$ m/s, $v_2 = 2$ m/s, $v_3 = 2$ m/s, and $v_4 = -1$ m/s. We use Eq. [2.9] in segments 1 and 3 (constant acceleration), and we use Eq. [2.4] in segments 2 and 4 (constant velocity). We find after Δt_1:

$$x_1 = x_i + 1\,\text{m} \quad \textbf{(2)}$$

We use x_1 and Δt_1 to find:

$$x_2 = x_1 + 4\,\text{m} = x_i + 5\,\text{m} \quad \textbf{(3)}$$

We can now use x_2 and Δt_3 to find:

$$x_3 = x_2 + 6\,\text{m} - 4.5\,\text{m} = x_i + 6.5\,\text{m} \quad \textbf{(4)}$$

In the last step we use x_3 and Δt_4 to find:

$$x_f = x_3 - 2\,\text{m} = x_i + 4.5\,\text{m} \quad \textbf{(5)}$$

Substituting the value found in Eq. [2] into the average velocity of Eq. [1] we find:

$$\vec{v}_{av} = +\frac{4.5\,\text{m}}{8\,\text{s}} = +0.56\,\text{m/s}$$

To find the average speed we need to calculate the total distance travelled by the object. We can use the positions calculated in the previous steps to find the respective distances in each one of the segments. From Eq. [2] the distance travelled in the first segment is $d_1 = 1$ m. From Eq. [3] the distance travelled in the second segment is $d_2 = 4$ m. From Eq. [4] the distance travelled in the third segment is $d_3 = 1.5$ m. From Eq. [5] the distance travelled in the fourth segment is $d_4 = 2$ m.

The total distance travelled is Δx:

$$\Delta x = d_1 + d_2 + d_3 + d_4 = 8.5\,\text{m} \qquad \textbf{(6)}$$

The average speed is now calculated as:

$$v_{\text{av}} = \frac{\Delta x}{\Delta t} = \frac{8.5\,\text{m}}{8\,\text{s}} = 1.1\,{}^{\text{m}}\!/_{\text{s}}$$

Alternatively you can calculate the average velocity at each segment using Eq. [2.7]. To find the overall average velocity you then calculate:

$$\vec{v}_{\text{av}} = \frac{\vec{v}_{1,\text{av}}\Delta t_1 + \vec{v}_{2,\text{av}}\Delta t_2 + \vec{v}_{3,\text{av}}\Delta t_3 + \vec{v}_{4,\text{av}}\Delta t_4}{\Delta t}$$

To find the average speed, the absolute value of each average velocity is used and the same averaging calculation is carried out.

Problem Problem 2.17

We use Eq. [2.10] with $v_1 = 0$:

$$a = \frac{v_2^2 - v_1^2}{2\cdot\Delta x} = \frac{(11\text{ km/s})^2}{2\cdot(220\text{ m})} = 28000\cdot g$$

Trained humans survive 30⊕g for 1 second, 15⊕g for 5 seconds, 8⊕g for one minute, and 6⊕g for less than four minutes.

Problem 2.19

(a) We find $y_{\max}$ using Eq. [2.10] as:

$$y_{\max} = \frac{v_{\text{initial}}^2}{2\cdot g} = 31.9\text{ m}$$

(b) To reach the highest altitude it takes a time of $t = 2.55$ s. This can be calculated using the last equation in Eq. [2.12]

(c) To reach the ground after reaching the highest altitude it will take the same time as the time to reach the highest altitude, that is, a time of $t = 2.55$ s

(d) The object will hit the ground with the a speed equal to the initial speed but directed down so that $v_{\text{final}} = -25$ m/s

Problem 2.21

The time it takes for the object to fall from height h when falling from rest can be calculated using Eq. [2.9]:

$$t = \sqrt{\frac{2h}{g}} \qquad \textbf{(1)}$$

For a height $h = 4$ m the time from Eq. [1] is then $t = 0.90$ s. If we double the height, the time will increase by a factor of $\sqrt{2} = 1.41$. The speed at the instant the object hits the ground can be calculated using Eq. [2.10]:

$$v = \sqrt{2gh} \qquad \textbf{(2)}$$

For a height of $h = 4$ m the speed from Eq. [2] is then $v = 8.9$ m/s. If we increase the height by a factor of four, the speed will increase by a factor of $\sqrt{4} = 2$. If the object starts with a non-zero initial speed v_0 directed down, we can use Eq. [2.10] to find the final speed as:

$$v = \sqrt{v_0^2 + 2gh} \qquad \textbf{(3)}$$

For a height of $h = 4$ m and an initial speed of $v_0 = 1$ m/s Eq. [3] yields $v = 8.91$ m/s. If instead the initial speed is $v_0 = 2$ m/s Eq. [3] yields $v = 9.08$ m/s. We can conclude that the relationship between initial speed and final speed is clearly not linear, a fact also evident from the expression in Eq. [3].

Problem 2.23

(a) The horizontal distance is:

$$\begin{aligned} x &= (v_0\cos\theta)t \\ &= (v_0\cos\theta)\left(\frac{2(v_0\sin\theta)}{g}\right) \\ &= 7.95\,\text{m} \end{aligned}$$

(b) The maximum height reached in the jump can be calculated as:

$$y_{\max} = (v_0\sin\theta)t - \frac{1}{2}gt^2,$$

where the time t needed to reach the maximum height is given by:

$$t = \frac{v_0\sin\theta}{g}$$

Substituting the values given in the problem we find $t = 0.38$ s and $y_{\max} = 0.72$ m.

Problem 2.25

The time for football to reach goal is:

$$t = \frac{\Delta x}{v_{\text{initial}} \cdot \cos\theta} = 3.3 \text{ s}$$

The height at that instant is:

$$y = \left(v_{\text{initial}} \cdot \sin\theta\right)t - \frac{1}{2}g \cdot t^2 = -0.6 \text{ m}$$

Therefore we can conclude that the ball hits the ground before reaching the goal.

Problem 2.27

We use Eq. [2.10] in the vertical direction, where, for the elevator starting from rest $v_1 = 0\,\text{m/s}$, $v_2 = 6\,\text{m/s}$, and $y_2 - y_1 = 30\,\text{m}$:

$$a = \frac{v_2^2 - v_1^2}{2(y_2 - y_1)} = 0.60\,\text{m/s}^2$$

Problem 2.29

(a) To find the centripetal acceleration of the child we need to have the radius of the Ferris wheel (which is given) and the speed of the Ferris wheel, which we will need to determine. The period of the ride is given in the information "spins four times per minute". This means one period takes 15 s. The speed of the ride is then the total distance travelled in one period (the circumference) divided by that time, $v = 2 \cdot \pi \cdot r/t$ which yields 3.77 m/s. The centripetal acceleration is then: $a = 1.6\ \text{m/s}^2$.

(b) At the top, gravity exerts a force downward equal to the child's weight, $W = 390$ N, while the seat exerts a normal force upwards. Together these forces must sum like vectors to create a net force, which causes the centripetal acceleration found in part (a). The centripetal acceleration will point downward because the child is accelerated toward the centre of the circular path, which is downward because the child is at the top of the circle. This means:

$$F_{net} = -W + N_{top} = -m \cdot a_{\perp}$$

which yields:

$$N_{top} = 390 \text{ N} - 64 \text{ N} = 330 \text{ N}$$

At the bottom, gravity exerts a force downward equal to the child's weight (still 390 N) while the seat exerts a normal force upward. Together these forces must sum like vectors to create a net force, which causes the centripetal acceleration found in part (a). The centripetal acceleration will in this case point *upward* because the child is accelerated toward the centre of the circular path, which is upward at the bottom of the circle. This means:

$$F_{net} = -W + N_{bottom} = +m \cdot a_{\perp}$$

which yields:

$$N_{top} = 390 \text{ N} + 64 \text{ N} = 450 \text{ N}$$

Halfway between the top and the bottom, gravity will still exert a force of 390 N downward and since the child is moving with constant speed the seat must exert a normal force which balances the child's weight. The normal force must also have a component directed horizontally since the centre of the circular path is directly horizontal from the child. No component of the weight can exert a force toward the centre so the normal force must provide the entire centripetal acceleration, a horizontal component of 64 N acts toward the centre of Ferris wheel.

CHAPTER THREE

Forces

MULTIPLE CHOICE QUESTIONS

Multiple Choice 3.1

Correct Answer (e).

$$M_p = \frac{1}{2} M_E \text{ and } R_p = 2R_E$$

If the acceleration on earth and the planet are $g_E = \frac{GM_E}{R_E^2}$ and $g_P = \frac{GM_P}{R_P^2}$,

respectively, the ratio $\frac{g_P}{g_E}$ is:

$$\frac{g_P}{g_E} = \frac{\frac{GM_P}{R_P^2}}{\frac{GM_E}{R_E^2}} = \frac{M_P R_E^2}{M_E R_P^2} = \frac{\left(\frac{1}{2} M_E R_E^2\right)}{M_E\left(4R_E\right)} = \frac{1}{8}$$

$$\frac{g_P}{g_E} = \frac{\frac{GM_P}{R_P^2}}{\frac{GM_E}{R_E^2}} = \frac{M_P R_E^2}{M_E R_P^2} = \frac{\left(\frac{1}{2} M_E R_E^2\right)}{M_E\left(4R_E\right)} = \frac{1}{8}$$

$$\therefore \frac{g_P}{g_E} = \frac{1}{8}$$

$$g_p = \frac{1}{8} g_E$$

Multiple Choice 3.3

Correct Answer (c).

Multiple Choice 3.5

Correct Answer (d). The force between two charges q1 and q2 is

$$F = \frac{kq_1q_2}{r^2}$$

The force is proportional to 1/r2. That means doubling the distance quarters the force. In this problem we decrease the distance by 5 times so the force increases by 52 times.

So

$$F_2 = 25F_1 = 24 \times 3 \times 10^{-7} N = 7.2 \times 10^{-6} N$$

The multiplicative factor is 25 not 24, and the answer is (d)

Multiple Choice 3.7

Easy way: Doubling the distance reduces the force by a factor of 4. Since F is proportional to q, doubling one of the charges doubles the force.

Combining these factors effects we get a factor of

$$\frac{1}{4} \bullet 2 = \frac{1}{2}$$

so the force is reduced by a factor of 2.

Longer way:

$$m^2 = \frac{Fr^2}{G}$$

$$\text{so m} = \sqrt{\frac{Fr^2}{G}} = \sqrt{\frac{0.50N \cdot (2.00m)^2}{6.67x10^{-11} \frac{Nm^2}{kg^2}}}$$

$$= 1.73x10^5 kg$$

Let

$$F_1 = \frac{kq_1q_2}{r_1^2}$$

then

$$F_2 = \frac{k(2q_1)q_2}{(2r_1)^2} = \frac{kq_1q_2}{2r_1^2} = \frac{1}{2}F_1$$

Multiple Choice 3.9

Correct Answer (d). The strong nuclear force is about a 100 times larger than the electric force over the same distance and only acts over very short distances.

Multiple Choice 3.11

Correct Answer (b).

Multiple Choice 3.13
Correct Answer (e). The forces T and F are contact forces. If the muscles were suddenly cut the tension would disappear. Similarly, if the dumbbell were released, the force F would disappear.

Multiple Choice 3.15
Correct Answer (a). The magnitude of the force exerted by a spring stretched a distance x from it's equilibrium position is F=kx. If x is doubled then the force must be doubled.

Multiple Choice 3.17
Correct Answer (b).

CONCEPTUAL QUESTIONS

Conceptual Question 3.1
The diagrams need to be drawn
(a) Two forces: The weight and the tension
(b) The weight and the normal to the bowl (along the radius)
(c) The weight and the normal to the bowl (vertical in this case)
(d) The weight and the normal force due to the table
(e) The weight, the normal due to the incline and the tension (no friction).
In the (b) case the object is not in static equilibrium.

Conceptual Question 3.3
Correct Answer (a)

ANALYTICAL PROBLEMS

Problem 3.1
The distance between the sphere centers is 1.0 m.
The gravitational force between them is:

$$F = \frac{Gmm}{r^2} = \frac{6.67x10^{-11}\frac{Nm^2}{kg^2}\cdot 15kg\cdot 15kg}{(1.0m)^2}$$

$$= 1.50x10^{-8}N$$

If the surface of spheres are separated by 2.0 m, then r=0.5m+2.0m+0.5m=3.0m. The gravitational force between them is now:

$$F = \frac{Gmm}{r^2} = \frac{6.67x10^{-11}\frac{Nm^2}{kg^2}\cdot 15kg\cdot 15kg}{(3.0m)^2}$$

$$= 1.68x10^{-9}N$$

Problem 3.3
The gravitational force between the spheres is

$$F = \frac{Gmm}{r^2} = 0.50N.$$

Solving for the mass m, we get:

$$m^2 = \frac{Fr^2}{G}$$

$$\text{so } m = \sqrt{\frac{Fr^2}{G}} = \sqrt{\frac{0.5N\cdot(2.00m)^2}{6.67x10^{-11}\frac{Nm^2}{kg^2}}}$$

$$= 1.73x10^5 kg$$

Problem 3.5
Two charged particles of
According to Newton's third law the force is equal in magnitude and opposite in direction on each charge. The magnitude of the force is given by:

$$F = \frac{kq_1q_2}{r^2}$$

$$= \frac{9x10^9\frac{Nm^2}{c^2}\cdot 1.00x10^{-5}c\cdot 1.00x10^{-6}c}{(1.00m)^2}$$

$$= 9.00x10^3 N$$

Problem 3.7

Both the electric and gravitational force have the same 1/r2 dependance so the r2 will cancel out when we take the ration of the two forces. Also, the electric force between two protons or two electrons is the same, because protons and electrons have the same amount of charge. The ration of the electric force to the gravitational force for two masses with the same charge can be written:

$$\frac{F_E}{F_s}=\frac{\frac{ke^2}{r^2}}{\frac{Gm_1m_2}{r^2}}=\frac{ke^2}{Gm_1m_2}$$

(a) Two protons m1=m2=1.67x10-27 kg so:

$$\frac{F_E}{F_s}=\frac{ke^2}{Gm_pm_p}$$

$$=\frac{9x10^9\frac{Nm^2}{c^2}\cdot\left(1.60x10^{-19}c\right)^2}{6.67x10^{-11}\frac{Nm^2}{kg^2}\cdot\left(1.67x10^{-27}\right)^2kg^2}$$

$$=1.24x10^{36}$$

$$\therefore\frac{F_E}{F_s}==1.24x10^{36}$$

(b) Two electrons m1=m2=me= 9.11x10-31 kg so:

$$\mathrm{T}=4.6\mathrm{x}9.81+100\mathrm{x}9.81/2=535.6\ \mathrm{N}$$

$$\therefore\frac{F_E}{F_s}==4.17x10^{42}$$

(c) A proton and an electron m1=mp=1.67x10-27 kg, m2=me=9.11x10-31 kg so:

11 kg The ration is largest for the force between two electrons. The electric force will be the same in all three cases but the gravitational mass will be smallest when the produce of the masses is smallest, that is, in the force between two electrons.

Problem 3.9

The magnitude of the force will be the same but the direction will be in the opposite direction. The force will be 7.8x10-5 N in the negative y direction.

Problem 3.11

$$F_1=\frac{kq_1q_2}{r^2}$$

$$=\frac{9x10^9\frac{Nm^2}{c^2}\cdot10^{-4}c\cdot45\times10^{-6}c}{(4m)^2}$$

$$=1.62N$$

$$F_2=\frac{kq_1q_4}{r^2}$$

$$=\frac{9x10^9\frac{Nm^2}{c^2}\cdot10^{-4}c\cdot25\times10^{-6}c}{(4m)^2}$$

$$=1.41N$$

$$F_3=\frac{kq_1q_3}{r^2}$$

$$=\frac{9x10^9\frac{Nm^2}{c^2}\cdot10^{-4}c\cdot125\times10^{-6}c}{\left(\sqrt{41}m\right)^2}$$

$$=2.75N$$

These the amplitudes of the three forces acting on the charge q1.We now evaluate the components along the vertical and horizontal axes.

$$F_v=F_2-F_3\times\frac{4}{\sqrt{41}}=1.41-2.75\times\frac{4}{\sqrt{41}}=-0.3N$$

$$F_h=F_3\times\frac{5}{\sqrt{41}}-F_1=2.75\times\frac{5}{\sqrt{41}}-1.62=0.5N$$

The magnitude of the force and its direction are given by:

$$F=\sqrt{F_v^2+F_h^2}=\sqrt{34}\times10^{-1}N$$

$$\tan(\theta)=-\frac{3}{5}$$

Problem 3.13

(a) The weight of the man is W=mg, that is W=70 (kg)x9.81 (m/s2)=687 N.
(b) The normal force acting on the man is equal and opposite to his weight.
(c) The man will read 687 N in principle. However, if the scale is not calibrated properly to zero, the weight might be off by the error in calibration. Moreover, the scale has a certain accuracy that may be greater than 1 N, which in turn means that there will be a round off error.

Problem 3.15

A $480\ \mathrm{kg}$ sea lion is resting on an inclined wooden surface $40°$ above the horizontal as illustrated in Figure 1. The coefficient of static friction between the sea lion and the wooden surface is 0.96. Find (a) the normal force on the sea lion by the surface; (b) the magnitude of force of friction; and (c) the maximum force of friction between the sea lion and the wooden surface.

Figure 1

Problem 3.17

A climber is secured by a rope hanging from a rock as shown in Figure 2. Find the tension in the rope

Figure 2

$$\sum F_y = 0$$
$$T + (-mg) = 0$$
$$T = mg$$
$$= 85kg \cdot 9.8\,m/s^2$$
$$= 833N$$

The climber is in static equilibrium so $\sum \vec{F} = 0$. There are no forces to consider in the x direction. In the y direction:

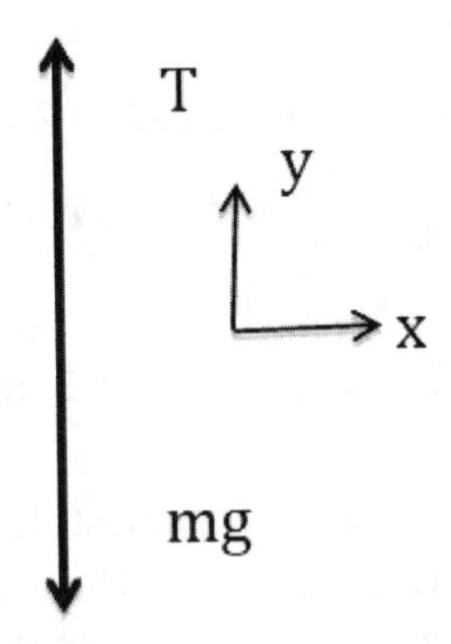

Figure 3

Problem 3.19

Casa (a):

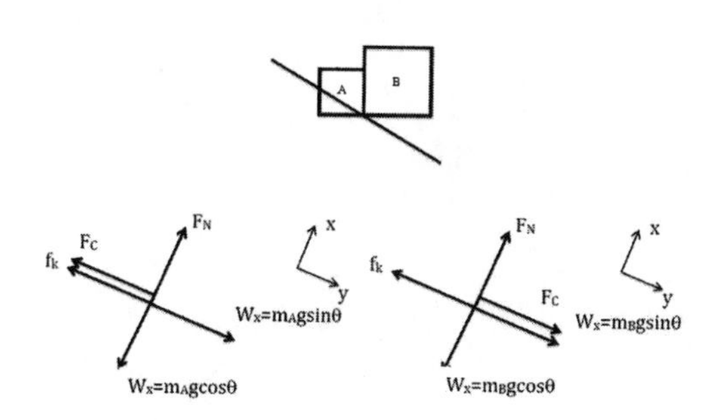

Figure 4a

Case (b):

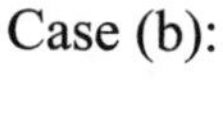

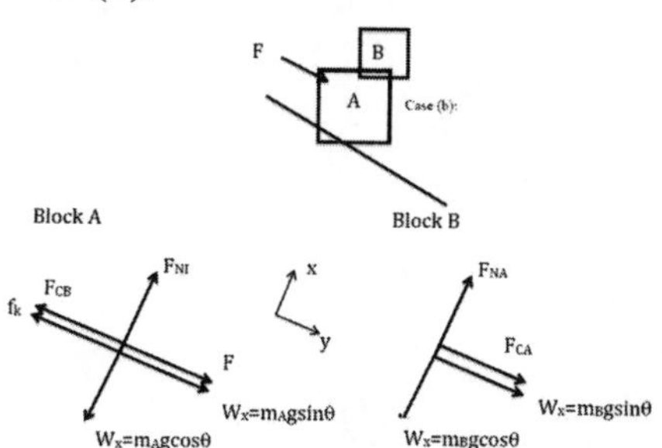

Figure 4b

In this case there are two contact forces between block A and B, one parallel to the incline FCA and one perpendicular to the incline FNA . FCA is exerted through friction so if the surfaces are smooth the top block will simply slip on the bottom block. If the surfaces are rough then as the force F is applied to block A the top block will first follow the bottom block without slipping until the maximum value of the static frictional force is reached. Then the top block B will slip on block A. There is the normal force FNA exerted by A on B and an equal and opposite force exerted FNB by B on A.

Case (c):

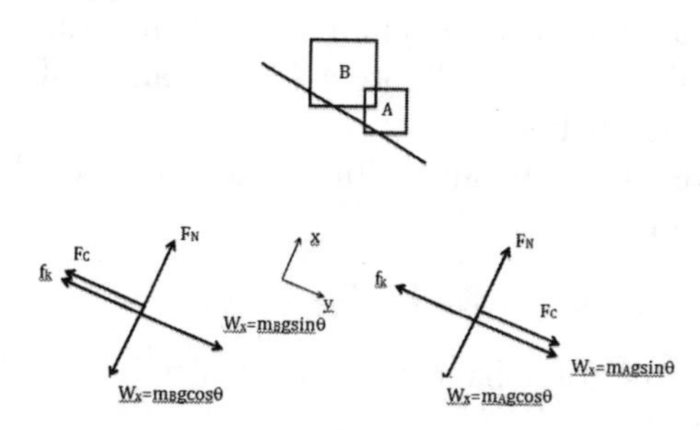

Figure 4c

Case (c) is similar to case (a). In fact the acceleration of the two block system will be the same. The main difference between the two cases is that the magnitude of the contact force will be different.

Problem 3.21

A box is lifted by a magnet suspended from the ceiling by a rope attached to the magnet as illustrated in Figure 3.46. Draw free body diagram for the box and for the magnet.

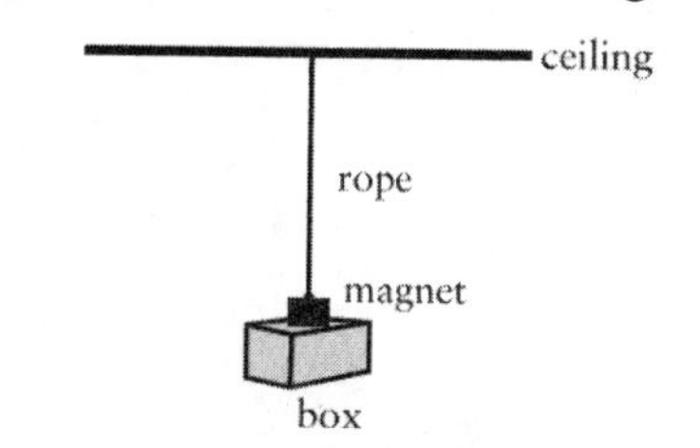

Figure 3.46

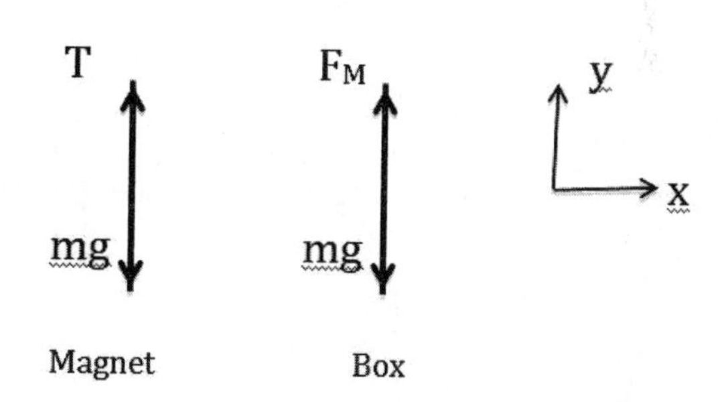

Figure 5

Problem 3.23
The freebody diagram for each arm is similar to that of figure 4.43 of example 4.25 in the textbook.
The force balance for each arm can be written as

$$T - F - F_{arm} = 0$$

and the force balance for the bar is

$$2F - W_{bar} = 0$$

combining the two equations, we find the expression for the tension on the shoulder

$$T = F_{arm} + W_{bar} / 2$$

Using the Table 4.1 we can estimate the tension

$$T = 4.6x9.81 + 100x9.81 / 2 = 535.6 \text{ N}$$

CHAPTER FOUR

Newton's Laws

MULTIPLE CHOICE QUESTIONS

Multiple Choice 4.1

Correct Answer (c). Note that (a) and (b) are indeed in translational equilibrium but the conditions described are sufficient and not necessary. The condition for translational equilibrium is described in Eq. [4.6]. Cases (d) and (e) describe objects that will be accelerating and will not satisfy Eq. [4.6].

Multiple Choice 4.3

Correct Answer (b). Only one additional force is needed, i.e., $\mathbf{F}_3 = (-F_1, -F_2)$. That one, plus the original two forces, makes for a total of three.

Multiple Choice 4.5

Correct Answer (d).

Multiple Choice 4.7

Correct Answer (a). The two forces form and action-reaction pair and thus they will have the same magnitude and opposite direction. Note that these two forces act on different objects; one force acts on the car the other force acts on the trailer.

Multiple Choice 4.9

Correct Answer (b). The scale shows the highest reading when the force made by the spring is largest. The force made by the spring is largest when the accelerating is the largest and directed upwards. Cases (c) and (e) have zero acceleration, while cases (a) and (d) have downwards acceleration. Only case (b) has an upward acceleration.

Multiple Choice 4.11

Correct Answer (d). Since the elevator is slowing down while descending the acceleration is directed up. Newton's Second Law for the person will read $N - mg = ma$, with positive directed up. The normal force exerted by the scale has magnitude of 931 N and reflects the reading on the scale. Converting to kg, the scale will read 95 kg.

Multiple Choice 4.13

Correct Answer (c). The interaction pair, or action-reaction pair, is composed of the force you exert on the desk and the force exerted by the desk on you.

Multiple Choice 4.15

Correct Answer (d). Since the skydiver has reached terminal velocity the drag will balance the gravitational force and the net force will be zero. Eq. [4.16] further illustrates this, and the drag from the wind is $R = mg = 677$ N.

Multiple Choice 4.17

Correct Answer (d). Newton's Second Law in the horizontal direction yields $N = F_{\text{App}} \cos\theta$, and we know $f_k = \mu_k N$.

Multiple Choice 4.19

Correct Answer (c). This example shows that the term "linear" has to be used with some caution. In particular, if Newton's Second Law leads to a linear equation it usually will not have a linear function as the solution $v(t)$. In the current case the horizontal equation of motion for the fish is:

$$F_{net} = -k \cdot v = m \cdot a \qquad \textbf{(1)}$$

with the weight and the buoyant force the only other forces acting on the fish, but both in the vertical direction. Eq. [1] is called a *differential equation* because the acceleration is the change of the speed with time, $a = \lim \Delta v/\Delta t$ with the limit for $\Delta t \to 0$. In differential calculus, Eq. [1] is then written as:

$$-k \cdot v = m\frac{dv}{dt} \qquad \textbf{(2)}$$

We don't discuss the solution to this equation here, but if you are interested and taking an introductory level calculus course, you should be able to use the method of separation of the variables with a subsequent integration to find the solution of Eq. [2]. However, a complete solution of Eq. [2] is not necessary to decide

whether the solution is linear. For this, we just substitute a linear solution and see whether it is consistent with this equation.
Such a linear function has the general form:

$$v(t) = a + b \cdot t \text{ ; } a \text{ and } b \text{ constant} \qquad \textbf{(3)}$$

We further note that $\Delta v/\Delta t$ for Eq. [3] leads to a constant value (slope of the linear function); i.e., $\Delta v/\Delta t = b$. Substituting this observation and Eq. [3] in Eq. [1] yields:

$$-k(a + b \cdot t) = m \cdot b \qquad \textbf{(4)}$$

We see now that Eq. [3] is not a solution to Eq. [1] because Eq. [4] is incorrect: the left hand side of the equation varies with time but the right hand side is time–independent. Choices (b) and (e) are inconsistent with Eq. [3] because the drag force becomes only zero when the fish is at rest. Choice (d) requires an infinite drag force, which could not be overcome by the fish in the first place.

Multiple Choice 4.21
Correct Answer (c). Though it is also true that the tension may not exert the same magnitude of force on both objects if the string passes over a pulley that is either massive, or not frictionless.

CONCEPTUAL QUESTIONS

Conceptual Question 4.1
No. For the object to be hanging, a vertical force directed up must exist in opposition to the gravitational force directed down. If the rope is perfectly horizontal there will be no vertical component of the tension and the object will accelerate down under the effects of gravity.

Conceptual Question 4.3
The correct free-body diagram is (E).

Conceptual Question 4.5
Provided that the angles that both forces make with respect to the horizontal are equal, case (B) may illustrate a block at rest or moving uniformly. Since the forces have equal magnitude, if the angles are equal, the horizontal components will be equal in magnitude but opposite in direction cancelling out each other. Furthermore, if the vertical component of each force is less than half of the weight of the block, then the block will remain in contact with the frictionless surface and not accelerate upward. In cases (A) and (C) there is a net horizontal force to the right, while in case (D) there is a net horizontal force to the left.

Conceptual Question 4.7
(a) No. This remains true even if we include friction. The friction force never acts in isolation.
(b) No, it only excludes that an unbalanced force acts on it. Again, this statement does not change when friction is included.

Conceptual Question 4.9
No. According to Newton's Second Law as stated in Eq. [4.8], the net force is the cause of the observed acceleration and thus the direction of the acceleration must be the same as the direction of the net force.

Conceptual Question 4.11
(a) It accelerates backward.
(b) Forward (i.e., toward the right in the figure). A muscle force across the hip interface can cause this force.
(c) **W**: The leg attracting Earth through gravitational interaction; **N**: The sole of the foot pushing down on the surface below; **F**: The leg pushing the hip upward and to the front.

Conceptual Question 4.13
(a) Both skaters push equally hard on account of Newton's Third Law; the forces from an action-reaction pair.
(b) From Newton's Second Law in Eq. [4.8], since the forces are equal, the skater with the smaller mass will accelerate the most and therefore gain a larger velocity; the acceleration is inversely proportional to the mass and larger acceleration will lead to larger velocity.

Conceptual Question 4.15

(a) Friction is caused at the microscopic level by electric interactions between atoms of the adjacent surfaces, and by the roughness of both surfaces causing interlocking of protrusions. When the two surfaces are at rest relative to each other (static friction case) both the electric and morphological surface features settle into the most stable state (which we will define as a state of minimum potential energy in Chapter 7 for mechanical systems and in Chapter 18 for electric systems). Setting the system into motion out of this state means that we separate both surfaces while in a stable state. This requires a larger force than sliding them past each other, when only a small fraction of stronger interactions form across the surface at any given time.

(b) In classical philosophy and mathematics, but rarely in scientific inquiry, statements can be verified by assuming that they are not true, then proving this assumption to be inconsistent with other observations. To demonstrate this approach, let's assume that there is a system for which $\mu_s < \mu_k$. We use Eqs. [3.8] and [3.9] to describe the resulting motion as we tilt the underlying surface to steeper and stepper angles; up to angle θ_1 the system is governed by Eq. [3.8], correctly predicting that the two objects remain at rest relative to each other. When we now tilt the surface beyond angle θ_1, Eq. [3.8] requires the two objects to move relative to each other because the threshold of the static friction force is exceeded. More specifically, the dashed force in Figure 1(a) no longer exceeds the force component W_x that points downhill, leading to an acceleration. At that moment we switch to Figure 1(b) with the kinetic friction force f_k. With our assumption above, this force will exceed the force component W_x for a range of tilt angles θ_1 to θ_2 with $\theta_2 > \theta_1$. In that interval, the motion is decelerated, i.e., the object comes to a rest. At that point, Eq. [3.8] applies again, requiring the object to accelerate. Thus, with the assumption $\mu_s < \mu_k$ we can show that Eqs. [3.8] and [3.9] become mutually contradictory in a range of angles for Figure 1. The only way to resolve this problem is to require $\mu_s \geq \mu_k$.

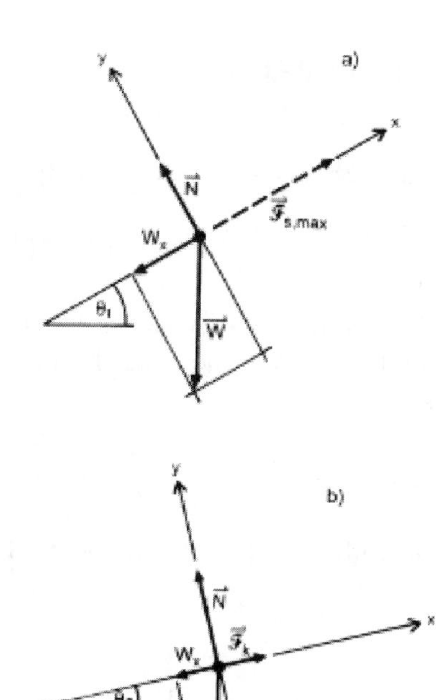

Figure 1

We compare the answers in part (a) and (b) to see why scientists don't like to use the mathematical approach of arguing: in part (a) we learn new details about friction, in part (b) we only confirm that a given fact is the case. Gathering evidence for a scientific statement allows research to proceed and new knowledge to be uncovered; in the current case we develop a greater sense of relevance of the microscopic nature of interfaces. The answer in part (b) does not allow us to learn more about the underlying principles of the phenomenon.

Conceptual Question 4.17

The third law is already included in the first law. Newton did not try to find a minimum system of laws to describe mechanical systems. His intention was to establish a set of laws that could be practically and effectively applied. Given that we are still using them hundreds of years later is testimony to the fact that he did so successfully.

ANALYTICAL PROBLEMS

Problem 4.1

(a) To find the mass we use the density:

$$\rho = \frac{1.0\ \text{g}}{1.0\ \text{cm}^3} = \frac{1.0\ \text{g}}{1.0\times10^{-6}\,\text{m}^3} = 1.0\times10^3\ \frac{\text{kg}}{\text{m}^3}$$

Thus, the mass of 1 m^3 of water is 1000 kg.
(b) To find the mass of the water in the bacterium:

$$m = \rho\cdot V = \rho\cdot\frac{4}{3}\pi\cdot r^3 = \frac{\rho}{6}\pi\cdot d^3 \qquad \textbf{(1)}$$

with r the radius and d the diameter. Eq. [1] yields:

$$m_{\text{bacterium}} = 0.98\cdot\frac{1000\dfrac{\text{kg}}{\text{m}^3}}{6}\pi\cdot(1.0\ \mu\text{m})^3$$

which results in $m_{\text{bacterium}} = 5\times10^{-16}$ kg.
(c) The mass of the fly is:

$$m = \rho\cdot V = \rho\cdot\pi\cdot r^2\cdot l$$
$$= \left(1000\frac{\text{kg}}{\text{m}^3}\right)\pi(1\text{mm})^2(4\text{mm})$$
$$= 1.3\times10^{-5}\text{kg} = 0.013\ \text{g}$$

Problem 4.3

If the airplane is in level flight at constant speed it must be in equilibrium. An upward lift force balances the downward weight of the airplane. The lift is generated by the exchange of *momentum* (see Chapter 5), between the airplane and the air, due to the motion of the airplane through the air at a specific *angle of attack*. In other words, since the wings of the airplane deflect the air by exerting a force directed down, the air exerts a reaction force on the wings directed up. In the horizontal direction, the drag from the wind is balanced by the airplane's thrust. The engine of the airplane pushes exhaust materials in one direction and due to Newton's Third Law the exhaust materials push the airplane in the opposite direction generating the force we call thrust. A diagram of this simplified model will identify four forces: the weight directed down, the lift directed up, the thrust directed forward and the drag directed backward. This is a very simplified description of a more complex situation that involves the motion of the airplane through a fluid. We will study fluids in later chapters.

Problem 4.5

(a) The object of interest is the bird while sailing without flapping its wings. Four forces are involved in flight: thrust and drag in the horizontal direction, lift and weight in the vertical direction. To achieve flight at constant speed, the thrust must compensate the drag force. In the current problem, we are interested in leveled flight, which requires that the lift force compensate the weight. The free–body diagram in the vertical direction has F_{lift} straight up and W straight down. Leveled flight implies that no vertical acceleration occurs, thus:

$$F_{lift} - W = 0$$

in which we have chosen the direction up as the positive axis. The weight is entered as a negative value as it is directed downward. Substituting the magnitude of the weight as $W = m\cdot g$ with m the given mass of a Franklin's gull, we find:

$$F_{lift} = m\cdot g = (0.28\ \text{kg})\left(9.8\frac{\text{m}}{\text{s}^2}\right) = 2.74\ \text{N} \qquad \textbf{(1)}$$

Note that the mass of the bird has been used in standard unit kg. This is necessary because the standard unit of the resulting force, N, contains the unit kg not g.
(b) The only difference in part (b) is the much larger mass of the American white pelican. Rewriting Eq. [1] with the mass of the pelican, we find F_{lift} = 68.6 N. Thus, a pelican needs a 25-fold higher lift force to sail than the small gull.

Problem 4.7

(a) The frictionless surface is a part of the environment. Object 1 is the object of (primary) interest as all forces named in the problem act on it. Thus, we choose it as the system. This leaves open what role object 2 plays. It could either be part of the environment or it could be a second system. The difference is that we need to develop a free–body diagram for a system but not for a component of the environment. It is fair at this point to choose either role for object 2. However, if you choose to consider object 2 to be part of the environment you may have to come back and change that choice. If you choose object 2 to be a second system and this is not necessary, you invest some superfluous effort, however without adversely affecting your ability to solve the problem. As it turns out, in the current case we have to identify object 2 as a second system, because we need some formulas derived from its free–body diagram to solve the problem. Consequently, several of the following steps have to be done twice, once for object 1 and once for object 2. There are four forces acting on object 1, its weight, a normal force upward due to the contact with the frictionless surface, the external contact force **F** toward the right, and the interaction force (also a contact force) between the two objects, $\mathbf{f}_1$. This force is directed toward the left as it is exerted by object 2 on object 1. Only the two anti–parallel forces **F** and $\mathbf{f}_1$ are considered further because we are exclusively interested in effects along the horizontal surface. Three forces act on object 2. These are its weight, the normal force due to the frictionless surface and the interaction force between the two objects, $\mathbf{f}_2$. Newton's third law relates the magnitudes of the two forces $\mathbf{f}_1$ and $\mathbf{f}_2$ to each other:

$$f_1 = f_2 \qquad \textbf{(1)}$$

These two forces point in opposite directions.

f₁ F m₁ f₂ m₂

Figure 2

The free–body diagrams for objects 1 and 2 are shown in Figure 2. We choose in both cases the positive axis toward the right. An acceleration is observed along this axis. Thus, Newton's second law applies. We use Figure 4 to apply Newton's law to each system. For simplicity, we drop the indices of forces $\mathbf{f}_1$ and $\mathbf{f}_2$, rewriting Eq. [1] in the form $f_1 = f_2 = f$. This yields:

$$\begin{aligned} \textit{system } 1: &\quad F - f = m_1 \cdot a \\ \textit{system } 2: &\quad f = m_2 \cdot a \end{aligned} \qquad \textbf{(2)}$$

Note that the same acceleration a is assumed. This is justified because the two blocks always move together. Using the second formula in Eq. [2] to eliminate the acceleration a in the first formula, we find:

$$a = \frac{f}{m_2} \quad \Rightarrow \quad F - f = \frac{m_1}{m_2} f \qquad \textbf{(3)}$$

$$f = \frac{F \cdot m_2}{m_1 + m_2} = 1.0\ \text{N}$$

(b) In this part the same reasoning applies, except that the force **F** is this time applied to object 2 (i.e., objects 1 and 2 change places in the free–body diagrams of Figure 2). Following this approach, we find instead of Eq. [3]:

$$f = F \frac{m_1}{m_1 + m_2} = 2.0\ N$$

Why is the force in part (b) different in spite of the fact that the two bodies have the same acceleration a? The force **f** is responsible for accelerating the object on which the external force **F** does not act. In the second case the force **f** must accelerate the more massive object, and therefore, must be larger.

Problem 4.9

Even if there are several distinct objects present in a problem, it is not always necessary to treat them as separate systems. This problem is an example of this: we initially choose to treat the two connected objects together as a single system, and only in part (b) choose as system one of the objects separately.

(a) Since the two objects are connected with a taut, massless string, they must move and accelerate together, which enables us to treat both objects as a single system. The external force is the only horizontal force acting on this system. We don't study forces in the vertical direction because the problem is confined to the horizontal direction. For a single force we do not need to draw a free–body diagram. We define the positive *x*–axis in the direction of the external force. As an acceleration is explicitly mentioned, this problem is an application of Newton's second law. It reads for the *x*–component of the force:

$$F_{ext} = (m_1 + m_2)a$$

which yields for the magnitude of the acceleration **a**:

$$a = \frac{50\text{ N}}{(10\text{ kg}) + (20\text{ kg})} = 1.67\frac{\text{m}}{\text{s}^2}$$

(b) We obtained in part (a) no information regarding the tension in the string between the objects. Therefore, the definition of the system must now be modified: we consider object 1 as the system and object 2 as part of its environment to solve for the tension **T**. This case leads again to a simple free–body diagram as the tension is the only horizontal force that acts on object 1. Keeping the same *x*–axis as in part (a), Newton's second law is written in the form:

$$T = m_1 \cdot a$$

which yields:

$$T = (10\text{ kg})\left(1.67\frac{\text{m}}{\text{s}^2}\right) = 16.7\text{ N}$$

Problem 4.11

The object shown as a rectangular box on the inclined plane in Figure 4.55 is the system; the inclined plane is part of the environment. Three forces act on the system: its weight, the external force and the normal force due to the contact with the inclined surface. Note that the normal force acts perpendicularly to the underlying surface, i.e., in this problem the normal force is not opposite to the weight! The free–body diagram is shown in Figure 3. The angle between the weight **W** and the negative *x*–axis is labelled $90^0 - \theta$. Make sure you understand why that angle is correct. We choose the coordinate system as shown in Figure 6. Remember, when an inclined plane is part of a problem, it is advisable to choose one axis to be directed along the inclined plane. This problem is an application of Newton's first law since the object does not accelerate along the inclined surface. Using Figure 3, the following two equations are derived for the *x*– and the *y*–components of the net force:

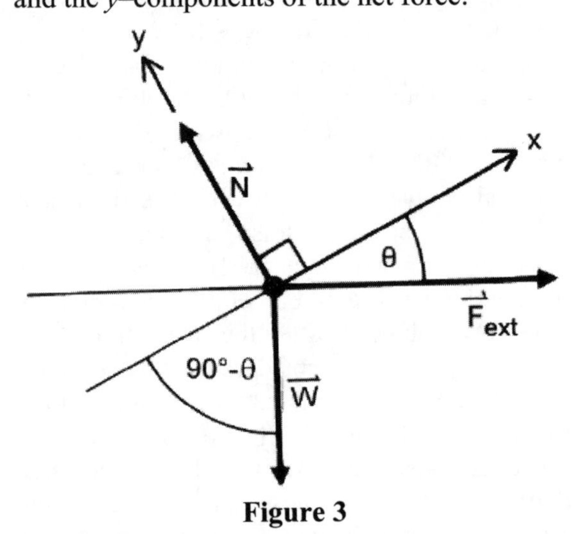

Figure 3

(1)

$$x-direction:$$

$$F_{ext}\cos\theta - W\ \cos\left(90^0 - \theta\right) = 0$$

$$y-direction:$$

$$N - F_{ext}\sin\theta - W\ \sin\left(90^0 - \theta\right) = 0$$

(a) The magnitude of the external force is obtained from the first formula in Eq. [1]:

$$F_{ext} = \frac{W \cos 50^0}{\cos 40^0} = 617 \text{ N} \qquad \textbf{(2)}$$

where $\theta = 40^0$, $90^0 - \theta = 50^0$ and the weight is:

$$W = Mg = (75 \text{ kg})(9.8 \text{ m/s}^2) = 735 \text{ N}$$

(b) The force exerted by the inclined plane is the normal force. Substituting the result of Eq. [2] into the second formula in Eq. [1], we find:

$$N = F_{ext} \sin 40^0 + W \sin 50^0 = 960 \text{ N}$$

Problem 4.13

The system is the standard man. Four forces act on the person: the body weight **W**, the normal force due to the

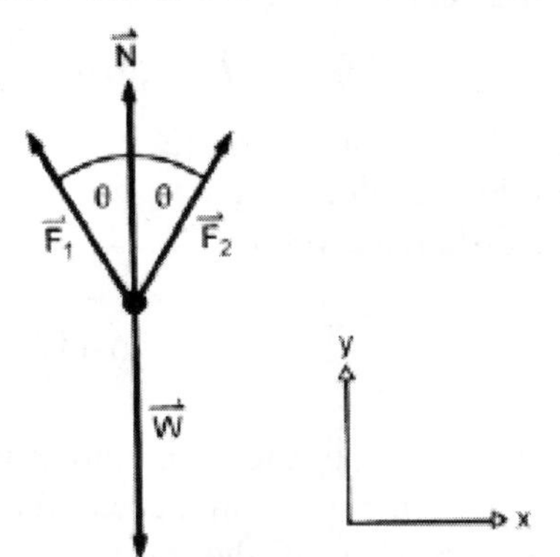

Figure 4

ground **N**, and two contact forces each along the crutches. We label these $\mathbf{F_1}$ and $\mathbf{F_2}$. The free–body diagram is shown in Figure 4. Note the directions of $\mathbf{F_1}$ and $\mathbf{F_2}$: these forces are shown in the direction in which they act on the person, i.e., $\mathbf{F_1}$ is due to the crutch shown in Figure 4.57 at the right. Figure 4 shows also the chosen coordinate system with a horizontal *x*– and a vertical *y*–axis. The problem is an application of Newton's first law because the person does not accelerate in any direction. This leads to the following two formulas for the *x*– and *y*–components of the net force:

$$\begin{aligned} &x - direction: \\ &\quad -F_1 \sin\theta + F_2 \sin\theta = 0 \\ &y - direction: \\ &\quad F_1 \cos\theta + F_2 \cos\theta + N - W = 0 \end{aligned} \qquad \textbf{(1)}$$

From the first formula in Eq. [1] we find $F_1 = F_2$, consistent with our intuition due to the symmetry in Figure 4.57. We call this force magnitude F without an index because the two magnitudes are the same. We further know that $N = W/2$ because the problem text states that half the weight of the person is supported by the normal force. Substituting these two findings in the second formula of Eq. [1] we get:

$$2 \cdot F \cos\theta - \frac{W}{2} = 0 \qquad \textbf{(2)}$$

Substituting the given values in Eq. [2] allows us to calculate the magnitude F:

$$F = \frac{W}{4 \cos\theta} = \frac{(70 \text{ kg})\left(9.8 \frac{\text{m}}{\text{s}^2}\right)}{4 \cos 25^0} = 189 \text{ N}$$

Problem 4.15

(a) The net force is: $F_{net} = m \cdot a = 12$ N.
(b) The acceleration is: $a = F_{net}/M = 3 \text{ m/s}^2$.

Problem 4.17

The mechanical equilibrium in the horizontal direction yields:

$$m_2 \cdot g \cdot \cos\theta - m_1 \cdot g \cdot \cos\varphi = 0$$

and in the vertical direction:

$$m_2 \cdot g \cdot \sin\theta + m_1 \cdot g \cdot \sin\varphi - W_{leg} = 0$$

This yields: $\theta = 61.4^0$ and $W_2 = 172.5$ N.

Problem 4.19

Throughout the problem we will use positive up and to the right while keeping in mind that all parts of the system are in equilibrium. Newton's Second Law applied to the hanging weight yields for the tension T in the rope:

$$T = W = 36 \text{N} \qquad \textbf{(1)}$$

(a) Assuming the rope and pulleys are all ideal, the tension in the rope is the same at all points. This means that at the pulley part of the apparatus that is attached to the foot, the vertical components of the tension cancel out. Therefore, the vertical component of F_{ap} is the vertical force supporting the leg so that:

$$F_{ap,y} = T \qquad \textbf{(2)}$$

The horizontal component of F_{ap} is the net horizontal force at the foot, so that:

$$F_{ap,x} = 2T\cos\theta \qquad \textbf{(3)}$$

Combining Eq. [1], Eq. [2], Eq. [3] and the given angle of $\theta = 30°$ we obtain:

$$\begin{aligned} F_{ap} &= \sqrt{F^2_{ap,x} + F^2_{ap,y}} \\ &= \sqrt{4T^2\cos^2\theta + T^2} = 72\,\text{N} \end{aligned} \qquad \textbf{(4)}$$

(b) The horizontal component of the traction force acting on the leg is given by Eq. [3] and has a magnitude of:

$$F_{ap,x} = 2T\cos\theta = 62\,\text{N} \qquad \textbf{(5)}$$

(c) If the leg has a weight of 36 N, this weight will balance the vertical component of the applied force in Eq. [2] so that:

$$\begin{aligned} \left(\vec{F}_{ap} + \vec{F}_g\right)_y &= 0 \\ \left(\vec{F}_{ap} + \vec{F}_g\right)_x &= F_{ap,x} = 62\,\text{N} \end{aligned} \qquad \textbf{(6)}$$

From Eq. [6] the magnitude of the resultant force $F_{ap} + F_g$ is 62 N.

(d) Since the leg is in equilibrium, the femur exerts on it a horizontal force that balances the resultant of $F_{ap} + F_g$ as found in Eq. [6]. Therefore, the force that the leg exerts on the femur has equal magnitude and thus $F_c = 62$ N.

Problem 4.21

We assume that the height is sufficient for the skydiver to reach his terminal speed. When the skydiver reaches his terminal velocity the drag force will have balanced his weight. This was calculated in Eq. [4.16]:

$$R = mg = 735\,\text{N}$$

Problem 4.23

(a) We can use Eq. [4.14] to find the horizontal acceleration of the sprinter:

$$\begin{aligned} a &= \frac{F_N\cos\alpha}{m} = \frac{(820\,\text{N})(\cos 21°)}{63\,\text{kg}} \\ &= 12.2\,\text{m/s}^2 \end{aligned} \qquad \textbf{(1)}$$

(b) We can use kinematics to find the speed with which she leaves the starting block, staring from rest (see Eq. [2.6]):

$$\begin{aligned} v &= v_0 + at \\ &= (0\,\text{m/s}) + (12.2\,\text{m/s}^2)(0.4\,\text{s}) \\ &= 4.9\,\text{m/s} \end{aligned}$$

Problem 4.25

(a) In her reaction time of 2 s she moves a further distance of:

$$\begin{aligned} d &= vt \\ &= (80.0\,\text{km/h})(2\,\text{s}) = 44.4\,\text{m} \end{aligned}$$

The breaking distance available to avoid hitting the deer is then:

$$x = 200\,\text{m} - d = 156\,\text{m} \qquad \textbf{(1)}$$

We use kinematics (Eq. [2.10]) to find the acceleration needed to go from 80.0 km/h to rest in a distance given by Eq. [1]:

$$a = \frac{v_f^2 - v_0^2}{2x} = -1.59\,\text{m/s}^2 \qquad \textbf{(2)}$$

Note that the sign of the acceleration in Eq. [2] is negative indicating an acceleration in the opposite direction of the initial velocity, as expected for the car to slow down. In all our calculations, make sure to convert the given speed in km/h to m/s.

(b) The normal force from the road on the car is given by $N = mg$, so that the kinetic friction force between the sliding tires and the ground is $f_k = \mu_k mg$. Choosing positive in the direction of the initial velocity of the car we can use Newton's Second Law to write:

$$\begin{aligned} -f_k &= ma \\ -\mu_k mg &= ma \end{aligned} \qquad \textbf{(3)}$$

Solving for the coefficient of kinetic friction in Eq. [3] and substituting the value previously found for a in Eq. [2] yields:

$$\mu_k = -\frac{a}{g} = 0.16$$

Problem 4.27

We use Eq. [4.15] for the air resistance:

$$R = \frac{D}{2}\rho \cdot A \cdot v_{system}^2 \quad \textbf{(1)}$$

and Eq. [3.9] for the combined friction effect:

$$f_k = \mu_k \cdot N \quad \textbf{(2)}$$

The information given in the problem text allows us to circumvent the coefficient for kinetic friction. A 1 % slope means that the road drops by 1 m for every 100 m length, i.e., the road has an angle of θ with tanθ = 1/100. At this small angle we use the approximation that tanθ = sinθ = θ and cosθ = 1. Figure 4.36 can be used again in this case, this time with N = W (because cosθ = 1) and $\mathbf{F}_k = W \sin\theta = 0.01 \cdot W$ due to the mechanical equilibrium that applies along the direction of the inclined surface. We set Eqs. [1] and [2] equal to find the speed at which the two resistance forces match each other:

$$R = \frac{D}{2}\rho \cdot A \cdot v_{system}^2 = 0.01 \cdot w = f_k$$

This yields the speed of the system (if we neglect the mass of the bicycle and use 70 kg for the standard man):

$$v_{system} = \sqrt{\frac{2 \cdot 0.01 \cdot W}{D \cdot \rho \cdot A}} = \sqrt{\frac{0.02(70\,\text{kg})\left(9.8\frac{\text{m}}{\text{s}^2}\right)}{0.5\left(1.2\frac{\text{kg}}{\text{m}^3}\right)\left(0.5\text{m}^2\right)}} = 6.76\frac{\text{m}}{\text{s}} = 24.3\frac{\text{km}}{\text{h}}$$

At speeds below 24 km/h the friction on the road and in the axles dominates, at speeds above 25 km/h the air resistance dominates due to the v^2 term in the air drag formula, Eq. [39]. Note that this is the relative speed between the bicycle and the air. Thus, a 25 km/h head wind will dominate the cyclist's motion even if the bicycle is moving very slowly with respect to the ground.

Problem 4.29

For m_1 the kinetic friction is $f_k = \mu_k \cdot \text{N} = (0.3) \cdot (98\ \text{N}) = 29\ \text{N}$. The tension acting on m_1 is T. For m_2, the same tension acts upward, and its weight is:

$$W_2 = m_2 \cdot g = (4\ \text{kg}) \cdot (9.8\frac{\text{m}}{\text{s}^2}) = 39\text{N}$$

It acts downward. Newton's laws in the direction of the acceleration are:

$$T - f_k = m_1 \cdot a$$
$$-T + W_2 = m_2 \cdot a$$

which yields:

$$a = \frac{W_2 - f_k}{m_1 + m_2} = \frac{39\text{N} - 29\text{N}}{10\ \text{kg} + 4\ \text{kg}} = 0.7\frac{\text{m}}{\text{s}^2}$$

Problem 4.31

We chose positive to the right and up. Using the vertical equations of motion for each mass, since they remain in contact with the surface we find that:

$$N_1 = m_1 g \qquad N_2 = m_2 g \quad \textbf{(1)}$$

Using the normal forces in Eq. [1] we find the friction forces acting on each of the crates:

$$f_1 = \mu_k N_1 = \mu_k m_1 g \qquad f_2 = \mu_k N_2 = \mu_k m_2 g \quad \textbf{(2)}$$

Newton's Second Law in the horizontal direction for m_1 yields:

$$\sum F_{x,1} = T - f_1 = m_1 a_1 \quad \textbf{(3)}$$

Newton's Second Law in the horizontal direction for m_2 yields:

$$\sum F_{x,2} = F - T - f_2 = m_2 a_2 \quad \textbf{(4)}$$

Since the string connecting the two masses is ideal the accelerations of both crates must be the same so $a_1 = a_2 = a$, and Eq. [3] yields:

$$a = \frac{T}{m_1} - \frac{f_1}{m_1} \quad \textbf{(5)}$$

Substituting Eq. [5] into Eq. [4] we find:

$$\frac{F}{m_2} - \frac{T}{m_2} - \frac{f_2}{m_2} = \frac{T}{m_1} - \frac{f_1}{m_1} \qquad \textbf{(6)}$$

Substituting f_1 and f_2 from Eq. [2] into Eq. [6] and reorganizing terms we find:

$$\frac{F}{m_2} - \frac{T}{m_2} - \cancel{\mu_k g} = \frac{T}{m_1} - \cancel{\mu_k g} \qquad \textbf{(7)}$$

Solving for T in Eq. [7] and using the given values from the problem we find:

$$T = \left(\frac{m_1}{m_1 + m_2} \right) F = 38.4\,\text{N}$$

Note that this result is independent of the coefficient of kinetic friction as long as it is the same for both crates, as illustrated by the cancellation in Eq. [7].

Problem 4.33

We set the positive y-axis as vertically up. Newton's Second Law for the box under the maximum tension before the string breaks yields the maximum positive acceleration:

$$T_{max} - mg = ma_{max} \qquad \textbf{(1)}$$

Solving Eq. [1] for a_{max} and using the given data we find:

$$a_{max} = \frac{T_{max}}{m} - g = 0.82\,\text{m/s}^2$$

If the elevator descends at a_{max} the tension in the string will obey:

$$T - mg = -ma_{max},$$

and solving for T we find:

$$T = m(g - a_{max}) = 233.5\,\text{N}$$

Since this is less than 276.1 N, the string will not break and will continue to hold the box.

CHAPTER FIVE

Centre of Mass and Linear Momentum

MULTIPLE CHOICE QUESTIONS

Multiple Choice 5.1

Correct Answer (a).

Multiple Choice 5.3

Correct Answer (a). The raven's linear momentum is $p_{\text{raven}} = 0.24$ kg · m/s and the sparrow's is $p_{\text{sparrow}} = 0.23$ kg · m/s. Let's assume that the window withstands the impact and that the collisions occur over the same amount of time. In an inelastic collision, linear momentum is reduced to zero during the collision if the window panel withstands the impact. That means that the raven exerts the larger force, though only slightly larger than the sparrow. If the collision is not inelastic, the momentum change is even greater as the birds bounce back. The respective forces are proportional to the linear momentum changes.

Multiple Choice 5.5

Correct Answer (f). We exert an unbalanced external force on the system, thus its centre of mass must accelerate. This acceleration can be the result of just one object's motion relative to the others. Inspect Eqs. [5.12] and [5.13] to rule out the first five choices given.

CONCEPTUAL QUESTIONS

Conceptual Question 5.1

N_2 in room temperature air moves with an average speed (root–mean–square speed) of $v_{\text{rms}} = 515$ m/s (compare with Example 8.7).

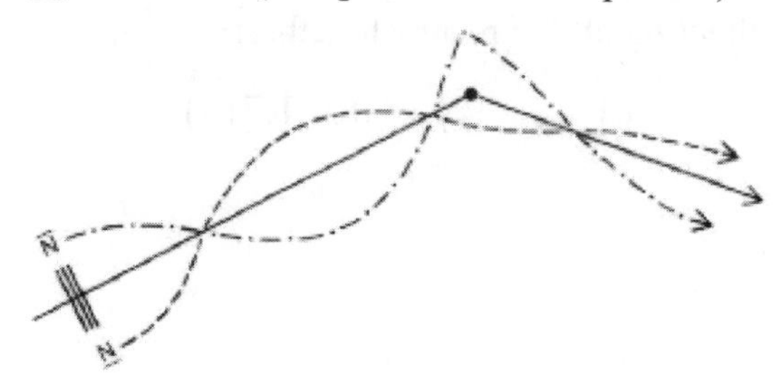

Figure 1

This value is a translational speed, i.e., a speed along a straight paths. Neglecting vibrations, the nitrogen molecule can rotate during its translational motion in any possible orientation. When we superimpose a rotation on a motion along a straight line, a wiggle line results as shown in Figure 1. However, Eq. [5.13] states that the centre of mass for a system of particles moves along a straight line unless external forces act on the system. A gas molecule can be modelled as free of external forces between collisions; thus, the centre of mass position of a nitrogen molecule moves exactly along a straight line.

Conceptual Question 5.3

No. Note that you are not an isolated system. You interact with the surface of Earth; it takes up the same momentum in the opposite direction. Due to Earth's huge mass, its change in speed is negligible.

Conceptual Question 5.5

Conceptual answer: Draw a dashed line at 45^0 with the horizontal. The problem is symmetric to this line, i.e., the combined object will move after the collision along the dashed line toward the lower left.

Quantitative answer: We start with Eq. [5.18]:

$$m_1 \cdot \mathrm{v}_1 + m_2 \cdot \mathrm{v}_2 = const$$

which is written for a perfect inelastic collision with $\mathbf{v}_{\text{final}}$ the final velocity:

$$m_1 \cdot \mathrm{v}_1 + m_2 \cdot \mathrm{v}_2 = (m_1 + m_2)\mathrm{v}_{\text{final}}$$

Using $m_1 = m_2 = m$ and $v_{1,\,y} = v_{2,\,x} = -\,v$ we find in component form:

$$(I) \qquad -m \cdot v = 2 \cdot m \cdot v_{final,x}$$

$$(II) \qquad -m \cdot v = 2 \cdot m \cdot v_{final,y}$$

from which we find $v_{\text{final, x}} = v_{\text{final, y}} = -\,v/2$. Thus, the final speed v_{final} is:

$$v_{final} = \sqrt{v_{final,\,x}^2 + v_{final,\,y}^2}$$

$$= \sqrt{2\frac{v^2}{4}} = \sqrt{2}v$$

The direction is expressed as the angle θ of the final velocity with the positive x–axis:

$$\frac{v_{final,y}}{v_{final,x}} = \frac{-v}{-v} = \tan\theta = 1$$

i.e., θ = 225^0. This angle exceeds 90^0 because both components of the final velocity are negative, as illustrated in Figure 2. The value θ represents the angle with the positive x–axis in a counter–clockwise fashion.

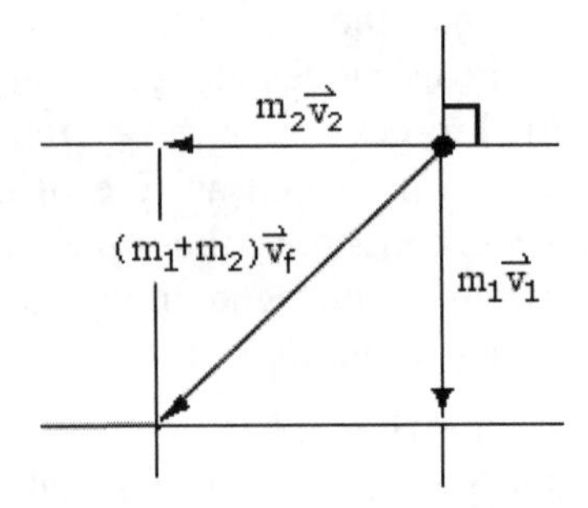

Figure 2

ANALYTICAL PROBLEMS

Problem 5.1

(a) We can use Eq. [5.3] for the centre of mass between two bodies. Measuring distances from the daughter:

$$x_{\text{c.m.}} = \frac{0\,\text{m}\cdot 20\,\text{kg} + 4\,\text{m}\cdot 80\,\text{kg}}{20\,\text{kg} + 80\,\text{kg}} = 3.2\,\text{m}$$

That is, the centre of mass for the man-daughter system is at a distance of 3.2 m from the daughter.

(b) If we assume the plank to have its mass distributed uniformly, the centre of mass of the plank would be at the exact mid-point of the plank, that is, 2 m from either end. This point is then where the mass of the plank can be located to calculate the centre of mass for the man-daughter-plank system. Using Eq. [5.2] in the x-direction for three objects:

$$x_{\text{c.m.}} = \frac{0\,\text{m}\cdot 20\,\text{kg} + 4\,\text{m}\cdot 80\,\text{kg} + 2\,\text{m}\cdot 10\,\text{kg}}{20\,\text{kg} + 80\,\text{kg} + 20\,\text{kg}}$$

$$= 2.8\,\text{m}$$

That is, the centre of mass for the man-daughter-plank system is at a distance of 2.8 m from the daughter.

(c) To balance the plank with the man and the daughter on it the pivot should be placed under the centre of mass found in part (b). If the pivot is placed under the centre of mass from part (a) the mass of the plank will not be balanced and the plank will tip towards the daughter. In Chapter 6 we will learn more about objects in static equilibrium, where not only there is absence of translational motion, but there is also absence of rotational motion.

Problem 5.3

(a) If we assume all birds have the same mass, the symmetry of the V-formation implies that $x_{\text{c.m.}} = 0$ m. Label the vertical coordinates as y_1 for the lead goose, y_2 and y_3 for the next closest pair, y_4 and y_5 for the pair following, and y_6 and y_7 for the trailing pair. With the lead goose at the origin $y_1 = 0$ m and:

$$y_2 = y_3 = d\cos(\theta/2) \equiv y_{23}$$

$$y_4 = y_5 = 2d\cos(\theta/2) \equiv y_{45}$$

$$y_6 = y_7 = 3d\cos(\theta/2) \equiv y_{67},$$

where d = 1 m and θ = 30°. The vertical coordinate of the centre of mass $y_{\text{c.m.}}$ is then:

$$y_{\text{c.m.}} = \frac{(y_1 + 2y_{23} + 2y_{45} + 2y_{67})m}{7m}$$

$$= \frac{2d\cos(\theta/2)(1+2+3)}{7}$$

$$= \frac{12}{7}d\cos(\theta/2)$$

Collecting all the results together:

$$(x_{\text{c.m.}}, y_{\text{c.m.}}) = (0\,\text{m}, 1.7\,\text{m}).$$

Problem 5.5

(a) Using Eq. [5.2] and since the mass at each point is M, the three coordinates of the centre of mass are:

$$x_{\text{c.m.}} = \frac{-1\,\text{m}\cdot M + 3\,\text{m}\cdot M + 9\,\text{m}\cdot M}{M + M + M}$$

$$y_{\text{c.m.}} = \frac{5\,\text{m}\cdot M + 3\,\text{m}\cdot M - 5\,\text{m}\cdot M}{M + M + M}$$

$$z_{\text{c.m.}} = \frac{7\,\text{m}\cdot M + 3\,\text{m}\cdot M - 2\,\text{m}\cdot M}{M + M + M}$$

Simplifying these expressions:

$$\left(x_{\text{c.m.}}, y_{\text{c.m.}}, z_{\text{c.m.}}\right) = \left({}^{11}\!/_{3}\,\text{m}, 1\,\text{m}, {}^{8}\!/_{3}\,\text{m}\right)$$

(b) If the masses at the three points P_1, P_2, and P_3 are $m_1 = 2m_2 = 4m_3 = M$, then $m_2 = M/2$, and $m_3 = M/4$. Using Eq. [5.2] the three coordinates of the centre of mass are:

$$x_{\text{c.m.}} = \frac{-1\,\text{m}\cdot M + 3\,\text{m}\cdot {}^{M}\!/_{2} + 9\,\text{m}\cdot {}^{M}\!/_{4}}{M + {}^{M}\!/_{2} + {}^{M}\!/_{4}}$$

$$y_{\text{c.m.}} = \frac{5\,\text{m}\cdot M + 3\,\text{m}\cdot {}^{M}\!/_{2} - 5\,\text{m}\cdot {}^{M}\!/_{4}}{M + {}^{M}\!/_{2} + {}^{M}\!/_{4}}$$

$$x_{\text{c.m.}} = \frac{7\,\text{m}\cdot M + 3\,\text{m}\cdot {}^{M}\!/_{2} - 2\,\text{m}\cdot {}^{M}\!/_{4}}{M + {}^{M}\!/_{2} + {}^{M}\!/_{4}}$$

Simplifying these expressions:

$$\left(x_{\text{c.m.}}, y_{\text{c.m.}}, z_{\text{c.m.}}\right) = \left({}^{11}\!/_{7}\,\text{m}, 3\,\text{m}, {}^{32}\!/_{7}\,\text{m}\right).$$

Problem 5.7

The centre of mass is located on the symmetry–line through the molecule, at a distance of 6.6×10^{-3} nm from the oxygen atom, in the direction of the hydrogen atoms.

Problem 5.9

We assign the names m_E, m_S, and m_M for the masses of the Earth, Sun, and Moon respectively, and the names r_{EM} and r_{ES} for the distances from the Earth to the Moon and to the Sun respectively.

(a) We use Eq. [5.3] to find the position of the centre of mass for the Earth-Moon system, with the origin of coordinates at the position of the Earth:

$$r_{\text{c.m.}} = \frac{r_E \cdot m_E + r_{EM} \cdot m_M}{m_E + m_M} = r_{EM}\left(\frac{m_M}{m_E + m_M}\right),$$

where $r_E = 0$. Using the values given by the problem we find $r_{\text{c.m.}} = 5 \times 10^6$ m, that is, the centre of mass for the Earth-Moon system is at about five thousand kilometers from the centre of the Earth. It is worth noting that since the radius of the Earth is about 6400 km, our calculation places the centre of mass of the Earth-Moon system inside the Earth, at about a depth of 2000 km below the surface.

(b) We use again Eq. [5.3] to find the position of the centre of mass for the Earth-Sun system, with the origin of coordinates at the position of the Sun:

$$R_{\text{c.m.}} = \frac{r_S \cdot m_S + r_{ES} \cdot m_E}{m_S + m_E} = r_{ES}\left(\frac{m_E}{m_S + m_E}\right),$$

where $r_S = 0$. Using the values given by the problem we find $R_{\text{c.m.}} = 3.00 \times 10^5$ m, that is, the centre of mass for the Earth-Sun system is at about three hundred kilometers from the centre of the Sun. It is worth noting that since the radius of the Sun is about 7×10^5 km, our calculation places the centre of mass of the Earth-Sun system well inside the Sun, quite close to the centre of the Sun.

(c) With respect to the Sun, that is, measuring all coordinates from the centre of the Sun, if the Sun, Earth, and Moon are all aligned, we have two possible scenarios: Sun-Earth-Moon (R_{SEM}) and Sun-Moon-Earth (R_{SME}). Using Eq. [5.3]:

$$R = \frac{r_S \cdot m_S + r_E \cdot m_E + r_M \cdot m_M}{m_S + m_E + m_M},$$

where in both scenarios $r_S = 0$ and $r_E = r_{ES}$. However, note that in the first case calculating R_{SEM} we have $r_M = r_{ES} + r_{EM}$, while in the second case calculating R_{SME} we have instead $r_M = r_{ES} - r_{EM}$. With these observations in mind we find:

$$R_{SEM} = 3.04 \times 10^5 \text{ m}$$

$$R_{SME} = 3.03 \times 10^5 \text{ m} .$$

Therefore, the configuration Sun-Earth-Moon changes the position of the centre of mass of the system the most with respect to the Sun-Earth system. The maximum change is given by $R_{SEM} - R_{c.m.}$, where $R_{c.m.} = 3.00 \times 10^5$ m is the result from part (b) for the position of the centre of mass of the Earth-Sun system. The difference is $R_{SEM} - R_{c.m.} = 4 \times 10^3$ m. We can thus say that the position of the centre of mass of the Earth-Sun system changes a maximum of 4 km if we were to include the Moon in the system. This distance is negligible when compared to all other distances involved.

(d) It is important to be very clear as to the reference being used to talk about the motion of the centre of mass. From our study of Newton's Laws in the previous chapters, we know that we must select an inertial frame of reference. Given their orbital motions due to the effect of the gravitational forces, the Sun, the Earth, and the Moon are not suitable choices. However, if we arbitrarily select a coordinate system and designate such system as an inertial frame of reference we can describe the motion of the centre of mass of the Sun-Earth-Moon system. Given that the system is isolated, no external forces act on it. Therefore, the centre of mass can only move in a straight line with constant speed as implied by Newton's First Law.

Problem 5.11

Given that no net external forces act on the student-backpack system in the horizontal direction, the horizontal position of the centre of mass will not change. This means $v_{x;c.m.} = 0$; the horizontal speed of the centre of mass is zero. We can use conservation of linear momentum measuring speeds with respect to the centre of mass, which coincides with measuring speeds with respect to the ground. Using Eq. [5.23] in the x-direction, with the sub-indices i for initial and f for final, b for backpack and s for student, and assuming all quantities are along the x-direction:

$$p_i = p_f$$

$$p_{i,b} + p_{i,s} = p_{f,b} + p_{f,s} .$$

Since before the throw both the backpack and the student are not moving $p_{i,\,b} = p_{i,\,s} = 0$. Using Eq. [5.19] for the definition of momentum we find:

$$0 = m_b \cdot v_{f,b} + m_s \cdot v_{f,s} \quad \textbf{(1)}$$

Both velocities in this equation are measured with respect to the centre of mass. Note that if the backpack moves to the right of the centre of mass, then the student will move to the left of the centre of mass. This means one of the velocities is positive while the other velocity will be negative. However, since we are only interested in the speeds, we can rewrite Eq. [1] with v_b for the speed of the backpack relative to the centre of mass, and v_s for the speed of the student relative to the centre of mass:

$$v_b = \left(\frac{m_s}{m_b}\right) v_s = 5 v_s \quad \textbf{(2)}$$

If v is the speed of the backpack relative to the student, then, taking into consideration the relative direction of motion of the backpack and the student, we can say:

$$v = v_s + v_b \quad \textbf{(3)}$$

Substituting v_b from Eq. [2] into Eq. [3] we can solve for v_s:

$$v_s = \tfrac{1}{6} v \quad \textbf{(4)}$$

Substituting v_s from Eq. [4] back into Eq. [2] we obtain for v_b:

$$v_b = \tfrac{5}{6} v \quad \textbf{(5)}$$

(a) Using Eq. [5] and a speed of $v = 2$ m/s for the backpack with respect to the student, we find $v_b = 1.7$ m/s for the speed of the backpack relative to the centre of mass.

(b) Using Eq. [4] and a speed of $v = 2$ m/s for the backpack with respect to the student, we find $v_s = 0.3$ m/s for the speed of the backpack relative to the centre of mass.

(c) If the student throws the backpack straight up, the linear momentum of the student-backpack system is not conserved. Gravity from the Earth on the backpack is an external force that acts on the backpack as it moves up. For the total momentum to be conserved, the system would need to include the agent of the gravitational force, in this case the Earth. If our system includes the Earth, the student, and the backpack, total momentum is now conserved.

Problem 5.13

(a) Conceptually, the conservation of momentum requires that the lead nucleus and the α–particle move in opposite directions. We define this common line of motion as the *x*–axis.

(b) We use the x–components in Eq. [5.18] with const = 0 for the initial state (particle at rest):

$$m_{\mathrm{Pb}} \cdot v_{\mathrm{Pb},final} + m_{\mathrm{a}} \cdot v_{\mathrm{a}} = 0$$

This is solved for the final speed of the Pb nucleus:

$$\begin{aligned} v_{Pb,final} &= -\frac{m_{\alpha}}{m_{Pb}} v_{\alpha} \\ &= -\frac{4.002\,u}{205.974\,u}\left(1.6\times10^{7}\,\frac{m}{s}\right) \\ &= -3.1\times10^{5}\,\frac{m}{s} \end{aligned}$$

The lead nucleus moves with 3.1×10^5 m/s in the direction opposite to the α–particle.

(c) Both speeds are significantly below the speed of light in vacuum with the α–particle moving at 5 % of the speed of light and the lead particle at 1 ‰. Note that we would have to be more careful if any of the calculated speeds came closer to the speed of light; classical mechanics fails for objects moving with a significant fraction of the speed of light and has to be replaced by relativistic calculations.

Problem 5.15

This is a perfectly inelastic collision, so we will use conservation of linear momentum in the direction along the collision. Using one direction of Eq. [5.23]:

$$p_i = p_f$$

$$p_{i,m} + p_{i,M} = p_{f,(m+M)} \qquad \textbf{(1)}$$

If the initial speed of mass *m* is *v*, then the initial speed of mass *M* will be *v*/2. Calling the final speed v_f, Eq. [1] becomes:

$$m \cdot v - M \cdot \frac{v}{2} = (m+M) \cdot v_f, \qquad \textbf{(2)}$$

where we have chosen mass *m* as moving in the positive direction, while mass *M* moves in the negative direction. Reorganizing Eq. [2] and solving for M, we find that:

$$M = 2m\left(\frac{v - v_f}{v + 2v_f}\right)$$

$57.7^0 = 12.3^0$. Hawks do not just crash into

Problem 5.17

(a) We first convert the given values into standard units. The volume flow rate of blood into the aorta is $\Delta V/\Delta t$ = 5.0 L/min = 8.33×10^{-5} m³/s; the average blood speed is 0.22 m/s; the density of blood is 1060 kg/m³ and the mass of the heart is 0.3 kg.

We model the heart in analogy to the water ejecting squid in Example 5.6. For this, we first need the mass flow rate of blood out of the heart, which we obtain by combining the volume flow rate and the density (in analogy to Eq. [5.29]):

$$\begin{aligned} \frac{\Delta m}{\Delta t} &= \rho \frac{\Delta V}{\Delta t} \\ &= \left(1060\frac{kg}{m^3}\right)\left(8.33\times10^{-5}\,\frac{m^3}{s}\right) \\ &= 0.088\frac{kg}{s} \end{aligned}$$

i.e., the heart output is by a factor of about 100 smaller than the water ejection of the squid. This is a good start since we do not want the heart to escape from our chest! In the next step, the mass flow rate is combined with the speed of blood in the aorta. This leads to the change of the linear momentum of the blood because we assume for this calculation that the blood was previously at rest in the heart:

$$\frac{\Delta|p_{water}|}{\Delta t} = \frac{\Delta m}{\Delta t} v = \left(0.088\frac{kg}{s}\right)\left(0.22\frac{m}{s}\right) = 0.02\frac{kg \cdot m}{s^2} \quad \textbf{(1)}$$

which is almost 10,000 times smaller than the linear momentum change of the squid. Thus, the force acting on the heart is of the order of a factor 10^4 smaller than the force acting on the squid while ejecting water. We continue this discussion in part (b) because we could argue that the squid and the heart do not differ much but for their respective size: the squid has a mass of 50 kg and the heart only 0.3 kg. Thus, the change in the linear momentum isn't large enough to let our heart bounce rhythmically against the ribs.

(b) We continue with Eq. [1] and use Newton's second law to convert the force into an acceleration in analogy to the step from Example 5.6 in the textbook:

$$a_{heart} = \frac{F_{net}}{m_{heart}} = \frac{0.02\frac{kg \cdot m}{s^2}}{0.3\ kg} = 0.067\frac{m}{s^2} \quad \textbf{(2)}$$

which is still 50 times less than the acceleration for the squid in Example 4.3 in the textbook. Therefore, we are satisfied with the fact that we don't feel how our heart pounds in our chest.

(c) We obtain an even smaller effect if we transfer the linear momentum of the ejected blood to the entire human, and not just to the heart. In this case Eq. [2] is rewritten in the form:

$$a_{standard\ man} = \frac{F_{net}}{m_{standard\ man}} = \frac{0.02\frac{kg \cdot m}{s^2}}{70\ kg} = 2.9 \times 10^{-4}\frac{m}{s^2}$$

in which we used the mass of the standard man from Table 4.1. This appears to be a negligible result. Still, the effect can be measured and is even used to estimate the blood volume ejected by a patient. The set–up for this purpose is called a *ballistocardiograph.* It consists of a flat, frictionless surface (floating on an air cushion) for which the displacement is measured as a function of time in the direction opposite to the direction of the blood flow in the aorta, i.e., in the direction of the legs. Typical data include a displacement of 50 to 100 μm within 0.1 to 0.2 seconds of the blood ejection.

(d) For the result in part (c) to be useful, we require the blood to be treated as if it is a second object while the heart and the rest of the standard man are rigidly connected. This assumption is at best acceptable for a very short period after blood ejection, because the blood then rushes into the aortic arch. In the aortic arch a significant redistribution of the linear momentum of blood occurs.

(e) We expect a notably larger effect than the one we calculated with the average data given. First, the heart ejects about twice as much blood per cycle with the other 50 % flowing through the pulmonary artery to the lungs. The pulmonary artery and the aorta leave the heart in about the same direction, thus the two effects should be combined. Secondly, the blood flows through the aorta with peak speeds exceeding the average speed up to a factor of 10. This is described as pulsatile flow. Thus, the forces on the heart may for short periods exceed the calculated values by an order of magnitude.

Problem 5.19

(a) We analyze both ejections separately, with the motion after the first ejection labeled *int* for intermediate. We call the mass of the initial object *M*. An ejection is the inverse process to a perfectly inelastic collision, that is, the linear momentum of the combined object initially is equal to the sum of the linear momentums of the two fragments after the ejection. We are interested in the *x*–direction motion of the heavier fragment in the intermediate stage:

$$Mv_{x,i} = 0.9Mv_{x,int} - 0.1M(1\,\text{m/s}) \qquad (1)$$

The object remains at rest with respect to the *y*–axis during the first ejection. With $v_{x,i} = 0$ we find:

x-direction:

$$v_{x,int} = \frac{0.1}{0.9}(1\,\text{m/s}) = 0.11\,\text{m/s}$$

y-direction: $\qquad (2)$

$$v_{y,int} = 0$$

The second ejection occurs along the *y*–axis and does therefore not affect the motion along the *x*–direction. Thus, the intermediate *x*–component of the velocity is also its final *x*–component. For the *y*–direction the perfectly inelastic process yields in analogy to Eq. [1]:

$$0.9\,Mv_{y,int} = 0.81\,Mv_{y,f} - 0.09\,M(1\,\text{m/s}) \qquad (3)$$

this yields with $v_{y,int} = 0$:

x-direction:

$$v_{x,f} = 0.11\,\text{m/s}$$

y-direction: $\qquad (4)$

$$v_{y,f} = \frac{0.09}{0.81}(1\,\text{m/s}) = 0.11\,\text{m/s}$$

From Eq. [4] the magnitude of the final velocity of the largest fragment is determined:

$$|\mathbf{v}_f| = \sqrt{v_{x,f}^2 + v_{y,f}^2} = \sqrt{2\cdot(0.11\,\text{m/s})^2} = 0.16\,\text{m/s}$$

Its direction is 45° above the positive *x*–axis, on the first quadrant, because both of its components are identical and positive.

b) Similar to part (a) but instead of an object starting at rest with $v_{x,i} = 0$ and $v_{y,i} = v_{y,int} = 0$, we have $v_{x,i}$ = 2 m/s and $v_{y,i} = v_{y,int}$ = 3 m/s. Repeating the calculations from Eq. [1-4] we find that the change in each direction is the same as the one found in part (a). It is important to note that while the ejected pieces move at 1 m/s with respect to the object, the velocity in Eq. [1] and Eq. [3] corresponds to the velocity of the ejected piece with respect to the external frame of reference. This means that for part (b) the ejected fragment in Eq. [1] moves at 2 m/s – 1 m/s = 1 m/s to the right, making the second term in the right-hand side of Eq. [1] positive. Also, the ejected fragment in Eq. [3] moves at 3 m/s – 1 m/s = 2 m/s to the right, making the second term in the right-hand side of Eq. [2] positive. With these considerations in mind, following the same procedure in Eq. [1] to Eq. [4], we obtain:

x-direction:

$$v_{x,f} = \left(\frac{1.90}{0.90}\right)\frac{\text{m}}{\text{s}} = 2.11\,\text{m/s}$$

y-direction: $\qquad (5)$

$$v_{y,f} = \left(\frac{2.52}{0.81}\right)\frac{\text{m}}{\text{s}} = 3.11\,\text{m/s}$$

Note that the change in v_x and the change in v_y are equal to those found in part (a). The reason for this lays in that the relative velocity of the ejected fragments are equal in both cases and thus carry equal amounts of momentum. Since the change in momentum is equal and the masses are the same, the change in velocity will be the same as well. If we want to compare the net change in speed, in part (a) the object goes from 0 m/s to 0.16 m/s, for a net change in speed of 0.16 m/s.

In part (b), the initial speed is:

$$|\mathbf{v}_i| = \sqrt{v_{x,i}^2 + v_{y,i}^2} = \sqrt{(2\,\text{m/s})^2 + (3\,\text{m/s})^2} = 3.61\,\text{m/s},$$

and using Eq. [5] the final speed is:

$$|\mathbf{v}_f| = \sqrt{v_{x,f}^2 + v_{y,f}^2} = \sqrt{(2.11\,\text{m/s})^2 + (3.11\,\text{m/s})^2} = 3.76\,\text{m/s}.$$

The change in speed is 0.15 m/s, different from the change in part (a) of 0.16 m/s. This is not a problem of precision or significant figures. Although the changes along each direction are equal, the change in the magnitude depends on those changes in a non-linear way; they are added in quadrature, that is, as squares under a square root. Said another way, remember that:

$$\sqrt{a^2+b^2} \neq a+b$$

(c) Given that:

$$1\,\text{m/s}\cdot\cos 45^\circ = 1\,\text{m/s}\cdot\sin 45^\circ = 0.71\,\text{m/s},$$

the velocity of the ejected piece is given by:

$$\left(v_{x,e}, v_{y,e}\right) = \left(0.71\,\text{m/s}, 0.71\,\text{m/s}\right).$$

Noting the direction of the motion of the ejected piece, conservation of momentum in the x-direction yields:

$$Mv_{x,i} = 0.8Mv_{x,f} + 0.2M\left(0.71\,\text{m/s}\right) \quad \textbf{(6)}$$

Conservation of momentum in the y-direction yields:

$$Mv_{y,i} = 0.8Mv_{y,f} + 0.2M\left(0.71\,\text{m/s}\right) \quad \textbf{(7)}$$

Solving Eq. [6] and Eq. [7], with the object initially at rest; we find the velocity of the largest fragment:

$$\begin{aligned} v_{x,f} &= -\frac{0.2}{0.8}\left(0.71\,\text{m/s}\right) = -0.18\,\text{m/s} \\ v_{y,f} &= -\frac{0.2}{0.8}\left(0.71\,\text{m/s}\right) = -0.18\,\text{m/s} \end{aligned} \quad \textbf{(8)}$$

From Eq. [8] the magnitude of the final velocity of the largest fragment is determined:

$$\begin{aligned} \left|\mathbf{v}_f\right| &= \sqrt{v_{x,f}^2 + v_{y,f}^2} \\ &= \sqrt{2\cdot\left(-0.18\,\text{m/s}\right)^2} = 0.25\,\text{m/s} \end{aligned}$$

Its direction is 45° below the negative x–axis, on the third quadrant, because both of its components are identical and negative.

Problem 5.21

Use kinematics to determine that the combined object is in falling for 0.45 seconds. Use that fact to determine that the velocity of the combined object just after the collision is 4.4 m/s. Then use the conservation of momentum to calculate the initial speed of the object with mass m; $v_{\text{m, initial}}$ = 143 m/s.

CHAPTER SIX

Torque and Equilibrium

MULTIPLE CHOICE QUESTIONS

Multiple Choice 6.1

Correct Answer (a). If the net force is also zero, then any point will work. However, if the net force is not zero, the point must be a point that lies along the line of the net force. The option (B) is only true if the object is in rotational and translational equilibrium. A simple illustration would be to consider an object with only one force acting on it and the torque initially calculated at the point of application of the force. That net torque will be zero. However, choosing any point that does not lie along the line of the force will yield a non-zero torque.

Multiple Choice 6.3

Correct Answer (a).

Multiple Choice 6.5

Correct Answer (b). The sign convention is designed such that the mathematical description will produce identical results regardless of point of view.

Multiple Choice 6.7

Correct Answer (c). Note $\tau \propto \sin\varphi$ is not a linear function in φ.

Multiple Choice 6.9

Correct Answer (c).

Multiple Choice 6.11

Correct Answer (b).

Multiple Choice 6.13

Correct Answer (d). The gravitational torque is negative and of magnitude $(mg\cos\theta)(l/2)$, while the torque made by the applied force is positive and of magnitude Fl. For the two torques to balance the force must have magnitude $F = (mg/2)\cos\theta = 27$ N. Note that this result is independent on the length of the trap door.

CONCEPTUAL QUESTIONS

Conceptual Question 6.1

The correct answer will be option (c):

$$\tau_{net} = -LW_1 - \frac{L}{2}W_2 + \frac{2}{3}LT\sin\theta = 0$$

Conceptual Question 6.3

In Figure 6.48, the points B and C are a distance l from the fulcrum on either of the ribs while this distance is L for points B' and C' ($L > l$). The muscles stretching between the ribs connect either points B and C' (*intercostales externi*), or points B' and C (*intercostales interni*). We first consider a contraction of the *intercostales externi*, i.e., the line connecting points B and C' shortens. This causes a torque on both the upper and the lower rib. On the upper rib the torque is $-F_{BC'}\cdot l$ (where we assume for simplicity that the sine–term in Eq. [6.1] is included in the magnitude of the force term $F_{BC'}$). This contribution is negative since it would lead to a clockwise rotation of the rib. For the lower rib, the torque is $+F_{BC'}\cdot L$. Thus, the torque on the lower rib is bigger and prevails, moving the lower rib upwards. Since all the ribs are connected in the same fashion by the *intercostales externi*, the entire rib cage moves up, which is the rib cage motion associated with inhalation. An equivalent argument applies to the *intercostales interni*, leading to the opposite motion.

Conceptual Question 6.5

In Figure 6.44 the pelvis and hip form a Class I lever system. This is clearly illustrated in Case Study 6.1, Figure 6.43 where the fulcrum is clearly between the load and the effort. For the situation in Figure 6.32(a) if we consider the external force on the foot as the load, and either the heel contact or the front contact as the fulcrum, the opposite normal force will represent the effort. Either way, the load lies between the fulcrum and the effort, describing a Class II lever system. In Figure 6.32(b) the load is the external force and the effort is the muscle tension. With respect to the point of contact with the diving board, the load is between the fulcrum and the effort, corresponding to Figure 6.30 and thus a Class II lever system.

Conceptual Question 6.7
The centre of mass of the bottle plus wine holder system must be located directly above the support point on the table because this leads to a net torque of zero.

Conceptual Question 6.9
The fulcrum is the shoulder joint, the effort is the tension in the deltoid muscle, and the load is the weight of the whole arm. Since the effort is closer to the fulcrum than the load, the system describes a Class III lever system.

ANALYTICAL PROBLEMS

Problem 6.1
The minimum force is $F_{min} = \tau / d$. The given values yield $F_{min} = (40\ \text{N·m}) / 0.3\ \text{m} = 133\ \text{N}$.

Problem 6.3
This is an application of the torque definition for an extended object, but contains a geometrical twist: there is only one force to be considered, but the angle θ is not the angle we need to analyze Eq. [6.1] for the torque. To use that equation, the angle between the exerted force, $\mathbf{F}_{ext}$, and the lever arm vector, that is **AB** = **r**, is needed. This is illustrated in Figure 2, where the angle between both vectors is defined as φ.(The figure below does not represent properly the angle between r and F_{ext}. In fact the angle between r and F_{ext} should be the complementary angle of the own shown on the figure; it should be (Pi-Phi). This does not change the answer since sine(Phi)=sine(Pi-Phi)

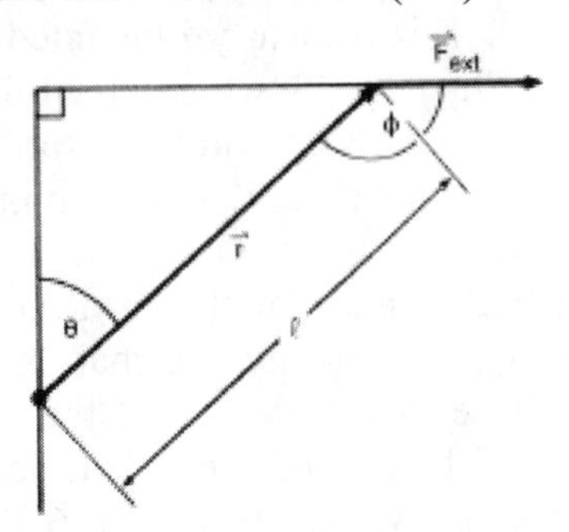

Figure 1

Confirm that the angle θ as shown in Figure 6.46 and the angle θ as shown in Figure 2 are indeed the same. Remember that vectors can be moved as long as their length and direction are kept the same. In this case, we can move vector $\mathbf{F}_{ext}$ while keeping the same angle between $\mathbf{F}_{ext}$ and **AB**. In particular, we can slide $\mathbf{F}_{ext}$ to the right in Figure 6.46 so that its tail end is located at point B. The angles in this problem are related in the following form:

$$\varphi = 180^0 - (90^0 - \theta) = 90^0 + \theta$$

With all necessary parameters defined, we use Eq. [6.1] to calculate the torque:

$$\tau = l \cdot F_{ext} \sin\varphi$$
$$= (1.3\times10^{-2}\text{m})(40\text{N})\sin 130^0 = 0.4\text{N}\cdot\text{m}$$

Problem 6.5
The lever arm for F_3 is:

$$r_{3,\perp} = (1\,\text{m})(\sin 30^\circ) = 0.5\,\text{m}$$

The lever arm for F_1 is:

$$r_{1,\perp} = (2\,\text{m})(\sin 60^\circ) = 1.7\,\text{m}$$

Problem 6.7
Start by considering the torques about one of the points where the rope attaches. Let's choose the point closest to where the person is standing. This gives us:

$$T_2(3\text{ m}) - (20.5\text{ kg})\left(9.8\frac{\text{m}}{\text{s}^2}\right)(1.5\text{ m})$$
$$-(70\text{ kg})\left(9.8\frac{\text{m}}{\text{s}^2}\right)(1\text{ m}) = 0$$

T_2 is the tension in the rope furthest from where the person is standing. Notice that by considering the torque about the point where one of the unknown forces is acting, we eliminate that variable from our equation. Solving this equation gives T_2 = 329 N. To find T_1, simply use the fact that the forces are in static equilibrium to find T_1 = 558 N.

Problem 6.9

If the man stands on the ladder 4 m from the ground, he is standing at a position $d_M = 4$ m / cos(60^0) along the ladder. Taking torques about the point where the ladder contacts the ground, we find the normal force:

$$N = \frac{m_L \cdot g \cdot \cos\theta \cdot d_{c.m.} + m \cdot g \cdot \cos\theta \cdot d_M}{l \cdot \sin\theta}$$

By balancing the forces acting in the horizontal direction, we find that the horizontal force exerted by the ground is equal in magnitude to the normal force. This gives $F_{\text{horizontal}} = 353$ N. By balancing the vertical force exerted by the ground with the two downward acting weights, we find $F_{\text{vertical}} = 1176$ N.

Problem 6.11

(a) The entire standard man in Figure 6.52 is the system. For this system we identify the conditions under which neither an acceleration along a straight line nor a rotational acceleration occur by using Eq. [6.11]. Since the system is an extended object, it is important to know where its centre of mass lies. In the particular case, this point is labeled *c.m.* in the figure. Three forces act on the system: the weight, and two normal forces at the two contact points of the system with its environment (at the toes and hands). It is important not to combine these two forces into a single force as they act at different points on the extended object. We need a free–body diagram and a balance of torque diagram. The balance of torque diagram is shown in Figure 2. To obtain it, first draw a bar representing the system. Next we indicate with a solid dot the fulcrum at the centre of mass. Remember that we limit the discussion to cases where all and (possible) motions occur in a plane perpendicular to the axis of rotation. Confirm for Figure 6.52 that any possible rotation would occur within the plane of the paper. Next we add the forces acting on the standard man to the sketch. Be careful to not only draw the forces in the correct direction, but also to attach them to the bar at the appropriate position. To make sure that you do this, always identify the distance from the fulcrum to the point where each force acts on the object.

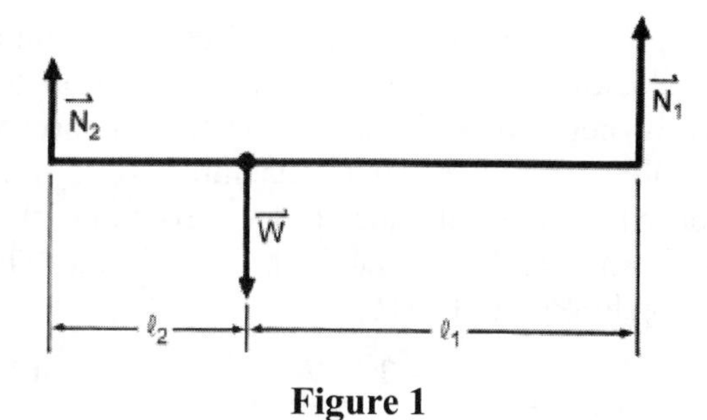

Figure 1

In Figure 2 the lengths l_1 and l_2 are included for that purpose.

The default choice of coordinate system for a balance of torque diagram is based on the fulcrum as the origin and the direction along the bar as the *x*–axis. From the free–body diagram and the balance of torque diagram the three formulas in Eq. [6.11] are developed: the first two represent the *x*– and *y*–components of Newton's first law and the third formula represents the torque equilibrium condition. In the current case none of the forces has a component acting in the *x*–direction, thus, the respective formula is omitted. This leaves two formulas for solving the problem:

$$\begin{aligned} &\textit{condition } 2: \quad N_1 + N_2 - W = 0 \\ &\textit{condition } 3: \quad N_1 \cdot l_1 - N_2 \cdot l_2 = 0 \end{aligned} \qquad \textbf{(1)}$$

Condition 3 in Eq. [1] does not contain a term with the magnitude of the weight, *W*. This is due to the fact that the weight acts at the fulcrum. Think of pulling a door out of its hinges or trying to push it into the hinges. No rotation occurs in either case. The two normal forces acting on the object in Figure 6.52 are present in the torque equilibrium formula. Based on the torque definition in Eq. [6.1], each of these forces is multiplied with the distance between the fulcrum and the point along the bar at which the force is applied. Note that the angle in Eq. [6.1] is also included, however, we find sin φ = 1 because both normal forces act perpendicular to the bar. In the torque equilibrium formula in Eq. [1], one term is positive and one is negative. This is the result of the sign–convention of Figure 6.9: imagine that the force $\mathbf{N_1}$ in Figure 2 succeeds in setting the bar in motion. This would be a counter–clockwise rotation; thus, the torque contribution of $\mathbf{N_1}$ is positive. In turn, if $\mathbf{N_2}$ were to succeed, the rotation would be clockwise; thus, the torque contribution of $\mathbf{N_2}$ is negative. We solve for the unknown variables, i.e., the two magnitudes of the normal forces, in the order given in the problem text: N_2 is found first. We isolate N_1 in condition 2 in Eq. [1]:

$$N_1 = W - N_2 \qquad (2)$$

Then we substitute Eq. [2] into condition 3 of Eq. [1] to eliminate N_1:

$$(W - N_2)\, l_1 - N_2 \cdot l_1 = 0$$

Using 70 kg for the mass of the standard man from Table 4.1 we find for the magnitude of the normal force at the hands:

$$N_2 = \frac{W \cdot l_1}{l_1 + l_2} = \frac{(686\ \text{N})\ (90\ \text{cm})}{(90\ \text{cm}) + (55\ \text{cm})} = 426\ \text{N}$$

(b) Substituting the value found in part (a) for N_2 into Eq. [2] yields for the magnitude of the normal force at the feet:

$$N_1 = W - N_2 = (686\ N) - (426\ N) = 260\ \text{N}$$

Problem 6.13

Given that r and F are perpendicular for the two forces being considered and $\sin 90° = 1$, Eq. [6.1] simplifies to:

$$\tau = r F \qquad (1)$$

As the arm is in rotational equilibrium, the net torque about any point must be zero. We chose the joint point as our reference.

(a) The magnitude of the torque due to the weight held in the hand is found using Eq. [1]:

$$\tau_W = r_W\, W = (35\,\text{cm})(70\,\text{N}) = 24.5\,\text{N}\cdot\text{m} \qquad (2)$$

Note that the torque made by W is negative and Eq. [2] just shows its magnitude.

(b) Using again Eq. [1], the magnitude of the torque due to the force T made by the biceps on the forearm is:

$$\tau_T = r_T\, T = (0.04\,\text{m})\,T \qquad (3)$$

Note that the torque made by T is positive.

(c) Since the arm is in rotational equilibrium:

$$\tau_T - \tau_W = 0 \qquad (4)$$

Substitute Eq. [2] and Eq. [3] into Eq. [4] to obtain:

$$T = \frac{r_W}{r_T} W = 613\,\text{N}$$

Problem 6.15

The system is the lower arm of the person. The object of mass M exerts an upward force on the left end of the lower arm (hand) that is equal to the weight of the object. We label this force $\mathbf{F_3}$. The lower arm also has a weight $\mathbf{W}$ that acts vertically down at its centre of mass. The other forces to be taken into account in this problem are identified in the text, and include the forces exerted on the lower arm by the triceps muscle (called $\mathbf{F_1}$) and by the Humerus through the elbow (called $\mathbf{F_2}$). Note that all four forces act vertically, but the lower arm forms an angle of 35^0 with the horizontal. The sketch in Figure 6.54 is not a balance of torque diagram. Thus, we draw both, a free–body diagram, shown in Figure 3(a), and a balance of torque diagram, shown in Figure 3(b).

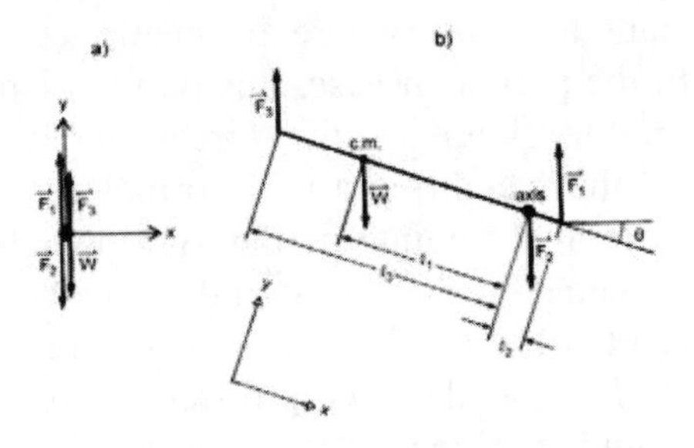

Figure 2

Note that the elbow does not lie at the end of the bar since the triceps tendon is attached to the right of the elbow. Figure 3 also contains the distances to the fulcrum for the various points at which the forces act on the bar. The standard choice of co-ordinate system for the balance of torque diagram is indicated below the bar in Figure 3(b). For the free-body diagram in Figure 3(a), a horizontal x– and a vertical y–axis have been chosen. Our use of different co-ordinate systems for both diagrams proves that such a choice is acceptable. Of the three conditions in Eq. [6.11] for the mechanical equilibrium of an extended object, the first condition can be omitted because no force components run along the x–axis in Figure 3(a). Thus, we write:

$$\begin{aligned}&\textit{condition}\,2: \\ &\qquad F_1 - F_2 + F_3 - W = 0 \\ &\textit{condition}\,3: \\ &\qquad l_1 F_1 \cos\theta + l_2 W \cos\theta - l_3 \mathrm{F}_3 \cos\theta = 0\end{aligned} \quad \mathbf{(1)}$$

The magnitudes $W = m \cdot g$ and $F_3 = M \cdot g$ are known. Condition 3 in Eq. [1] is analyzed first to find F_1:

$$F_1 = \frac{l_3 F_3 - l_2 W}{l_1} = \frac{(l_3 \mathrm{M} - \mathrm{l}_2 \mathrm{m}) g}{l_1} \quad \mathbf{(2)}$$

Substituting the given numerical values into Eq. [2] yields for the right hand side:

$$\frac{\big((0.4\,\mathrm{m})(10\,\mathrm{kg}) - (0.15\,\mathrm{m})(2.3\,\mathrm{kg})\big)(9.8\,\mathrm{m/s^2})}{0.02\,\mathrm{m}}$$

which results in F_1 = 1790 N. The term cosθ did not enter Eq. [2]. This is mathematically due to the fact that we can divide condition 3 in Eq. [1] on both sides by cosθ. It is important to notice, however, that there is one angle θ for which this mathematical operation is not valid: for $\theta = 90^0$ we find cosθ = 0 but cannot divide by zero. However, if $\theta = 90^0$ the whole problem makes no longer sense, and thus, this case can be excluded.

(b) Substituting the result from part (a) in condition 2 in Eq. [1], we obtain F_2:

$$\begin{aligned}F_2 &= F_1 + F_3 - W \\ &= (1790\,\mathrm{N}) + (10\,\mathrm{kg} - 2.3\,\mathrm{kg})(9.8\,\mathrm{m/s^2}) \\ &= 1865\,\mathrm{N}\end{aligned}$$

Compare the magnitude of the two forces $\mathbf{F}_1$ and $\mathbf{F}_2$ with the two weights, which are about 25 N for the lower arm and about 100 N for the lifted weight: tremendous forces act on an arm when performing typical physical tasks, here lifting an object of mass 10 kg.

Problem 6.17

Only one unknown variable is asked for in this problem text: the magnitude of the tension **T**. Thus, a single formula is sufficient to answer the question. The problem directs us to use the torque equilibrium formula. The lower leg without the foot is the system. The foot is kept separate because it must be treated as an additional object suspended from the lower leg. If the foot and the lower leg together were considered to form the system, their weights would have to be combined as a single force acting at the centre of mass of lower leg and foot. However, the position at which the weight of the foot acts is important because we are considering torque. All three forces acting on the system are shown in Figure 6.56(b). These are the weight of the system, the weight of the foot and the tension in the tendon of the large quadriceps muscle. The balance of torque diagram is given in Figure 6.56(b). Note that we do not need a free–body diagram to solve this problem since the only formula needed is the one resulting from the balance of torque diagram:

$$\frac{l}{5} T \sin\phi - \frac{l}{2} W_L \sin\theta - l F \sin\theta = 0 \quad \mathbf{(1)}$$

After division by l, Eq. [1] is solved for T:

$$T = \frac{\left(\frac{1}{2}(3\,\mathrm{kg}) + (1.2\,\mathrm{kg})\right) g \sin 35^\circ}{\frac{1}{5}\sin 30^\circ} = 150\,\mathrm{N}$$

Note that this result is independent of the length l.

Problem 6.19

(a) We are provided with a balance of torque diagram in Figure 6.57. Note that some of the forces do not act perpendicular to the bar, which represents the arm. As a consequence, all three formulas for the mechanical equilibrium of a rigid object in Eq. [6.11] must be written. For both the free–body diagram and the shown balance of torque diagram we choose the *x*–axis horizontally toward the right and the *y*–axis vertically upward. The fulcrum lies in the shoulder joint and is identified by the solid dot at the right end of the bar. Writing the various terms in Eq. [6.11] is simplified by identifying the *x*– and *y*–components of the forces in Figure 6.57. This is illustrated in Figure 4 for both the force $\mathbf{F}_{ext}$ and the tension $\mathbf{T}$.

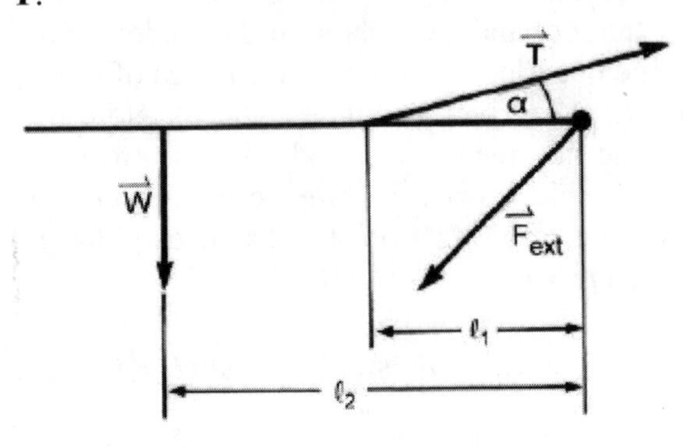

Figure 4

Using Figure 6.57 and Figure 5, we write:

$$\begin{aligned} &\textit{condition } 1: \quad - \quad + T\cos\alpha = 0 \\ &\textit{condition } 2: \quad - \quad + T\sin\alpha - \quad = 0 \qquad \textbf{(1)} \\ &\textit{condition } 3: \quad - \quad \alpha + \quad = 0 \end{aligned}$$

in which $T_x = |\mathbf{T}| \cos\alpha$, and $T_y = |\mathbf{T}| \sin\alpha$. Two notes about Eq. [1] are useful:

- We have chosen to introduce the *x*– and *y*–components for the force $\mathbf{F}_{ext}$. Because part (b) of the problem asks for the magnitude of the external force $\mathbf{F}_{ext}$, we will later have to calculate this magnitude from the two components using the Pythagorean theorem. Alternatively, you can introduce a second angle between the force $\mathbf{F}_{ext}$ and the negative *x*–axis. It might be useful to try this if you didn't do it in the first place. Note also that the force $\mathbf{F}_{ext}$ is not present in condition 3 in Eq. [1] since this force pushes into the fulcrum.
- Condition 3 in Eq. [1] reminds you once more how to deal with forces in the balance of torque diagram, which are not perpendicular to the bar. Any such force should be written in component form as done in Figure 5 with one component parallel and one perpendicular to the bar. The component parallel to the bar does not enter into the torque equilibrium formula since that component is directed either into or away from the fulcrum. Starting with condition 3 in Eq. [1] is the best approach. In the current case, this allows us to calculate the magnitude of the tension directly:

$$T = \frac{l_2 \cdot W}{l_1 \sin\alpha} = \frac{(35\ \text{cm})(44.6\ \text{N})}{(13\ \text{cm})\sin 15^0} = 465\ \text{N}$$

in which we used for the weight of the arm from Table 4.1, $W = (0.065 \cdot 70\ \text{kg})\ 9.8\ \text{m/s}^2 = 44.6\ \text{N}$.

(b) Substituting the result of part (a) into conditions 1 and 2 in Eq. [1], we find the two components of the external force:

$$F_{ext,x} = T\cos\alpha = (465\ \text{N})\cos 15^0 = 450\ \text{N}$$

and

$$\begin{aligned} F_{ext,y} &= T\sin\alpha - W \\ &= (465\ \text{N})\sin 15^0 - (44.6\ \text{N}) = 75\ \text{N} \end{aligned}$$

leading to F_{ext}:

$$F_{ext}\sqrt{(450\ \text{N})^2 + (75\ \text{N})^2} = 455\ \text{N}$$

Problem 6.21
(a) Read the solution to this problem carefully as there is a change in what we define as the system when proceeding from part (a) to parts (b) and (c). How can you anticipate this? Read part (a) only. This question deals with the entire body. It is the mass of the entire body, which hangs on the bar, not only the lower arms. The two forces mentioned in parts (b) and (c), $\mathbf{F}_{\mathbf{elbow}}$ and **T**, are, in turn, only relevant when we focus on physical effects which occur across the interface between the lower arm and the rest of the human body. In part (a), we are asked to determine the external forces exerted on each hand. The system is the entire body. Three forces act on the system: the weight and the two contact forces exerted by the bar on each hand. We label these forces $\mathbf{F}_{\mathbf{ext}}$ each because it is stated in the problem text that the person holds both lower arms parallel to each other (which leads to the higher score in a competition), and that these two forces are equal in magnitude. We need only a free–body diagram (and not a balance of torque diagram) to determine the external force. This is illustrated in Figure 7. For the human body to remain stationary, its centre of mass must be placed exactly below the hands to avoid a non–zero net torque. If the centre of mass were displaced to either side (front or back with respect to the high bar) a pendulum-type of motion would result similar to that of a child being released on a swing after pulling the child back.

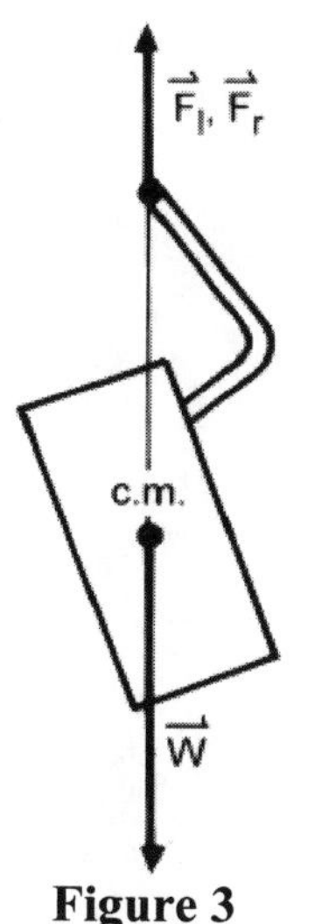

Figure 3

Newton's law in the vertical direction is:

$$2F_{ext} - W = 0$$

i.e.:

$$F_{ext} = \frac{W}{2} = \frac{70\ \text{kg}}{2}\left(9.8\frac{\text{m}}{\text{s}^2}\right) = 343\ \text{N}$$

(b) and **(c)** Now we redefine the system as the lower arm of the person, with the two forces $\mathbf{F}_{\mathbf{elbow}}$ and **T** acting across the interface between the lower arm and the rest of the body. Given in the problem are three contact forces that act on the lower arm, with their respective directions shown in Figure 6.59: **T**, $\mathbf{F}_{\mathbf{elbow}}$ and $\mathbf{F}_{\mathbf{ext}}$. Also, the weight of the lower arm, $\mathbf{W}_{\mathbf{la}}$, is included. The free–body diagram is shown in Figure 8. Note that the coordinate system in Figure 8 a vertical y– and a horizontal x–axis. The balance of torque diagram is already given in Figure 6.59. The elbow is the fulcrum. The force $\mathbf{F}_{\mathbf{elbow}}$ acts at the elbow while the biceps tendon, exerting the tension **T**, is attached a small distance l_3 away from the joint. **T** forms an angle φ with the vertical and $\mathbf{F}_{\mathbf{elbow}}$ forms an angle ψ with the lower arm. Given is the angle θ, which defines the angle between the vertical and the lower arm.

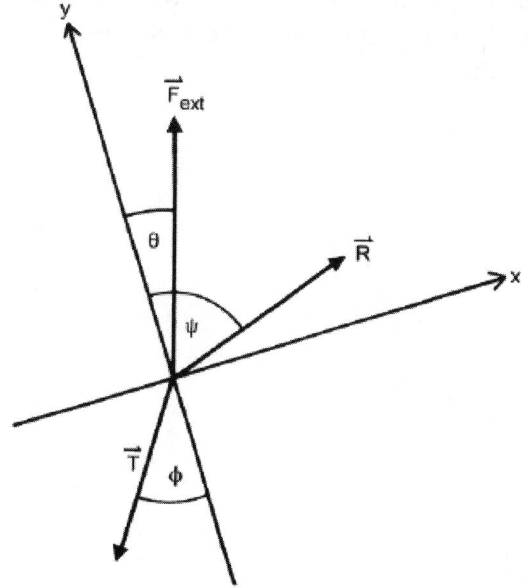

Figure 4

Using Eq. [6.11], we write the following three formulas for the mechanical equilibrium of the lower arm:

condition 1:

$$-F_{elbow}\sin(\psi-\theta)+T\sin\varphi=0$$

condition 2:

$$F_{ext}-W_{la}+F_{elbow}\cos(\psi-\theta)-T\cos\varphi=0 \quad \textbf{(1)}$$

condition 3:

$$-l_3T\sin(\varphi+\theta)-l_2W_{la}\sin\theta$$
$$+l_1F_{ext}\sin\theta=0$$

Note that condition 3 in Eq. [1] does not contain a reference to $\mathbf{F_{elbow}}$ since this force acts along a line through the fulcrum. In parts (b) and (c) we are asked to find F_{elbow}, T and ψ, of these only T is present in condition 3 and can be calculated first.

(b) The third condition in Eq. [1] we find:

$$T=\frac{l_2W_{la}\sin\theta+l_1F_{ext}\sin\theta}{l_3\sin(\varphi+\theta)}$$
$$=\frac{(-(15\text{ cm})(22.5\text{ N})+(40\text{ cm})(343\text{ N}))\sin 8^0}{(4\text{ cm})\sin 16^0}$$

which yields T = 1690 N. This means that the force pulling on the hands while hanging on a high bar is equal to half the person's weight, but the tension in each of the biceps tendons is more than twice the weight! Thus, that tendon better be made of very strong tissue and be attached very firmly to the bone and the muscle.

(c) To obtain the two remaining unknown variables, F_{elbow} and ψ, we use conditions 1 and 2 in Eq. [1]. We isolate the terms that contain the two unknown variables first:

condition 1:

$$F_{elbow}\sin(\psi-\theta)+T\sin\varphi$$
$$=(1690\text{ N})\sin 8^0=235\text{ N} \quad \textbf{(2)}$$

condition 2:

$$F_{elbow}\cos(\psi-\theta)=T\cos\varphi+W_{la}-F_{ext}$$
$$=1355\text{ N}$$

To find F_{elbow}, both formulas are squared, and then the left and right sides are added, respectively. This eliminates the sine and cosine terms because $\sin^2\alpha+\cos^2\alpha=1$:

$$F_{elbow}=\sqrt{(235\text{ N})^2+(1355\text{ N})^2}=1375\text{ N} \quad \textbf{(3)}$$

The angle ψ is found by substituting the result in Eq. [3] in either one of the two conditions in Eq. [2]. We choose the first condition:

$$\sin(\psi-\theta)=\frac{235\text{ N}}{1375\text{ N}}=0.17$$

This yields $\psi-\theta=10^0$, or $\psi=18^0$. Again, note that the force $\mathbf{F_{elbow}}$ is a large force, in each arm twice the weight of the person!

CHAPTER SEVEN

Energy and its Conservation

MULTIPLE CHOICE QUESTIONS

Multiple Choice 7.1

Correct Answer (c). Note that since we have defined the joule so that 1 J = 1 N·m, another valid answer to this question would be J.

Multiple Choice 7.3

Correct Answer (b).

Multiple Choice 7.5

Correct Answer (f). The work done by the force is positive because the force is increasing the energy of the object.

Multiple Choice 7.7

Correct Answer (d). The work done by the system on the environment can be positive if for example the force and the displacement are in the same direction. It can be negative if for example the force and the displacement are in opposite directions. And it can be zero if for example the force and the displacement are perpendicular to each other.

Multiple Choice 7.9

Correct Answer (c).

Multiple Choice 7.11

Correct Answer (e). Increasing the speed will increase the object's kinetic energy, but we do not know that the increase in kinetic energy is related to a decrease in potential energy. Even if the sum of kinetic and potential energy of the system were conserved answer (E) remains correct because we can only quantify changes in potential energy but the absolute value is arbitrary.

Multiple Choice 7.13

Correct Answer (d).

Multiple Choice 7.15

Correct Answer (b). At the peak of its surge, the whale's centre of mass is ½ · 18 m = 9 m above the surface of the water. If that height is achieved by its speed at the instant it breaks the water surface, the speed can be calculated as follows.

$$v = \sqrt{2gh} = \sqrt{2\left(9.8\ m/s^2\right)\left(9m\right)} = 13.3\ m/s$$

The closest answer to this result is 15 m/s.

Multiple Choice 7.17

Correct Answer (d). The value of the gravitational potential energy (see Eq. [7.11]) depends on the choice of zero for the measurement of the height. If I chose the zero at ground level, my gravitational potential energy will be positive since I am sitting on a chair a bit higher than the ground, and $y > 0$. If I chose the zero at the chair level, my gravitational potential energy will be zero, and $y = 0$. If I chose the zero at the level of the ceiling, my gravitational potential energy will be negative, and $y < 0$.

Multiple Choice 7.19

Correct Answer (d). The maximum height is attained when all the kinetic energy is converted into gravitational potential energy. That is, if the zero for potential energy is chosen at the initial point, the initial potential energy is zero. Since the final kinetic energy is zero as the object reaches the maximum point then conservation of mechanical energy implies for this case:

$$E_{\text{kin};i} = E_{\text{pot};f}$$

Using the kinetic energy given by Eq. [7.7] and Eq. [7.11] for the gravitational potential energy, we find that:

$$h_f = \frac{v_i^2}{2g}$$

Note that this result is independent on the mass of the object. With the information given, we can calculate $h_f = 11.5$ m.

Multiple Choice 7.21
Correct Answer (d). Since the objects start from rest, the increase in kinetic energy is equal to the final kinetic energy. Given the connection through the ideal string the final speeds of both objects will be identical. This means that the object with the larger mass will have a larger final kinetic energy and thus will have experienced a larger increase in kinetic energy (see Eq. [7.7]). However, in Chapter 4 we found that for a frictionless table, the objects in Figure 4.4 will move regardless of whether $m_1 < m_2$, $m_1 = m_2$, or $m_1 > m_2$. Therefore, more information is needed to be able to determine which object experiences a larger increase in kinetic energy.

Multiple Choice 7.23
Correct Answer (c). The total energy of the system composed of both objects is conserved. This means that the energy gained by the object on the table is exactly equal to the energy lost by the hanging object. Therefore both objects changed their total energy by the same amount. You can show that this amount is exactly equal to:

$$\left(\frac{m_1}{m_1 + m_2}\right) m_2 g y ,$$

positive for the object on the table and negative for the hanging object.

Multiple Choice 7.25
Correct Answer (c). Since the object starts from rest its initial kinetic energy is zero. We can choose the zero-point for gravitational potential energy at the lowest point in the swing so that the final potential energy of the object is zero. Using Eq. [7.12] for the conservation of energy we find:

$$E_{\text{pot};i} = E_{\text{kin};f}$$

Using the kinetic energy given by Eq. [7.7] and Eq. [7.11] for the gravitational potential energy, we find that:

$$v_f = \sqrt{2h_i g} \qquad \textbf{(1)}$$

Given the geometry of the problem, you can show that:

$$h_i = L - L\sin\theta , \qquad \textbf{(2)}$$

where L is the length of the string and θ is the initial angle in the figure. Replacing the result from Eq. [2] into Eq. [1] we find:

$$v_f = \sqrt{2L(1-\sin\theta)g}$$

Note that this result is independent on the mass of the object. With the information given, we can calculate $v_f = 7.6$ m/s.

CONCEPTUAL QUESTIONS

Conceptual Question 7.1
You need less force but for a longer distance. In the end, you end up doing the same amount of work. Note that, if there is also friction acting on the object, you will end up doing extra work by increasing the distance over which that force acts.

Conceptual Question 7.3
Yes. We can see this in Eq. [7.11]. Since y is a vertical coordinate measured with respect to a chosen reference point it would be negative for any point below the reference. It is very important to note that in Eq. [7.11] the value of g does not have a sign.

Conceptual Question 7.5
To hold the object as depicted in the figure your muscles must remain in a non-relaxed state of contraction or extension. However, to maintain this state, at the microscopic level the muscles are contracting/expanding and relaxing by small amounts as the electrical excitation signals are received. The small contractions and expansions of the muscles then do work on the tendons and bones to which they are attached.

ANALYTICAL PROBLEMS

Problem 7.1

(a) The man is doing work against the gravitational force, therefore the work he does has the same magnitude and opposite sign of the work done by the gravitational force. Since the normal force is always perpendicular to the road, it does zero work. Using Eq. [7.1] the work done by the gravitational force is:

$$W_g = m\mathbf{g}\bullet\Delta\mathbf{r}. \quad \textbf{(1)}$$

Given the dot product in Eq. [1] only the displacement collinear with the gravitational force ends up being relevant. That is, only the vertical displacement or height above the point of departure. Furthermore, since the gravitational force is directed down and the vertical displacement is directed up, the work done by gravity will be negative. The result is that Eq. [1] becomes:

$$W_g = -mgh, \quad \textbf{(2)}$$

where $h = 250$ m, $g = 9.8$ m/s^2 and $m = m_s + m_b$ is the mass of the standard man and the bicycle combined, so that m = 100 kg is the mass of the standard man and the bicycle combined. Since the work done by the standard man W_s is of the same magnitude and opposite sign of the work done by the gravitational force, we find:

$$\begin{aligned} W_s &= -W_g = mgh \\ &= 250\,\text{kJ} \end{aligned} \quad \textbf{(3)}$$

(b) Recall that power is the rate at which energy is absorbed or released. In this problem, the energy is released in the form of work done by the standard man. Therefore:

$$\begin{aligned} \mathcal{P} &= \frac{W_s}{\Delta t} = \frac{250\,\text{kJ}}{1800\,\text{s}} \\ &= 140\,\text{W} \end{aligned}$$

Problem 7.3

As the man climbs the stairs he is doing work against the gravitational force. This means that the work he does has the same magnitude and opposite sign of the work done by the gravitational force. From Eq. [7.1] the work done by the gravitational force is:

$$W_g = m\mathbf{g}\bullet\Delta\mathbf{r}. \quad \textbf{(1)}$$

Given the dot product in Eq. [1] only the displacement collinear with the gravitational force ends up being relevant. That is, only the vertical displacement from the ground floor to the fourth floor. Furthermore, since the gravitational force is directed down and the vertical displacement is directed up, the work done by gravity will be negative. The result is that Eq. [1] becomes:

$$W_g = -mgh, \quad \textbf{(2)}$$

where $h = 16$ m, $g = 9.8$ m/s^2 and $m = 70$ kg is the mass of the standard man. Since the work done by the man W is of the same magnitude and opposite sign of the work done by the gravitational force, we find:

$$\begin{aligned} W &= -W_g = mgh \\ &= 11\,\text{kJ} \end{aligned} \quad \textbf{(3)}$$

Power is the rate at which energy is absorbed or released, and in this problem, the energy is released in the form of work done by the standard man. Therefore:

$$\begin{aligned} \mathcal{P} &= \frac{W}{\Delta t} = \frac{11\,\text{kJ}}{15\,\text{s}} \\ &= 730\,\text{W} \end{aligned}$$

Problem 7.5

A chin-up lifts the man a distance close the length of his arm. This distance is roughly the same as the distance for the knee-bend in problem P-7.4, that is, 60 cm. As the man lifts his body for one chin-up he is doing work against the gravitational force. This means that the work he does has the same magnitude and opposite sign of the work done by the gravitational force. The work done by the gravitational force (see Eq. [7.1]), is given by:

$$W_g = m\mathbf{g}\bullet\Delta\mathbf{r}. \quad \textbf{(1)}$$

Given the dot product in Eq. [1] only the displacement of 60 cm collinear with the gravitational force ends up being relevant. Furthermore, since the gravitational force is directed down and the vertical displacement is directed up, the work done by gravity will be negative. The result is that Eq. [1] becomes:

$$W_g = -mgh, \quad \textbf{(2)}$$

where h = 60 cm, g = 9.8 m/s^2 and m = 70 kg is the mass of the standard man. Then the work done by the man W for one knee-bend is:

$$W = -W_g = mgh \\ = 410\,\text{J} \qquad (3)$$

The total work done for the 12 knee-bends is thus W_{tot} = 4.9 kJ. Using Eq. [3] to find the power as the rate at which the man does work, we find:

$$\mathcal{P} = \frac{W_{tot}}{\Delta t} = \frac{4.9\,\text{kJ}}{60\,\text{s}} \\ = 82\,\text{W} \qquad (4)$$

In contrast, the power from P-7.4 was 2500 W, thirty times larger. We can conclude that, at least for short periods of time, human legs offer better performance than human arms.

Problem 7.7

The work done by the man is of the same magnitude but opposite sign of the work done by gravity. This is made even clearer in this problem by stating that the weight is lifted at constant speed so that the net force is zero. Therefore the lifting force balances the gravitational force. Since the gravitational force is collinear with the displacement but opposite in direction, the work done W_g is:

$$W_g = -mgh, \qquad (1)$$

where m = 40 kg, g = 9.8 m/s^2 and h = 1.9 m. Since the work done by the man is $W = -W_g$, from Eq. [1] we obtain:

$$W = -W_g = mgh \\ = 740\,\text{J}$$

Problem 7.9

The work done by the pushing force on the shopping cart can be calculated according to Eq. [7.2]:

$$W = |F| \cdot |\Delta r| \cdot \cos\theta, \qquad (1)$$

where the magnitude of the force is 40 N, the displacement of the cart is 10 m in magnitude, and the angle between the force and the displacement is 30°. Note that the work will be positive, as the force and the displacement are on the same direction.

Substituting the given values into Eq. [1] we find the work to be:

$$W = (40\,\text{N}) \cdot (10\,\text{m}) \cdot \cos 30° \\ = 350\,\text{J}$$

Problem 7.11

(a) We neglect air resistance. The diver is not in mechanical equilibrium as a continuous acceleration occurs. We use the conservation of energy with the initial state of the system when the diver leaves the platform and the final state when the diver reaches the water surface. The initial state is chosen because we know all required parameters at that point: the diver starts from rest and is 35 m above the water surface. The final state is chosen at the water surface because the unknown parameter, the final speed v_{final}, applies at that point. We write:

$$E_{kin,initial} + E_{pot,initial} = E_{kin,final} + E_{pot,final} \qquad (1)$$

The individual terms for the diver are:

$$E_{kin,initial} = 0 \\ E_{pot,initial} = m \cdot g \cdot h \\ E_{kin,final} = \frac{1}{2} m \cdot v_{final}^2 \\ E_{pot,final} \qquad (2)$$

The initial kinetic energy is zero because the diver starts from rest. The final potential energy is zero since we choose y = 0 at the surface of the water. Therefore, the initial height is $y = h$ = 35 m. We substitute the four formulas from Eq. [2] in Eq. [1]:

$$m \cdot g \cdot h = \frac{1}{2} m \cdot v_{final}^2$$

which yields:

$$v_{final} = \sqrt{2 \cdot g \cdot h} \qquad (3)$$

Note that Eq. [18] does not contain the mass of the system, i.e., it applies to all divers, whether they confirm to standard man data or not.

Substituting the values given in the problem text we find:

$$v_{final} = \sqrt{2\left(9.8\frac{m}{s^2}\right)35m}$$

$$= 26\frac{m}{s} = 94\frac{km}{h}$$

This result indicates why these dives are only done by professional athletes: you don't want to hit the water surface with that speed unless your body is perfectly aligned for the dive. Compounding the risk in Mexico is the fact that the water at the bottom of the cliff is rather shallow and the divers have to ensure that a wave has rolled in when they enter the water.

(b) Figure 1 shows a sketch of the diver and the corresponding energy plots (centre) and plots of speed versus height (left). The total mechanical energy is constant and the potential energy increases linearly with height. Due to energy conservation, the kinetic energy decreases linearly with height, $E_{kin} = ½ m \cdot v^2 \propto \text{const} - y$. The square–root of this relation describes the speed as a function of height, i.e., $v \propto (\text{const} - y)^{1/2}$. Note that the graph of velocity versus time for an object in free–fall is a parabola, whereas this curve is a square root. This is because we are plotting versus distance in this problem.

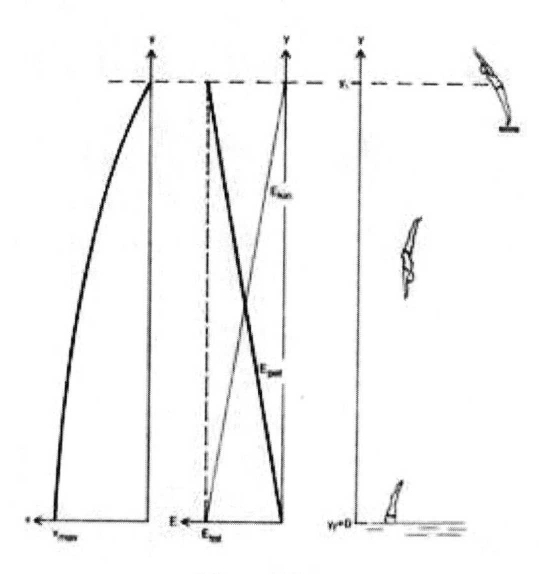

Figure 1

Problem 7.13

We apply the conservation of energy. The initial instant is chosen at the release of the objects from rest, and the final instant when mass m_3 has moved 0.4 m downward:

$$E_{kin,initial} + E_{pot,initial} = E_{kin,final} + E_{pot,final} \quad \textbf{(1)}$$

For each of the three objects, we identify all the terms in Eq. [1] separately:

- The initial kinetic energy of all three objects is zero since they are connected by taut strings. When one of the objects is at rest, the other two must be at rest, too.
- The initial potential energy we choose to be zero by defining the initial position of each object as the respective origin along the vertical axis.
- The final kinetic energy contains the unknown variable. Thus, we leave that term unchanged in Eq. [1] for now.
- The final potential energy has three contributions, one due to each of the three objects. Since the object of mass m_2 moves across a horizontal surface only, its potential energy does not change; the other two objects, however, contribute:

$$E_{pot,final} = m_1 g y_{1,final} + m_3 g y_{3,final}$$

$$= (5kg(0.4m) + 15kg(-0.4m))\left(9.8\frac{m}{s^2}\right)$$

where a downward displacement of $\Delta y_3 = -0.4$ m for the object of mass m_3 means an upward displacement of the object of mass m_1 because the connecting strings are taut: $\Delta y_1 = +0.4$ m. This yields:

$$E_{pot,final} = -39.2J$$

Next we enter all energy contributions at the initial and final states into Eq. [1]:

$$0 = -39.2J + \frac{1}{2}(m_1 + m_2 + m_3)v_{final}^2$$

There is only one speed, v_{final}, associated with the total final kinetic energy because all three objects move at the same speed at all times. The final speed is:

$$v_{final} = \sqrt{\frac{2(39.2J)}{(5+10+15)kg}} = 1.62\frac{m}{s}$$

Problem 7.15

At the highest point, the baseball will have a velocity equal to its initial velocity in the horizontal direction. Thus E_{kin} = ½ m (v cos(30^0))^2 = 90 J.

Problem 7.17

This problem is solved in the same fashion as Problem 7.17:

$$h = \frac{\left(v_{final}^2 - v_{initial}^2\right)}{2 \cdot g} = 46\ cm$$

Problem 7.19

We use Eq. [7.7] for the kinetic energy of an object of mass m travelling at speed v.

(a) Since m = 0.5 kg and v_1 = 2.5 m/s, at position 1 the kinetic energy is:

$$E_{\text{kin;1}} = \frac{1}{2}mv_1^2$$
$$= 1.6\,\text{J}$$

(b) Since m = 0.5 kg and $E_{\text{kin;2}}$ = 10.0 J at position 2, we can solve Eq. [7.7] for the speed to obtain:

$$v_2 = \sqrt{\frac{2E_{\text{kin;2}}}{m}}$$
$$= 6.3\,\text{m/s}$$

(c) Using Eq. [7.8] also know as the Work – Kinetic Energy Theorem, the total work W done as the object moves from position 1 to position 2 is:

$$W = E_{\text{kin;2}} - E_{\text{kin;1}}$$
$$= 10.0\,\text{J} - 1.56\,\text{J} = 8.44\,\text{J}\,,$$

where we used the result from part (a). Note that the work done is positive, in agreement with the fact that the speed of the object increased.

Problem 7.21

The gravitational potential energy of an object is given by Eq. [7.11]:

$$E_{\text{pot}} = mgy\,, \qquad \textbf{(1)}$$

where m = 1.8 kg is the mass of the object, the gravitational acceleration is g = 9.8 m/s^2, and y is the height of the object with respect to the reference point.

(a) The height of the object with respect to the ceiling is y_a = −1.2 m. Therefore, replacing in Eq. [1] we find:

$$E_{\text{pot};a} = mgy_a$$
$$= -21\,\text{J}$$

(b) The height of the object with respect to the floor is y_b = 2.8 m – 1.2 m = 1.6 m. Therefore, replacing in Eq. [1] we find:

$$E_{\text{pot};b} = mgy_b$$
$$= 28\,\text{J}$$

(c) The height of the object with respect to its equilibrium position is y_c = 0 m. Therefore, replacing in Eq. [1] we find:

$$E_{\text{pot};c} = mgy_c$$
$$= 0\,\text{J}$$

Problem 7.23

We assume that an object moves with speed v_{object} through a medium of density ρ. To achieve this motion, fluid in front of the object must be pushed aside, which is only possible if this fluid is accelerated to a speed v_{fluid}. For simplicity we assume that $v_{object} = v_{fluid} = v$. The mass of fluid, m_{fluid}, accelerated during time interval Δt is:

$$m_{fluid} = \rho \cdot A \cdot v \cdot \Delta t$$

in which $v \cdot \Delta t$ is the length of the column of the fluid affected by the moving object and A is the cross–sectional area of the moving object.

The acceleration of the fluid to velocity v means that energy has been transferred to the fluid equal to its final kinetic energy:

$$E_{transfer} = \Delta E_{kin,fluid}$$

$$= \frac{1}{2} m_{fluid} \cdot v_{fluid}^2 = \frac{1}{2} \rho \cdot A \cdot v^3 \cdot \Delta t \quad \textbf{(1)}$$

Dividing Eq. [1] by Δt gives us the rate at which energy is transferred, which is a power term:

$$P = \frac{\Delta E_{kin,fluid}}{\Delta t} = \frac{1}{2} \rho \cdot A \cdot v^3 \quad \textbf{(2)}$$

In general, power is defined as:

$$P = \mathrm{F} \bullet \mathrm{v}$$

i.e., the power is the applied force multiplied with the velocity. In the current case the force is the drag force, F thus Eq. [2] yields:

$$\mathscr{F} = \frac{1}{2} \rho \cdot A \cdot v^2$$

which is equal to the drag force in Chapter 3 except for a missing drag coefficient D.

Problem 7.25

Write the conservation of momentum equations for the system that is the ball and the club. For illustration, we further use a slightly different notation with capital and small letters for the different velocities instead of indices 1 and 2:

$$MV_{initial} + mv_{initial} = MV_{final} + mv_{final}$$

The capital letters refer to the club, the lowercase letters refer to the ball. Rearrange and solve for the speed of the golf ball just after impact:

$$v_{final} = \frac{MV_{initial} + mv_{initial} - MV_{initial}}{m}$$

Substituting the given data, this gives us v_{final} = 65 m/s. Given the ratio of the masses, this seems like a reasonable value.

Problem 7.27

To set up the problem, let m represent the mass of each object moving initially with speed v; in the positive direction for the first object, in the negative direction for the second object. Furthermore, let v_1 represent the final velocity of the first object and v_2 the final velocity of the second object after the collision. Eq. [7.15] for conservation of momentum yields:

$$m \cdot v - m \cdot v = m \cdot v_1 + m \cdot v_2$$

$$v_2 = -v_1 \quad , \quad \textbf{(1)}$$

where we simplified the equation in the last step. Similarly, Eq. [7.16] for conservation of mechanical energy yields:

$$\frac{1}{2} m v^2 + \frac{1}{2} m v^2 = \frac{1}{2} m v_1^2 + \frac{1}{2} m v_2^2$$

$$2v^2 = v_1^2 + v_2^2 \quad , \quad \textbf{(2)}$$

where we simplified terms of $m/2$ in the last step. We substitute Eq. [1] into Eq. [2] to obtain:

$$v_1^2 = v^2 \quad \textbf{(3)}$$

Eq. [3] has $v_1 = v$ as a possible solution. This solution is unphysical since it means that the first mass passes through the second mass continuing to move unaffected in the positive direction, while the second mass passes through the first mass continuing to movee unaffected in the negative direction. The physically meaningful solution of Eq. [3] is:

$$v_1 = -v \qquad (4)$$

Substituting Eq. [4] back into Eq. [1]:

$$v_2 = v \qquad (5)$$

Eq. [4] and Eq. [5] mean that each mass reverses direction with the same exact speed as it had before the collision.

(b) Using Eq. [7.7], the initial kinetic energy of the first mass is:

$$E_{\text{kin;i}} = \frac{1}{2}mv^2 \qquad (6)$$

Using Eq. [7.7] and Eq. [4], the final kinetic energy of the first mass is:

$$E_{\text{kin;1}} = \frac{1}{2}mv_1^2 = \frac{1}{2}mv^2 \qquad (7)$$

Given that $E_{\text{kin;1}} = E_{\text{kin;i}}$ no kinetic energy is transferred.

(c) When an object collides elastically with an stationary wall its kinetic energy is unchanged as found in Eq. [8], while its velocity changes direction keeping the same magnitude as found in Eq. [4]. The two situations described are identical in the end result from the perspective of one of the objects.

Problem 7.29

We solve this problem in two parts. In part (a) object 1 swings down from rest to a final speed at the lowest point in the swing. In part (b) object 1 moving at the speed found in part (a) collides elastically with object 2.

(a) There are only two forces acting on the object: gravity and the tension from the string. Since the tension from the string is perpendicular to the displacement it does zero work and thus does not affect the total mechanical energy. Since the other force is gravity we can use conservation of mechanical energy. Since the object starts from rest $v_i = 0$ and $E_{\text{kin,i}} = 0$. Furthermore, if we set the lowest point in the swing as the reference zero for potential energy, $y_f = 0$ and $E_{\text{pot,f}} = 0$. Using Eq. [7.12] we obtain:

$$E_{\text{kin,i}} + E_{\text{pot,i}} = E_{\text{kin,f}} + E_{\text{pot,f}}$$

$$0 + m_1 g y_i = \frac{1}{2}m_1 v_f^2 + 0 \qquad (1)$$

From Figure 7.19 $y_i = h$ so that:

$$y_i = L - L\cos\theta$$
$$= L(1-\cos\theta) \qquad (2)$$

Substituting Eq. [2] into Eq. [1] and solving for v_f yields:

$$v_f = \sqrt{2gL(1-\cos\theta)}$$
$$= 2.65\ \text{m/s} \qquad (3)$$

(b) Right before the elastic collision object 1 starts with a velocity $v_{1;i} = 2.65$ m/s as found in Eq. [3] of part (a), and collides with object 2 found at rest so $v_{2;i} = 0$. Let $v_{1;f}$ and $v_{2;f}$ represent the final velocities of objects 1 and 2 respectively. The gravitational force, being a conservative force, allows us that the lowest point in the swing. We can use the result from P-7.30 for the elastic collision:

$$v_{1;i} + v_{1;f} = \cancel{v_{2;i}} + v_{2;f}, \qquad (4)$$

which can be reorganized into:

$$v_{1;f} = v_{2;f} - v_{1;i} \qquad (5)$$

From Eq. [15] for conservation and momentum we can write:

$$m_1 v_{1;i} + \cancel{m_2 v_{2;i}} = m_1 v_{1;f} + m_2 v_{2;f} \qquad (6)$$

Substituting Eq. [5] into Eq. [6] we find:

$$m_1 v_{1;i} = m_1\left(v_{2;f} - v_{1;i}\right) + m_2 v_{2;f}$$

$$2m_1 v_{1;i} = \left(m_1 + m_2\right) v_{2;f} \qquad (7)$$

We can simplify Eq. [7] to find the final speed of object 2:

$$v_{2;f} = \frac{2m_1 v_{1;i}}{m_1 + m_2} \qquad (8)$$

Since the result for v_f from Eq. [3] in part (a) is precisely $v_{1;i}$ from part (b) we can write:

$$v_{2;f} = \left(\frac{2m_1}{m_1 + m_2}\right)\sqrt{2gL(1-\cos\theta)}$$
$$= 3.5\,\mathrm{m/s} \quad ,$$

using the values of $m_1 = 0.1$ kg, $m_2 = 0.05$ kg, $L = 1.0$ m, $\theta = 50°$, and $g = 9.8\ \mathrm{m/s^2}$.

Problem 7.31

With the convention of positive to the right and negative to the left, the initial velocities are given by $v_{1;i} = 25$ cm/s and $v_{2;i} = -45$ cm/s. We can use the result from problem P-7.30 for elastic collisions:

$$v_{1;i} + v_{1;f} = v_{2;i} + v_{2;f}\ , \qquad \textbf{(1)}$$

where we are trying to find $v_{1;f}$ and $v_{2;f}$. We can reorganize Eq. [1] into:

$$v_{1;f} = v_{2;i} + v_{2;f} - v_{1;i} \qquad \textbf{(2)}$$

Reorganizing Eq. [15] for conservation of momentum, we can write:

$$m_2 v_{2;f} = m_1 v_{1;i} + m_2 v_{2;i} - m_1 v_{1;f} \qquad \textbf{(3)}$$

Substituting $v_{1;f}$ from Eq. [2] into Eq. [3] and reorganizing similar terms we find:

$$(m_1 + m_2)v_{2;f} = (m_2 - m_1)v_{2;i} + 2m_1 v_{1;i} \quad \textbf{(4)}$$

Solving for $v_{2;f}$:

$$v_{2;f} = \left(\frac{2m_1}{m_1 + m_2}\right)v_{1;i} + \left(\frac{m_2 - m_1}{m_1 + m_2}\right)v_{2;i} \quad \textbf{(5)}$$

Taking Eq. [5] into Eq. [2] will yield $v_{1;f}$ as:

$$v_{1;f} = \left(\frac{m_1 - m_2}{m_1 + m_2}\right)v_{1;i} + \left(\frac{2m_2}{m_1 + m_2}\right)v_{2;i} \quad \textbf{(6)}$$

The given values of $m_1 = 7.5$ g, $m_2 = 12.5$ g, $v_{1;i} = 25$ cm/s, and $v_{2;i} = -45$ cm/s when substituted into Eq. [5] and Eq. [6] yield:

$$v_{1;f} = -62.5\,\mathrm{cm/s} \quad \text{and} \quad v_{2;f} = 7.5\,\mathrm{cm/s}$$

Problem 7.33

We split the problem in two parts. In part (a) the bird flies off horizontally making the base of the swing recoil backwards with a speed that can be found using conservation of momentum. This is a process similar to an inelastic collision in reverse, much like the ejection process in P-5.19. Then, in part (b) the base of the swing moves up until it reaches its maximum height after converting all of its kinetic energy into potential energy. Energy is conserved in part (b) because the only other force besides gravity is the tension in the string of the swing. Since the tension is perpendicular to the displacement it does no work and thus does not affect conservation of energy.

(a) We call m_b the mass of the bird and m_s the bass of the base of the swing. From Chapter 3 we know that:

$$w = mg\ ,$$

so that:

$$m_b = \frac{w_b}{g} \quad \text{and} \quad m_s = \frac{w_s}{g} \qquad \textbf{(1)}$$

We can use the values $w_b = 0.6$ N, $w_s = 1.6$ N, and g = 9.8 m/s^2 in Eq. [1] to find m_b and m_s. From Eq. [15] for conservation of momentum:

$$0 = m_b v_b + m_s v_s\ , \qquad \textbf{(2)}$$

where the initial momentum is zero because both the bird and the base of the swing are at rest. We can solve Eq. [2] for the velocity of the base of the swing v_s:

$$v_s = -\left(\frac{m_b}{m_s}\right)v_b$$
$$= -\left(\frac{w_b}{w_s}\right)v_b\ , \qquad \textbf{(3)}$$

where in the last step we also used Eq. [1] to write the result in terms of the weights. It is worth noting that as expected the velocity of the base of the swing is opposite in direction to the velocity of the bird.

(b) We now use conservation of mechanical energy in the form of Eq. [7.12]. Note that since we are trying to find the highest point that the base of the swing reaches, its speed at that point will be zero and thus the final kinetic energy is also zero. Furthermore, if we set the zero for potential energy at the lowest point in the swing, the initial potential energy is also zero. With these considerations in mind, conservation of energy from Eq. [7.12] gives:

$$E_{\text{kin,i}} + 0 = 0 + E_{\text{pot,f}}$$

$$\frac{1}{2} m_s v_s^2 = m_s g h \quad , \qquad \textbf{(4)}$$

where v_s is the initial speed of the base at the start of the swing, and h is the maximum height the base of the swing reaches. Substituting Eq. [3] into Eq. [4] and simplifying:

$$h = \frac{v_s^2}{2g} = \left(\frac{w_b}{w_s} \right)^2 \frac{v_b^2}{2g} \qquad \textbf{(5)}$$

Using the values given by the problem, we find that $h = 4.5$ cm, is the maximum height that the base of the swing reaches with respect to its original position.

CHAPTER EIGHT

Gases

MULTIPLE CHOICE QUESTIONS

Multiple Choice 8.1

Correct Answer (b). Choices (C), (D) and (E) do not result in $T = \alpha$ at $h = H$. Choice (A) implies $T \propto -h$, i.e., the mercury column would shrink for rising temperatures.

Multiple Choice 8.3

Correct Answer (d).

Multiple Choice 8.5

Correct Answer (c).

Multiple Choice 8.7

Correct Answer (e). As shown in Eq. [8.25], v_{rms} is proportional to the square root of the temperature and inversely proportional to the square root of the molar mass, so it cannot be (A) or (B). If we interpret the quantity of gas in (C) as the mass in one mol, it is the same as (A). If we interpret the quantity of gas in (C) as the volume in one mol, using the ideal gas law in Eq. [8.16] into Eq. [8.25] we find that v_{rms} is proportional to the square root to the molar volume. Also, using Eq. [8.16] into Eq. [8.25] we find that v_{rms} is proportional to the square root of the pressure.

Multiple Choice 8.9

Correct Answer (d). The new law reads:

$$p = \frac{\rho R T}{M}$$

The pressure across the envelope is equal inside and outside the blimp. The density of helium is less than the density of air. This is needed for the buoyant force to balance the gravitational force and keep the blimp airborne. A typical helium blimp has no heating source, as it is not needed. The pressure is the same on account of the lower molar mass of helium. No quantity must increase as the decrease in density and the decrease in molar mass are sufficient conditions for the blimp to stay airborne.

Multiple Choice 8.11

Part (a): Correct Answer (a).

$$v_{rms} = \sqrt{\frac{3\,(8.314\dfrac{\text{J}}{\text{K}\cdot\text{mol}})(323\text{ K})}{0.002\text{ kg/mol}}} = 2007\frac{\text{m}}{\text{s}}$$

Part (b): Although the energy of the molecule will be also distributed amongst the rotational and vibrational degrees of freedom, only the translational energy contributes to the v_{rms} of the gas molecule and thus the calculation is correct for molecules.

Part (c): Correct Answer (a). The molecular mass of H is half the molecular mass of H_2 so the v_{rms} of the H-atoms is $\sqrt{2}$ larger than the v_{rms} of the H_2-molecules at the same temperature.

Multiple Choice 8.13

Correct Answer (a).

Multiple Choice 8.15

Correct Answer (d). The pressure would be doubled.

Multiple Choice 8.17

Correct Answer (a). Helium, being the lighter gas, has the greater root–mean–square speed at the same temperature.

Multiple Choice 8.19

Correct Answer (c). We know that:

$$\frac{\Delta U}{U} = \frac{\frac{3}{2} n \cdot R(T_{\text{final}} - T_{\text{initial}})}{\frac{3}{2} n \cdot R T_{\text{initial}}}$$

In this case, $T_{\text{final}} = 310$ K and $T_{\text{initial}} = 293$ K. When evaluated, this shows that the internal energy of the air increases by about 5% over the initial value.

Multiple Choice 8.21

Correct Answer (b). We use Eq. [8.24] and the Key Point right after it.

CONCEPTUAL QUESTIONS

Conceptual Question 8.1

In the case of such an astronomically large temperature, the difference is less than 0.002%. Chances are good that such a small difference would be insignificant. But, check out the percentage error you would get when reporting the temperature that water freezes if you need to convince yourself that it is important to know which unit is being used.

Conceptual Question 8.3

At fixed volume and amount of gas, the pressure is proportional to temperature, $p \propto T$. Thus, on a warmer day the bubbles are more bulging.

Conceptual Question 8.5

Cylinder A has three times the pressure of cylinder B.

Conceptual Question 8.7

Molecules attract each other (otherwise gases would never condense). Boiling leads to an increase in volume of the system, which means an increase of inter– molecular distances at a molecular scale. Energy is needed to separate molecules against this attractive force.

Conceptual Question 8.9

The velocity is a vector with three components. In a given coordinate system, as many gas particles move in the direction of a positive axis as move in the direction of the corresponding negative axis; thus, the average is zero. Were this not so, we would have to notice a direction of preferential air motion (like in an operating wind–tunnel).

Conceptual Question 8.11

Dry air consists mostly of nitrogen and oxygen molecules with respective molar masses of 28 g/mol and 32 g/mol. In humid air of otherwise identical parameters, water molecules with a molar mass of 18 g/mol displace some of the nitrogen and oxygen molecules. Thus, in humid air, lighter molecules replace heavier ones, and therefore, humid air is lighter than the same amount of dry air. Note that this applies only as long as the air remains a single phase. Once phase separation occurs, e.g., in clouds where water condensation on dust particles leads to levitating water droplets in the air, the argument remains no longer valid as each phase develops separately. In particular, the denser liquid water phase undergoes a ripening process until droplets are large enough to fall toward the ground (rain).

ANALYTICAL PROBLEMS

Problem 8.1

(a) We use the ideal gas law in the form:

$$p \cdot V = n \cdot R \cdot T$$

For the first plot, we need the volume to be the dependent variable and the temperature to be the independent variable:

$$V = \frac{n \cdot R}{p} T$$

In this equation is n = 1.0 mol and the pressure is either p = 0.2 atm = 20.26 kPa, or p = 5.0 atm = 506.5 kPa. We plot in Figure 1:

$$(I) \quad V(\mathrm{m}^3) = 4.1 \times 10^{-4} T(\mathrm{K})$$
$$(II) \quad V(\mathrm{m}^3) = 1.6 \times 10^{-5} T(\mathrm{K})$$

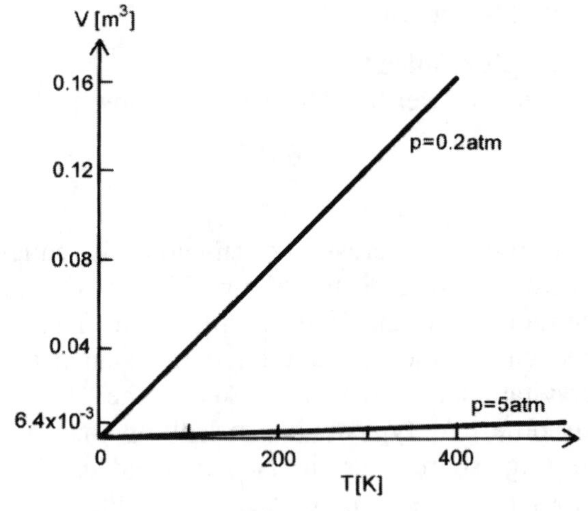

Figure 1

(b) The ideal gas equation is rewritten such that the pressure is the dependent variable and the volume is the independent variable:

$$p = \frac{n \cdot R \cdot T}{V}$$

Using again $n = 1.0$ mol, we plot Figure 2:

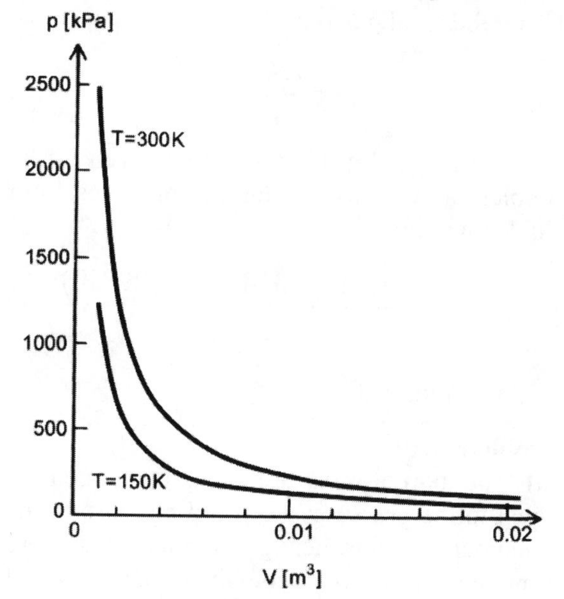

Figure 2

$$(I) \quad T = 300\,\text{K} \Rightarrow p(\text{kPa}) = \frac{2.494}{V(\text{m}^3)}$$

$$(II) \quad T = 150\,\text{K} \Rightarrow p(\text{kPa}) = \frac{1.247}{V(\text{m}^3)}$$

Problem 8.3

This problem is an application of the ideal gas law. Since the mass of the gas is given and the molar mass is sought, we rewrite the ideal gas law in the form $p \cdot V = (m/M)\, R \cdot T$:

$$M = \frac{m \cdot R \cdot T}{p \cdot V} \qquad (1)$$

In Eq. [1], m is the mass of air, which is obtained from:

$$m = m_{full} - m_{evacuated} = 0.4807 \times 10^{-3}\,\text{kg}$$

By substituting the remaining data given in the problem, including a temperature of 20°C = 293 K, and the air pres-sure in the container as 1.0 atm = 1.013×10^5 Pa, we find:

$$M = \frac{0.4807 \times 10^{-3}\,\text{kg}\left(8.314\,\frac{\text{J}}{\text{K mol}}\right)293\,\text{K}}{(1.013 \times 10^5\,\text{Pa})(400 \times 10^{-6}\,\text{m}^3)}$$

$$= 0.0289\,\frac{\text{kg}}{\text{mol}} = 28.9\,\frac{\text{g}}{\text{mol}}$$

We usually use a value of 29 g/mol for the molar mass of air.

Problem 8.5

We have $V_{\text{final}}/V_{\text{initial}} = 3/2$ because

$$\frac{V_2}{V_1} = \frac{p_1}{p_2}\frac{T_2}{T_1} = \left(\frac{2}{1}\right)\left(\frac{3}{4}\right) = \frac{3}{2}$$

Problem 8.7

The final pressure is $p_{\text{final}} = 5.87$ atm because

$$p_2 = \frac{n_2}{n_1}\frac{T_2}{T_1}p_1 = 5.87\,\text{atm}$$

Be sure to convert the temperatures into kelvin.

Problem 8.9

Use the ideal gas law to find:

$$r_1 = \left(\frac{T_1}{T_2}\frac{p_2}{p_1}r_2^3\right)^{1/3} = 15.3\,\text{m}$$

Note that the subscript 1 refers to the state on the ground, and the subscript 2 refers to the state in the air. Also, recognize that what is given in the question is a diameter, when what we use in this formula is the radius.

Problem 8.11

(a) Use

$$v_{rms} = \sqrt{\frac{3RT}{M}}$$

with $M_{H2} = 0.002$ kg/mol and $M_{CO2} = 0.044$ kg/mol to find $v_{\text{rms}}(H_2) = 1.73$ km/s and $v_{\text{rms}}(CO_2) = 370$ m/s.

(b) We have $v_{\text{escape}}/6 = 1.71$ km/s. Since $v_{\text{rms}}(H_2)$ is slightly larger than this, it will eventually be depleted from Venus.

Problem 8.13

(a) We use the ideal gas law to find:

$$n = \frac{PV}{RT} = \frac{(1.45 \times 10^7 \text{ Pa})(0.12 \text{ m}^3)}{(8.314 \text{ J/K·mol})(293 \text{ K})} \quad (1)$$
$$= 714 \text{ mol}$$

(b) We use again the ideal gas law with the number of moles found in Eq. [1] at the new pressure to find the total final volume:

$$V_f = \frac{nRT}{p} = \frac{(714 \text{ mol})(8.314 \text{ J/K·mol})(293 \text{ K})}{(1.013 \times 10^5 \text{ Pa})} \quad (2)$$
$$= 17.2 \text{ m}^3 = 1.72 \times 10^4 \text{ L}$$

The volume that escaped the cylinder, V_{escape}, would be the volume found in Eq. [2] minus the 120 L remaining in the cylinder, that is:

$$V_{left} = V_f - V_i = 1.71 \times 10^4 \text{ L}$$

Problem 8.15

Assuming the gas is monoatomic and there are no other forms of energy besides the thermal energy (that is, no potential energies, chemical or mechanical), we use Eq. [8.24] and the ideal gas law to write:

$$U = \frac{3}{2} nRT = \left(\frac{3}{2} \cancel{nR}\right)\left(\frac{pV}{\cancel{nR}}\right) \quad (1)$$
$$= \frac{3}{2} pV$$

Substituting the given values into Eq. [1]:

$$U = \frac{3}{2}(5 \times 1.013 \times 10^5 \text{ Pa})(0.010 \text{ m}^3)$$
$$= 7.6 \text{ kJ}$$

Problem 8.17

Since the molar mass of N_2 is $M = 14$ g/mol, a mass $m = 25$ g of nitrogen gas will contain a total of:

$$n = \frac{m}{M} = 1.79 \text{ mol} \quad (1)$$

Using the ideal gas law:

$$p = \frac{nRT}{V} \quad (2)$$

Substituting in Eq. [2] the values given in the problem as well as the number of moles from Eq. [1] we find:

$$p = \frac{(1.79 \text{ mol})(8.314 \text{ J/K·mol})(298 \text{ K})}{(1.0 \times 10^{-3} \text{ m}^3)}$$
$$= 4.42 \times 10^6 \text{ Pa}$$

Problem 8.19

(a) The partial pressure of a component is equal to the pressure we would measure in the container if all other gas components were removed from the container. The partial pressure of the oxygen component is treated as an ideal gas:

$$p_{O_2} = \frac{n_{O_2} \cdot R \cdot T}{V} \quad (1)$$

To substitute the given values in Eq. [1] we need to determine the amount of oxygen gas in the container:

$$n_{O_2} = \frac{m_{O_2}}{M_{O_2}} = \frac{0.25 \text{ g}}{32 \frac{\text{g}}{\text{mol}}} = 7.8 \text{ mmol}$$

This yields for the partial pressure of oxygen:

$$p_{O_2} = \frac{7.8 \text{ mmol}\left(8.314 \frac{\text{J}}{\text{K} \cdot \text{mol}}\right) 293 \text{ K}}{2.0 \times 10^{-3} \text{ m}^3}$$
$$= 9.5 \text{ kPa}$$

(b) The calculation for the nitrogen component is done in an analogous fashion. We thus find $n(N_2) = 53.6$ mmol and for the partial pressure $p(N_2) = 65.25$ kPa.

(c) The total pressure of the system follows from the single partial pressures:

$$p = p_{O_2} + p_{N_2} = 74.75 \text{ kPa}$$

Problem 8.21

The difference in mass between the evacuated bulb and the bulb filled with dry air is then the mass of dry air in the bulb:

$$\begin{aligned} m_{\text{air}} &= m_{\text{total}} - m_{\text{empty}} \\ &= 46.0529\,\text{g} - 45.9214\,\text{g} \\ &= 131.5\,\text{mg} \end{aligned} \quad \textbf{(1)}$$

As the molar mass of air is $M_{\text{air}} = 29$ g/mol, we can use Eq. [1] to find the number of moles of air in the bulb:

$$\begin{aligned} n_{\text{air}} &= \frac{m_{\text{air}}}{M_{\text{air}}} = \frac{0.1315\,\text{g}}{29.0\,\text{g}/\text{mol}} \\ &= 4.5345\,\text{mmol} \end{aligned} \quad \textbf{(2)}$$

With the bulb filled with the gas mixture, since the volume, pressure, and temperature are the same as when the bulb is filled with air, the ideal gas law implies that we have the same number of moles as found in Eq. [2] of the gas mixture, that is:

$$n_{\text{mix}} = 4.5345\,\text{mmol} \quad \textbf{(3)}$$

The difference in mass between the evacuated bulb and the bulb filled with the gas mixture is the mass of gas mixture in the bulb:

$$\begin{aligned} m_{\text{mix}} &= m_{\text{total}} - m_{\text{empty}} \\ &= 46.0141\,\text{g} - 45.9214\,\text{g} \\ &= 92.70\,\text{mg} \end{aligned} \quad \textbf{(4)}$$

If the mass of methane in the mix is m_e and the mass of ethane in the mix is m_m then:

$$\begin{aligned} m_{\text{mix}} &= m_m + m_e \\ &= n_m M_m + n_e M_e \\ &= n_{\text{mix}} x_m M_m + n_{\text{mix}} x_e M_e \end{aligned} \quad , \quad \textbf{(5)}$$

where M_m and M_e are the molar masses of methane and ethane respectively, and x_m and x_e are the molar fractions of methane and ethane respectively.

We can rewrite Eq. [5] as:

$$\frac{m_{\text{mix}}}{n_{\text{mix}}} = x_m M_m + x_e M_e \quad \textbf{(6)}$$

Given that methane and ethane make up the entire gas mix, their molar fractions must obey:

$$x_m + x_e = 1 \quad \textbf{(7)}$$

Eq. [6] and Eq. [7] form a linear system in the two unknowns x_m and x_e and thus can be solved simultaneously for both variables using the values from Eq. [3], Eq. [4], and the molar masses of methane and ethane, $M_m = 16$ g/mol and $M_e = 30$ g/mol. Solving for the molar fraction of methane:

$$x_m = \frac{M_e - (m_{\text{mix}}/n_{\text{mix}})}{(M_e - M_m)} = 0.683$$

CHAPTER NINE

Work and Heat for Non-Mechanical Systems

MULTIPLE CHOICE QUESTIONS

Multiple Choice 9.1

Correct Answer (d). A system receiving mechanical work at constant pressure will decrease its volume. At the same time, its pressure will increase. However, in a process where the pressure changes inversely proportional to the volume the system will receive work at constant temperature. This also highlights the possibility of the pressure remaining constant or changing. These arguments highlight how (B) and (C) are not valid answers. The reason for (A) not being the correct answer is that our system need not be a non-mechanical system. If the system is for example a box falling under the influence of gravity, our discussion in Chapter 7 tells us that the box receives work from the gravitational force and yet its volume does not decrease or change.

Multiple Choice 9.3

Correct Answer (c).

Multiple Choice 9.5

Correct Answer (c). All three work terms are positive because $\Delta V < 0$ and $W = -p \cdot \Delta V$. The largest area under the curve in the p–V diagram then gives the largest value.

Multiple Choice 9.7

Correct Answer (b). We can break the cycle into an expansion section and a compression section. The expansion section on the path, going from left to right produces an area under the curve that is larger than the compression section on the path, going from right to left. This means that the expansion work during the cycle is larger than the compression work. Therefore the net work done during the cycle is negative and the system releases work per cycle. This feature of cyclic processes can be described qualitatively by noting that the net work for clockwise oriented processes is negative and thus the system releases work. In contrast, the net work for counter-clockwise oriented processes is positive and thus the system receives work per cycle.

Multiple Choice 9.9

Correct Answer (f). Remember that while compression work is positive, expansion work is negative. Step II has no change in volume so the work done is zero. Step I is an expansion so the work done is negative and therefore smaller than the work done in Step II. Step III is a compression so the work done is positive, larger than the work done in Step II or Step I.

Multiple Choice 9.11

Correct Answer (c).

Multiple Choice 9.13

Correct Answer (e). The change in temperature in a closed system is related to its change in internal energy. A closed system can change its internal energy due to a contribution from heat or work (see Eq. [9.9]). Therefore, although the heat is doubled, the temperature will not necessarily double on account of contributions from the work. Energy additions to the work can be in any amount completely unrelated to the heat being added.

Multiple Choice 9.15

Correct Answer (b). The ethyl alcohol temperature increase (ΔT) is about twice that of water. We are assuming that equal amounts, by mass, are being compared.

Multiple Choice 9.17

Keep in mind that, for the system experiencing the process (in this case the blood), compression work is positive, while expansion work is negative.

(a) Correct Answer (c). In Step I we have an expansion so $W < 0$. Step II does not contribute any extra work since it is done at constant volume.

(b) Correct Answer (a). In Step III we have a compression so $W > 0$. Step IV does not contribute any extra work since it is done at constant volume.

CONCEPTUAL QUESTIONS

Conceptual Question 9.1

(a) The same change occurs for the internal energy for all three paths because they have the same initial and final state.

(b) In decreasing order, (i) – (ii) – (iii). Heat transfer between the system and the environment is larger for paths that have changes in pressure occurring at higher temperatures. Since path (i) has all of its change in pressure occurring at high temperature, it has the most heat transfer between the system and the environment.

Conceptual Question 9.3

In cold winters the heat stored in the barrel of liquid water helped keep the temperature of the storage room above freezing.

Conceptual Question 9.5

Heat capacities and masses of the objects have been neglected.

ANALYTICAL PROBLEMS

Problem 9.1

The definition of work is based on the area under the curve representing a process in a p–V diagram. If the process occurs at constant pressure, p = const = p_0, the work is calculated as:

$$W = -p_0(V_{final} - V_{initial}) \quad (1)$$

For any other process, either graphic or numerical methods are needed to obtain the area. Fig. 9.19 represents an intermediate case: the pressure varies along straight-line segments. In this case, a geometrical method can be applied to obtain the work.

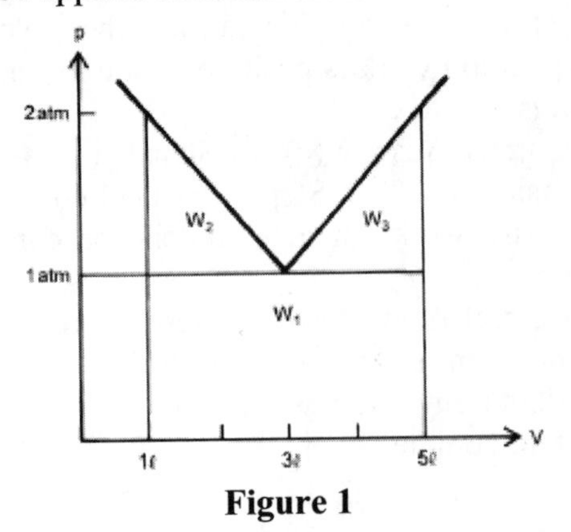

Figure 1

The area under the curve in Fig. 9.19 is divided into three simple–shaped areas, as shown in Fig. 1. We calculate the contribution to the total work of each of these three areas; the total work is then the sum of the three components. Using geometric identities for right triangles and rectangles, we find for the three areas:

$$\begin{aligned} A_1 &= (1\,atm)(5L - 1L) \\ &= 4\,atm \cdot L \\ A_2 &= \frac{1}{2}(2\,atm - 1\,atm)(3L - 1L) \\ &= 1\,atm \cdot L \\ A_3 &= \frac{1}{2}(2\,atm - 1\,atm)(5L - 3L) \\ &= 1\,atm \cdot L \end{aligned} \quad (2)$$

The terms in Eq. [2] were intentionally not labeled W_1, W_2 and W_3 because we must still apply the sign convention. The work is negative because the process in Fig. 6.43 is an expansion for which work is done by the gas on the piston. Thus, the total work is:

$$\begin{aligned} W &= -(A_1 + A_2 + A_3) \\ &= -6\,atm \cdot L = -608\,J \end{aligned} \quad (3)$$

The unit $atm \cdot L$ in Eq. [3] is not an SI energy unit and thus, has been converted with 1 L = 1 × 10^{-3} m³ and 1 atm = 1.013 × 10^5 Pa.

Note that Fig. 9.19 does not represent a realistic process. However, it is often possible to approximate a real process with a few straight-line segments. Thus, the method above is frequently used to obtain a first approximation of the work in a real situation.

Problem 9.3

The molar mass of water is 18.0 g/mol and we are given 1.0 mol of water, therefore the mass of water in the problem is m = 18.0 g.

(a) The density of liquid water at 0°C is approximately ρ_l = 1.00 g/cm³, while the density of ice is approximately ρ_i = 0.92 g/cm³. Since the density is the ratio of mass to volume we find:

$$V_l = \frac{m}{\rho_l} \quad \text{and} \quad V_i = \frac{m}{\rho_i}, \quad (1)$$

for the mass of water m = 18.0 g. To find the work, at constant pressure, we use Eq. [9.2]:

$$W_1 = -p \cdot \Delta V = -p(V_i - V_l), \quad (2)$$

where the initial volume corresponds to liquid water and the final volume corresponds to ice. Substituting Eq. [1] into Eq. [2]:

$$W_1 = -pm\left(\frac{1}{\rho_i} - \frac{1}{\rho_l}\right) = -159\,\text{mJ} \quad (3)$$

In the last step of Eq. [3], after converting to standard SI units, we substituted the given values for pressure, mass, and density. Note that the work done is negative. This means that the water releases work into the environment as the volume increases from that of liquid water into the volume of ice.

(b) The density of liquid water at 100°C is approximately ρ_l = 1.00 g/cm^3, while the density of steam (water vapour at 100°C) is approximately ρ_s = 0.59 kg/m^3. Since the density is the ratio of mass to volume we find:

$$V_l = \frac{m}{\rho_l} \quad \text{and} \quad V_s = \frac{m}{\rho_s}, \quad (4)$$

for the mass of water m = 18.0 g. We could also treat the steam as an ideal gas law and use Eq. [8.16] to find an approximate value for its volume. At constant pressure, we use Eq. [9.2] to find the work:

$$W_2 = -p \cdot \Delta V = -p(V_s - V_l), \quad (5)$$

where the initial volume corresponds to liquid water and the final volume corresponds to ice. Substituting Eq. [4] into Eq. [5]:

$$W_2 = -pm\left(\frac{1}{\rho_s} - \frac{1}{\rho_l}\right) = -3.09\,\text{kJ} \quad (6)$$

In the last step of Eq. [6], after converting to standard SI units, we substituted the given values for pressure, mass, and density. Note that the work done is negative. This means that the water releases work into the environment as the volume increases from that of liquid water into the volume of steam.

(c) The heat Q_1 needed to solidify 18.0 g of water can be found using E_{fusion}:

$$Q_1 = E_{\text{fusion}} \times m = 5.99\,\text{kJ} \quad (7)$$

Comparing Q_1 from Eq. [7] to W_1 from Eq. [3], in magnitude, Q_1 is almost forty thousand times larger than W_1. That is, the heat needed to turn water at 0°C into ice at 0°C is almost forty thousand times larger than the work put out by the water as it expands to form the ice. The heat Q_2 needed to vaporize 18.0 g of water can be found using $E_{\text{vaporization}}$:

$$Q_2 = E_{\text{vaporization}} \times m = 40.7\,\text{kJ} \quad (8)$$

Comparing Q_2 from Eq. [8] to W_2 from Eq. [6], in magnitude, Q_2 is over ten times larger than W_2. That is, the heat needed to turn water at 100°C into steam at 100°C is over ten times larger than the work put out by the water as it expands to form the steam.

Problem 9.5

(a) From Table 9.2, we find the metabolic rate for walking to be M = 1.0 cal/(s · kg). Note that the non–standard unit cal is often used in the context of energy content in food or other organic compounds. You also find the unit Cal (with a capital letter C) which converts as 1 Cal = 1 kcal = 1 × 10^3 cal. It is advisable to convert such non–standard units as early as possible. Here the result is M = 1.0 cal/(s · kg) = 4.184 J/(s · kg).

From this value of the metabolic rate M we determine the total energy when a standard man of 70 kg walks for 1 h = 3600 s. Note that the non–standard unit h (hour) is used. The energy consumption ΔE_{walk} is:

$$\Delta E_{walk} = \left(4.184\frac{J}{s\,kg}\right)(70kg)(3600s) = 1.05\times10^6 J = 1050 kJ$$

(b) Using the result in part (a) and Table 9.3, the fat consumption during the walking exercise is calculated. The table shows that 1 g = 0.001 kg fat provides 9300 cal = 39 kJ when converted into energy.
Thus, the total mass of fat consumed is:

$$m_{fat\,loss} = \frac{1050\,kJ}{39\,kJ/g}\left(1\times10^{-3}\frac{kg}{g}\right)$$
$$= 0.027\,kg$$

i.e., only 27 g of fat is lost.

Problem 9.7
4 horses perform work at a rate 4 · 750 J/s = 3000 J/s. If the total work is stored in the water in the form of thermal energy as implied in the problem text, the equivalence of work and heat applies in the form:

$$W = P\cdot\Delta t = m_{H_2O}c_{H_2O}\Delta T \qquad \textbf{(1)}$$

The temperature difference is obtained from Eq. [30]:

$$\Delta T = \frac{P\cdot\Delta t}{\rho_{H_2O}V_{H_2O}c_{H_2O}}$$
$$= \frac{\left(3000\frac{J}{s}\right)(3600s)}{\left(1\times10^3\frac{kg}{m^3}\right)(1.0m^3)\left(4.185\frac{kJ}{°C\,kg}\right)}$$
$$= 2.6°C \qquad \textbf{(2)}$$

in which ρ_{H2O} is the water density with ρ_{H2O} = 1.0 g/cm³ and the heat capacity of water at 25⁰C is c_{H2O} = 4185 J/(⁰C · kg), which, after unit conversion, is equal to c_{H2O} = 4185 J/(⁰C · kg). The temperature change in Eq. [2] is measurable but small, increasing from 25⁰C to 27.6⁰C.

Problem 9.9
The reverse amount of energy discussed in Section 10.1.1 (Metabolism at the Molecular Level: The Role of ATP), is required in the phosphorylation of ADP to ATP: – 29 kJ/mol. Thus, the formation of 38 mol of ATP requires 1100 kJ. The amount released per mol in the cellular respiration of glucose is 675 kcal = 2825 kJ.

This means that 1100 kJ/2825 kJ = 39% of the energy stored in the glucose molecule can be used to synthesize ATP from ADP.
The mitochondria work like small power plants, i.e., they operate as an open system applying a cyclic process. It must be a cyclic process because otherwise they would do their deed once and would become obsolete in no time. Read the discussion about the second law of thermodynamics in Chapter 10 to learn more about the efficiency of cyclic processes and their inadvertent loss of thermal energy during operation.

Problem 9.11
From Eq. [9.3] and Eq. [9.4] we can write:

$$\Delta T = \frac{E_{kin}}{c_{H_2O}m_{H_2O}} = \frac{m_{H_2O}gh}{c_{H_2O}m_{H_2O}},$$

where we have used conservation of energy between potential and kinetic. Given the result is independent of mass, we can solve and find:

$$\Delta T = \frac{g\cdot h}{c_{H_2O}} = 0.12^0C$$

Problem 9.13
In segments II and IV there is no change in volume so there is no work. Furthermore, since we are calculating a graphical estimate, we will assume that segment I is done at constant pressure of 0 torr so the work is zero. You can refine the estimate by taking into account the value of the pressure at the end of segment I, at about 10 torr for a volume of 100 mL. The work is the area under the curve, in this case, the area under the line for segment III which is broken into two trapezoids. These areas are calculated as the areas of rectangles and triangles. For the section where the volume goes from 100 mL to 60 mL and the pressure goes from 80 torr to 120 torr we find the work to be:

$$W_1 = 40\,\text{mL}\cdot80\,\text{torr} + \tfrac{1}{2}(40\,\text{mL}\cdot40\,\text{torr})$$
$$= 533\,\text{mJ},$$

where we converted from mL to m³ and from torr to Pa. Similarly, for the section where the volume goes from 60 mL to 35 mL and the pressure goes from 120 torr to 100 torr we find the work to be:

$$W_2 = 25\,\text{mL} \cdot 100\,\text{torr} + \tfrac{1}{2}(25\,\text{mL} \cdot 20\,\text{torr}) = 367\,\text{mJ},$$

with the appropriate conversions. Since segment III is a compression the work will be positive and equal to the sum of the previously calculated works. Therefore the total work W is given by:

$$W = W_1 + W_2 = 0.9\,\text{J},$$

or approximately one joule.

Problem 9.15

(a) Since we are assuming the man is an isolated system, the heat he produces is absorbed back into his body, so $Q = 1 \times 10^4$ kJ. We use Eq. [9.3] to find the change in temperature ΔT, with a mass $m = 70$ kg and the specific heat capacity of water $c = 4186$ J/kg·°C:

$$\Delta T = \frac{Q}{c \cdot m} = 34°\text{C}$$

Note that if this were the case, the man would in one single day increase his temperature form 37°C to 71°C, and in two days exceed the temperature of boiling water.

(b) To keep the temperature constant over one day, the heat produced must then used to evaporate water.

Since it takes 2405 J to evaporate 1 g of water, and we need to spend a total of 1×10^4 kJ, the mass of water is:

$$(1 \times 10^4\,\text{kJ}) \times \left(\frac{1\,\text{g}}{2405\,\text{J}}\right) = 4.2\,\text{kg},$$

that is, about 4 L of water.

Problem 9.17

Initially, the aluminium calorimeter and the water are in equilibrium at 10°C. Upon addition of the hot pieces of metal, heat will be absorbed by the cold water and the aluminium container, and will be released by the hot pieces of metal. Since the system is isolated, the heat lost by the metal pieces must be equal to the heat gained by the cold water and the calorimeter. Making sure that all these heats are positive quantities a balance of energy gives:

$$Q_u + Q_c = Q_a + Q_w$$
$$Q_u = Q_a + Q_w - Q_c, \qquad \textbf{(1)}$$

where Q_a is the heat gained by the cold aluminium calorimeter, Q_w is the heat gained by the cold water, Q_c is the heat lost by the hot piece of copper, and Q_u is the heat lost by the hot piece of unknown metal. We calculate each heat using Eq. [9.3] and Table 9.1:

$$Q_a = m_a c_a \Delta T_a = 0.90\,\text{kJ}, \qquad \textbf{(2)}$$

where $m_a = 0.1$ kg, $c_a = 900$ J/kg·°C, and the change in temperature of the aluminium calorimeter is ΔT_a = (20°C – 10°C) = 10°C. Also using Eq. [9.3] and Table 9.1:

$$Q_w = m_w c_w \Delta T_w = 10.5\,\text{kJ}, \qquad \textbf{(3)}$$

where $m_w = 0.25$ kg, $c_w = 4186$ J/kg·°C, and the temperature change of the cold water in the calorimeter is ΔT_w = (20°C – 10°C) = 10°C.
For the copper, using Eq. [9.3] and Table 9.1:

$$Q_c = m_c c_c \Delta T_c = 1.16\,\text{kJ}, \qquad \textbf{(4)}$$

where $m_c = 0.05$ kg, $c_c = 387$ J/kg·°C, and the temperature change of the copper inside the calorimeter is ΔT_c = (80°C – 20°C) = 60°C. For the unknown piece of metal:

$$Q_u = m_u c_u \Delta T_u = c_u \times (5.60\,\text{kg} \cdot °\text{C}), \qquad \textbf{(5)}$$

where $m_u = 0.07$ kg, c_u is unknown, and the temperature change of the unknown metal is ΔT_u = (100°C – 20°C) = 80°C. We can now substitute the results of Eq. [2] through Eq. [5] into Eq. [1] to obtain:

$$c_u = \frac{0.90\,\text{kJ} + 10.5\,\text{kJ} + 1.16\,\text{kJ}}{5.60\,\text{kg} \cdot °\text{C}} = 2240\,\text{J/kg·°C}$$

The unknown metal has a very large specific heat capacity.

Problem 9.19

(a) After supplementing the axes of Fig. 9.20 with linear axes for ln$h$, ln$E$ and ln$m$, Fig. 9.20 is used to read two data pairs of ln$h$ and ln$m$ from the straight line labelled (I). The data picked are listed in Table 2:

Table 1

h (mm)	ln$h$	m (kg)	ln$m$
186	5.23	1	0.0
3260	8.09	100	4.605

We use the formula:

$$h = a \cdot m^b \Rightarrow \ln h = \ln a + b \cdot \ln m \quad \textbf{(1)}$$

and substitute the data from Table 2 to write two linear formulas:

$$(I) \quad 5.23 = b \cdot (0.0) \quad + \ln a$$
$$(II) \quad 8.09 = b \cdot (+\ 4.605) + \ln a$$
$$(II) - (I) 2.86 = b \cdot 4.605$$

This yields b = 0.62 which is close to b = 2/3, and a = 186.

(b) From Fig. 9.20 we read two data pairs of ln$h$ and ln$m$ from the straight line labelled (II) as shown in Table 3:

Table 2

h (mm)	ln$h$	m (kg)	ln$m$
419	6.04	1	0.0
1860	7.53	100	4.605

Using the data from Table 3 in Eq. [1] we write two linear formulas:

$$(I) \quad 6.04 = b \cdot (0.0) \quad + \ln a$$
$$(II) \quad 7.53 = b \cdot (+\ 4.605) + \ln a$$
$$(II) - (I) 1.49 = b \cdot 4.605$$

Which yields b = 0.325, which is about b = 1/3, and a = 419.

(c) For the linear fit of the dashed line in Fig. 9.20, we read two data pairs of ln$E$ and ln$m$ from the curve labelled (III). These data are listed in Table 4:

Table 3

E (kcal/day)	ln$E$	m (kg)	ln$m$
181	5.20	1	0.0
5540	8.62	100	4.605

We substitute the data from Table 4 in:

$$E = a \cdot m^b \Rightarrow \ln E = \ln a + b \cdot \ln m$$

and obtain two linear formulas:

$$(I) \quad 5.20 = b \cdot (0.0) \quad + \ln a$$
$$(II) \quad 8.62 = b \cdot (+\ 4.605) + \ln a$$
$$(II) - (I) 3.42 = b \cdot 4.605$$

Which yields b = 0.74 which is close to b = 3/4, and a = 181.

(d) Fig. 2 shows the proportions of human bodies as a function of age. Height is clearly not by itself sufficient to predict the mass of a person as width and depth also contribute to the volume. It is the volume, which is ultimately linked to the mass, assuming a constant density of tissue and bone material.

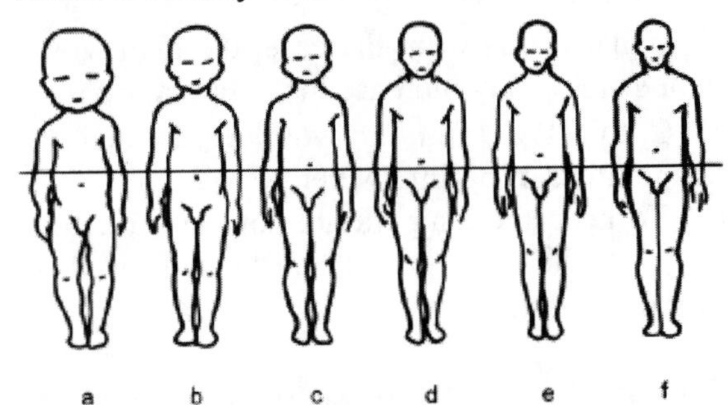

Figure 2

(a) 6 months old fetus, (b) 2 years old, (c) 5 years old, (d) 13 years old, (e) 17 years old, (f) adult

Problem 9.21

The surface of an animal A is proportional to r^2 if r is its size (its length in unit metre). The mass of the animal is proportional to its volume, $m \propto V$, and in turn, the volume of the animal V is proportional to r^3. The energy loss ΔE through the surface is proportional to the surface A, i.e., $\Delta E \propto A$ and therefore $\Delta E \propto r^2$. We want to express this last relation as a function of volume, not radius. Therefore, we use $r \propto V^{1/3}$. Substituting this leads to $M \propto \Delta E \propto r^2 \propto (V^{1/3})^2 = V^{2/3} \propto m^{2/}$

CHAPTER TEN

Thermodynamics

MULTIPLE CHOICE QUESTIONS

Multiple Choice 10.1
Correct Answer (e). The linearity of the p–V diagram shows this to be an isochoric process. Thus, we cannot supply energy to the system in the form of work, so the gas must be heated.

Multiple Choice 10.3
Correct Answer (e).

Multiple Choice 10.5
Correct Answer (c).

Multiple Choice 10.7
Correct Answer (c).

Multiple Choice 10.9
Part (A) Correct Answer (c).
Part (B) Correct Answer (d).

Multiple Choice 10.11
Correct Answer (d).

Multiple Choice 10.13
Correct Answer (a). Given that:

$$T = T_{\text{high}}\,(1 - (1.5)\,\eta_{\text{initial}}) = 200\text{ K}$$

Multiple Choice 10.15
Correct Answer (d).

CONCEPTUAL QUESTIONS

Conceptual Question 10.1
We must have $Q = -W$, because $\Delta U = 0$.

Conceptual Question 10.3
An isochoric process requires no change in the volume; isochoric processes occur at constant volume. This is impossible and should not be offered as a plausible option given that the premise of the problem states that the volume changes as it doubles going from V_0 to $2V_0$.

Conceptual Question 10.5
(a) Irreversible mixing.

(b) Figure 1 shows two gases that are separated by two pistons built with semi-permeable membranes. The left membrane allows gas I molecules to pass, while it is not permeable for gas II molecules. The right membrane in turn allows gas II to pass while blocking gas I.

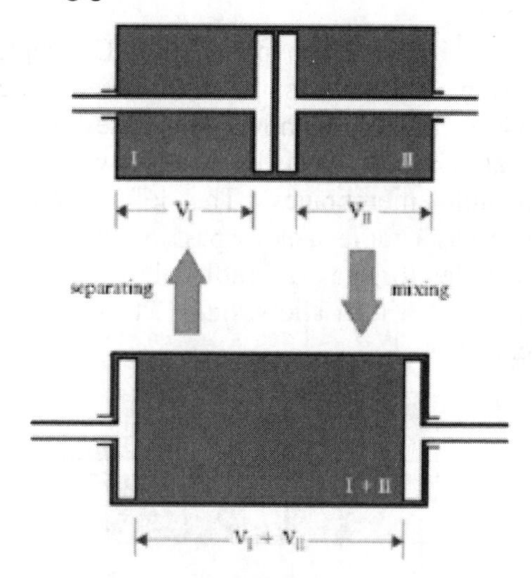

Figure 1

Allowing each gas to expand by pushing away the respective piston that blocks it leads to mixing of the gases with a constant volume. The process is reversible because the work done on the pistons can be used to push the pistons back to their initial position. The gases become separated as each gas can pass only one membrane.

Conceptual Question 10.7
The figure shows two cyclic processes operating between two heat reservoirs. System 1 is a super–engine and system 2 is a Carnot process that operates in the reverse direction.
(a) Yes, energy has neither been created nor destroyed.
(b) No, this would constitute a perpetual motion machine of the second kind. For example, a ship would no longer need fuel, but would extract the heat it needs for propulsion form the seawater.

Conceptual Question 10.9
The entropy change of the environment will obey $\Delta S_{environment} \geq +8.0$ J/K.

Conceptual Question 10.11
(a) The mixing process described in the question is irreversible because closing the valve at a later time cannot reverse the process. This is not surprising, because we did not store work from the initial process in the environment; usually such work has to be applied to the system when reversing the process.
(b) This is similar to part (b) of Conceptual Question 10.5. The same figure, reproduced below as Figure 2, shows two gases that are separated by two pistons built with semi-permeable membranes. The left membrane allows gas I molecules to pass, while it is not permeable for gas II molecules. The right membrane in turn allows gas II to pass while blocking gas I.

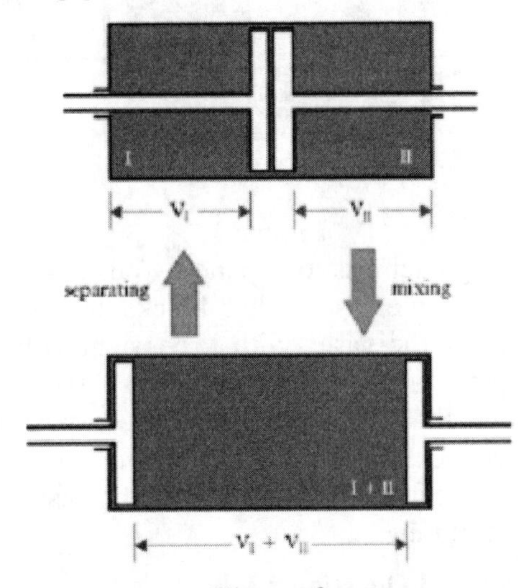

Figure 2

Allowing each gas to expand by pushing away the respective piston that blocks it leads to mixing of the gases with a constant volume. The process is reversible because the work done on the pistons can be used to push the pistons back to their initial position. The gases become separated as each gas can pass only one membrane.

ANALYTICAL PROBLEMS

Problem 10.1
(a) This problem requires that the same type of calculation is done twice, once for an isothermal expansion at $T_1 = 0^0\text{C} = 273$ K and once for an isothermal expansion at $T_2 = 25^0\text{C} = 298$ K. For the work of an isothermal expansion, we use the formula developed in Example 10.1 with the pressure as independent variable instead of the volume. We find at T_1:

$$W_1 = -n \cdot R \cdot T_1 \ln\left(\frac{p_{initial}}{p_{final}}\right)$$
$$= -(1\,\text{mol})\left(8.314\frac{\text{J}}{\text{K}\cdot\text{mol}}\right)(273\,\text{K})\ln\left(\frac{20}{5}\right)$$
$$= -3.15\,\text{kJ}$$

At T_2 we obtain $W_2 = -3.45$ kJ. This result can also be obtained by calculating:

$$W_2 = W_1\frac{T_2}{T_1}$$

(b) The change of the internal energy of an ideal gas during an isothermal process is zero, i.e., $\Delta U = 0$ since $\Delta T = 0$. This applies at any temperature.
(c) Using the first law of thermodynamics for closed systems, we obtain:

$$Q = \Delta U - W = -W \Rightarrow$$
$$Q_1 = +3.15\,\text{kJ}\ ;\ Q_2 = +3.45\,\text{kJ}$$

Problem 10.3
We start with the equation derived in the text, Eq. [10.16]. In this formula we replace the temperature by $p{\cdot}V/(n{\cdot}R)$ from the ideal gas law:

$$V \cdot T^{C_V/R} = V\left(\frac{p \cdot V}{n \cdot R}\right)^{C_V/R} = const \quad \textbf{(1)}$$

$$p^{\frac{C_V}{R}} \cdot V^{\frac{C_V}{R}+1} = const\,(n \cdot R)^{C_V/R} = const^*$$

in which const* is indeed a constant since both n and R in the middle term of the second formula in Eq. [1] do not vary. In the next step we rewrite the exponent of the volume term:

$$p^{\frac{C_V}{R}} \cdot V^{\frac{C_V}{R}+1} = p^{\frac{C_V}{R}} \cdot V^{\frac{C_V+R}{R}} = const^*$$

In the last step, we raise both sides of the formula to the (R/C_V)–th power:

$$p \cdot V^{\frac{C_V+R}{C_V}} = (const^*)^{\frac{R}{C_V}} = const^l \quad (2)$$

in which const' is also constant since the middle term in Eq. [1] does not contain any variables. Eq. [1] is easily transformed into Eq. [10.17] when using the relation between C_V and C_p and yields $\kappa = C_p/C_V$.

Problem 10.5

We rewrite the first law of thermodynamics, $\Delta U = W + Q$ in the form $W = -n{\cdot}p{\cdot}\Delta V$. The change of the internal energy is $\Delta U = n{\cdot}C_V{\cdot}\Delta T$. We further use the equation given in the problem and obtain:

$$\Delta U = n \cdot C_V \cdot \Delta T = -n \cdot p \cdot \Delta V + n \cdot C_p \cdot \Delta T$$

which leads to:

$$C_p - C_V = \frac{n \cdot p \cdot \Delta V}{n \cdot \Delta T} = \frac{p \cdot \Delta V}{\Delta T} = R$$

Problem 10.7

(a) See Figure 3(a)
(b) See Figure 3(b)
(c) Identifying the gas the system, we find $W(\text{a}) < W(\text{b}) < 0$.

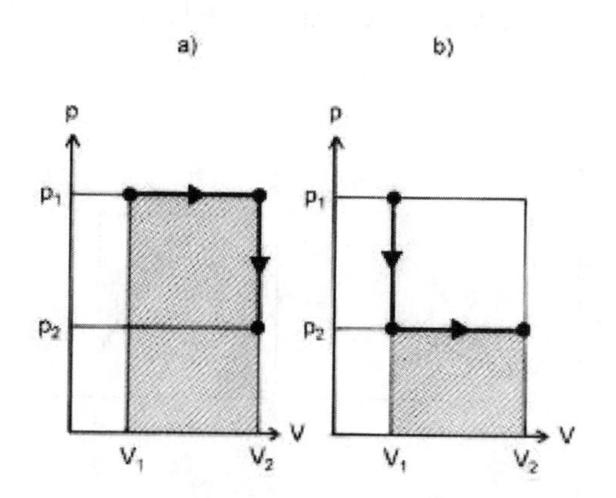

Figure 3

Problem 10.9

(a) The final temperature is:

$$T_2 = \frac{pV_2}{nR} = \frac{p4V_1}{nR} = \frac{4p\left(\frac{nRT_1}{p}\right)}{nR}$$

$$= 4T_1 = 1090\,\text{K}$$

(b) The work is:

$$W = -p(V_{final} - V_{initial}) = -6.81\,\text{kJ}$$

Problem 10.11

(a) Using Eq. [10.6] we find:

$$W = -nRT\ln\left(\frac{V_f}{V_i}\right)$$

$$= -(1.0\,\text{mol})(8.314\,\text{J/K·mol})(300\,\text{K})\ln\left(\frac{40\,\text{L}}{20\,\text{L}}\right)$$

$$= -1.73\,\text{kJ}$$

Note that the work is negative as it should be for the gas doing work on the surroundings and the gas expanding.

(b) With the ideal gas law we find the initial and final pressures as:

$$p_i = \frac{nRT}{V_i} = 125\,\text{kPa}$$

$$p_f = \frac{nRT}{V_f} = 62.4\,\text{kPa} \quad (1)$$

Using Figure 10.31(b) the work is:

$$W = -(A_1 + A_2)$$

Using the values given in the problem and the pressures calculated in Eq. [1], the areas are:

$$A_1 = \frac{(V_f - V_i)(p_i - p_f)}{2} = 624\,\text{J}$$

$$A_2 = (V_f - V_i)p_f = 1.25\,\text{kJ}$$

Therefore the work is $W = -1.87$ kJ which is larger by about 8% than the value we found in part (a) as the areas are an overestimate.

(c) Let the intermediate volume be $V_{\text{int}} = 30$ L so that the intermediate pressure is:

$$p_{\text{int}} = \frac{nRT}{V_{\text{int}}} = 83.1\,\text{kPa} \quad (2)$$

Using Figure 10.31(c) the work is:

$$W = -(A_1 + A_2 + A_3 + A_4)$$

Using the values given in the problem and the pressures calculated in Eq. [1] and Eq. [2], the areas are:

$$A_1 = \frac{(V_{\text{int}} - V_i)(p_i - p_{\text{int}})}{2} = 210\,\text{J}$$

$$A_2 = (V_{\text{int}} - V_i)\,p_{\text{int}} = 831\,\text{J}$$

$$A_3 = \frac{(V_f - V_{\text{int}})(p_{\text{int}} - p_f)}{2} = 104\,\text{J}$$

$$A_4 = (V_f - V_{\text{int}})\,p_f = 624\,\text{kJ}$$

Therefore the work is $W = -1.77$ kJ which although still an overestimate on the value found in part (a) by about 2%, is nevertheless lower than the value from part (b) and closer to the exact result.

Problem 10.13

(a) Any cyclic process of this type is treated the same way that we dealt with the Carnot process. In the first step we summarize the work, heat and internal energy contributions due to the single steps involved in the cyclic process. For this we need not to calculate any of the contributions since each individual step has been covered in this chapter.

Table 1

Step	Work W	Heat Q
I	$-n\,R\,T_1\,\ln(p_1/p_2)$	$-W_I$
II	0	$-(3/2)\,n\,R\,(T_1-T_2)$
III	$+(3/2)\,n\,R\,(T_1-T_2)$	0

The contributions are summarized in Table 1. To quantify the terms in Table 1, the temperatures of the two isothermal curves in Figure 10.32 must be calculated. The temperature T_1 is obtained from the ideal gas law applied to the first state of the system:

$$T_1 = \frac{p_1 \cdot V_1}{n \cdot R} = \frac{1.013\times10^5\,\text{Pa})(0.01\,\text{m}^3)}{\left(8.314\frac{\text{J}}{\text{K}\cdot\text{mol}}\right)1.0\,\text{mol}} = 121.8\,\text{K}$$

The second temperature is obtained from the adiabatic step (step III) in Figure 10.32, using $C_V/R = 3/2$ for an ideal gas:

$$T_2 = \left(\frac{V_1}{V_2}\right)^{2/3} T_1 = 0.5^{2/3}(121.8\,\text{K}) = 76.8K$$

in which the ratio of the two volumes is 0.5 because of Boyle's law applied to step (I) in Figure 10.32: $p_2/p_1 = V_1/V_2$. The total work is the sum of the three work terms in Table 1:

$$W_I = -1.0\,\text{mol}\left(8.314\frac{\text{J}}{\text{K}\cdot\text{mol}}\right)(121.8\,\text{K})\ln\frac{1.0}{0.5}$$

$$= -700\,\text{J}$$

$$W_{III} = +\frac{3}{2}1.0\,\text{mol}\left(8.314\frac{\text{J}}{\text{K}\cdot\text{mol}}\right)45\,\text{K}$$

in which $T_1 - T_2 = 121.8$ K $-$ 76.8 K = 45.0 K is the temperature difference in the third work term. Thus, the work per cycle is $W_{\text{cycle}} = W_I + W_{III} = -140$ J. Because this is a negative value, the work is done by the gas.

(b) From Table 1, we note that $Q_{II} = -W_{III}$ and $Q_I = -W_I$. Thus, $Q_{\text{cycle}} = -W_{\text{cycle}} = +140$ J. Since the value is positive, we conclude that the system receives this amount of energy as heat per cycle.

(c) For any cyclic process the change per cycle in the internal energy must be zero because the internal energy is a variable of state of the system. This can be confirmed by adding Q_{cycle} and W_{cycle}, which were calculated above.

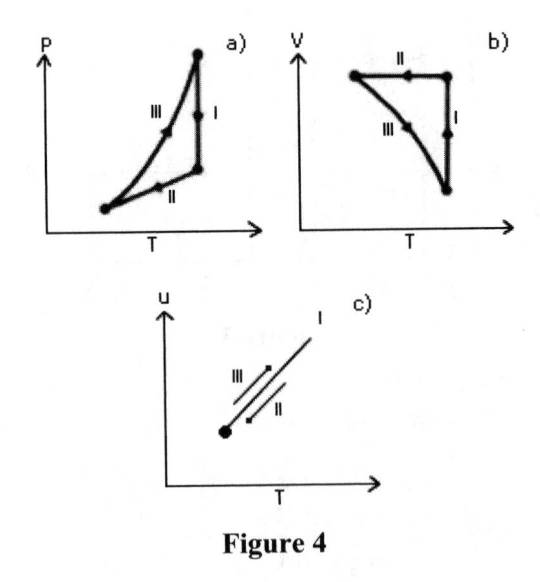

Figure 4

(d) The three graphs are shown in Figure 4. They are derived in the following fashion:

- *p–T* plot: The first step is an isothermal expansion or isothermal decompression. Since temperature is constant for isothermal processes, the initial and final state must lie on a common, vertical line. The second step is an isochoric cooling, i.e., both, temperature and pressure decrease while the volume stays constant. The third step must bring the system back to the initial state.
- *V–T* plot: The first step is an isothermal expansion, i.e., the volume increases and the temperature remains the same (vertical line). The second step is an isochoric cooling, i.e., the temperature is reduced while the volume is constant (horizontal line). The last step must connect back to the initial state. Both curves for the last step are bent because the adiabatic process is not a linear relation between either pressure and temperature or volume and temperature.
- *U–T* plot: Since the first step is isothermal, both the temperature and the internal energy of the ideal gas do not change. Thus, during the first step the system does not change its position in this type of plot. The second step is an isothermal cooling, i.e., the temperature decreases, and with it the internal energy. This relationship is linear due to $\Delta U \propto \Delta T$. The third step must bring the system back to the initial state.

Problem 10.15

First we find the number of moles in the sample as:

$$n = \frac{m}{M} = \frac{1000\,\text{g}}{18\,\text{g/mol}} = 55.6\,\text{mol} \qquad (1)$$

The total enthalpy change ΔH is broken down into three different processes as:

$$\Delta H = \Delta H_1 + \Delta H_2 + \Delta H_3, \qquad (2)$$

where process 1 is the heating of ice from −10°C to 0°C, process 2 is the melting of ice into water, and process 3 is the heating of water from 0°C to +10°C. Using Eq. [10.9], Eq. [10.10], and Eq. [1] for the number of moles we find for the first process:

$$\begin{aligned}\Delta H_1 &= n\,C_p\,\Delta T \\ &= (55.6\,\text{mol})(37.78\,\text{J/mol·K})(10\,\text{K}) \qquad (3) \\ &= 21.0\,\text{kJ}\end{aligned}$$

Note that in Eq. [3] we have used the value of C_p from Table 10.5 that corresponds to ice at −2.2°C as suggested in the problem. For the second process we use again Eq. [10.9] and Eq. [1] to find:

$$\begin{aligned}\Delta H_2 &= Q = n\,L_{\text{melting}} \\ &= (55.6\,\text{mol})(6.0\,\text{kJ/mol}), \qquad (4) \\ &= 333\,\text{kJ}\end{aligned}$$

where we have used the value given in the problem for the latent heat of melting. For the last process we use once more Eq. [10.9], Eq. [10.10], and Eq. [1]:

$$\begin{aligned}\Delta H_3 &= n\,C_p\,\Delta T \\ &= (55.6\,\text{mol})(75.86\,\text{J/mol·K})(10\,\text{K}) \qquad (5) \\ &= 42.1\,\text{kJ}\end{aligned}$$

In Eq. [5] we have used the value of C_p from Table 10.5 that corresponds to liquid water at 0°C as suggested in the problem.

Substituting the results from Eq. [4], Eq. [4], and Eq. [5] into Eq. [2] we obtain the total change in enthalpy:

$$\begin{aligned}\Delta H &= 21.0\,\text{kJ} + 333\,\text{kJ} + 42.1\,\text{kJ} \\ &= 396\,\text{kJ}\end{aligned}$$

Problem 10.17

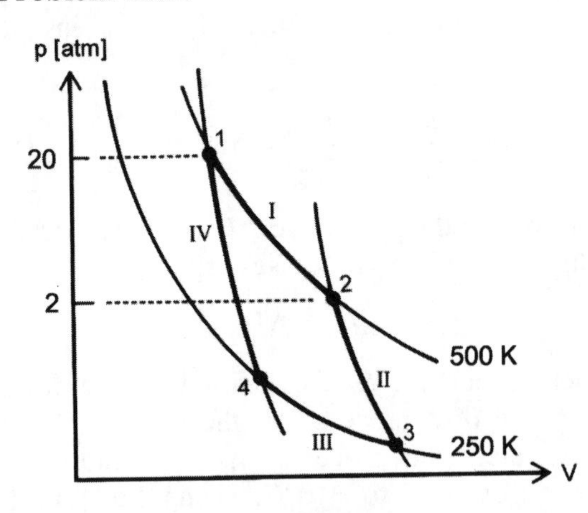

Figure 5

(a) Figure 5 shows the Carnot process with the two temperatures, 500 K and 250 K. The data given in the problem text for the four corner states of the Carnot process are supplemented with the initial volume in Table 2. The volume values are calculated using the ideal gas law.

Table 2

State	p	V	T
1	20 atm	2.05 L	500 K
2	2 atm	20.5 L	500 K
3			250 K
4			250 K

With these preliminary steps we can now answer the various parts of the problem. **For** the work, heat and energy terms of the Carnot process, we find Table 3. Note that volumes are related through $V_2/V_1 = V_3/V_4$.

Table 3

Process	work W	heat Q
I	– 9.6 kJ	+ 9.6 kJ
II	– 3.1 kJ	0
III	+ 4.8 kJ	– 4.8 kJ
IV	+ 3.1 kJ	0

(b) The efficiency is $\eta = 50\%$. This result can be found from Eqs. [10.20] or [10.21], e.g.:

$$\eta = \frac{|W_I + W_{m}|}{Q_I} = \frac{|-9.6\ kJ + 4.8\ kJ|}{+9.6\ kJ} = 0.5$$

in which the work and heat terms are taken from Table 3.

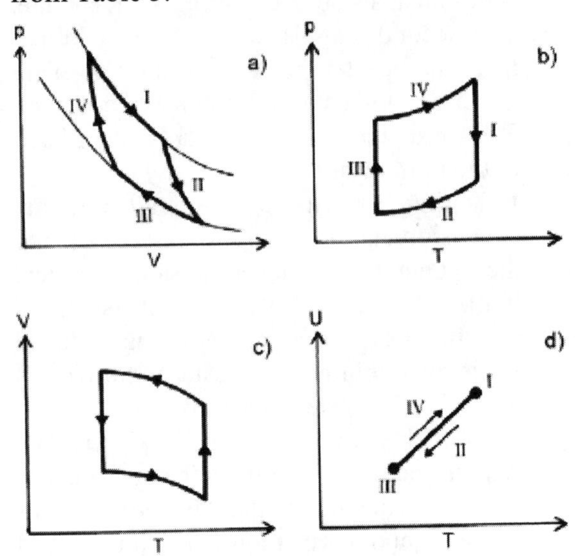

Figure 6

(c) Four of the plots are shown in Figure 6. The shape of the *S–T* diagram will be a rectangle since the branches of a Carnot process are either isentropic (constant S), or isothermal (constant T). Note that all plots illustrate the same cyclic process! In the *U–T* diagram, all processes are represented by straight line segments because the change of the internal energy and the temperature change are related in a linear fashion, $\Delta U \propto \Delta T$. To determine the curvature of the adiabatic steps in the *p–T* diagram, we rewrite the equation for the adiabatic process in with p and T as the variables by using the ideal gas law in the form $V = n \cdot R \cdot T/p$:

$$p^{-1}T^{C_V/R+1} = p^{-1}T^{C_p/R} = const^{*}w$$

$$\Rightarrow p \propto T^{5/2}$$

Problem 10.19

We use the definition of the entropy change for the process, $\Delta S = Q/T$. To express the entropy in unit J/(K · mol), we need to convert the latent heat to a molar value. The molar mass of benzene is:

$$M_{C_6H_6} = 6(M_C + M_H)$$
$$= 6\left(12.01\frac{g}{mol} + 1.01\frac{g}{mol}\right) = 78.1\frac{g}{mol}$$

With this mass, we convert the latent heat of melting, which is 30 kcal/mol = 126 kJ/mol:

$$\Delta H_{melt} = \left(126\frac{kJ}{kg}\right)\left(78.1\frac{g}{mol}\right) = 9.84\frac{kJ}{mol}$$

Note that the latent heat of melting is written as an enthalpy because the process occurs at constant pressure, not at constant volume. With the melting temperature T_{melt}, we find:

$$\Delta S_{melt} = \frac{\Delta H_{melt}}{T_{melt}} = \frac{9.84\frac{kJ}{mol}}{288.6 K} = 34.1\frac{J}{K \cdot mol}$$

Problem 10.21

(a) We first calculate the amount of energy needed to melt 150 g of ice. This energy must be extracted from the water at 80^{0}C, leaving that part of the system at a lower temperature. In the last step, we mix the 150 g water now liquid at 0^{0}C with the 250 g of warmer water. The energy needed to melt 150 g of water is obtained from the given latent heat of melting and the molar mass of water, M = 18 g/mol:

$$E_{melt} = \frac{5.98\frac{kJ}{mol}}{18\frac{g}{mol}} 150 g = 49.9 kJ$$

The same energy is obtained from cooling 250 g of water from $T_{initial}$ = 80^{0}C = 353 K to T_{final}. Because the process is done at constant pressure, we use C_p in:

$$\Delta H = -n \cdot C_p (T_{final} - T_{initial})$$

which yields for the final temperature:

$$T_{final} = -\frac{\Delta H}{n \cdot C_p} + T_{initial}$$

and with the given values substituted:

$$T_{final} = -\frac{49.9 kJ}{\frac{250 g}{18 g/mol}\left(75.3\frac{J}{K \cdot mol}\right)} + 363 K$$
$$= 315.3 K = 42.2°C$$

Mixing 150 g water at 0^{0}C and 250 g of water at 42.2^{0}C leads to 400 g of water at 26.4^{0}C.

(b) The entropy change is determined in two parts: the contribution of the phase change of ice and the contribution due to the temperature changes in the liquid water. The first contribution to the entropy change is the melting of 150 g ice. We saw that the energy needed for that process is 49.9 kJ. The associated entropy value is ΔS = + 182.6 J/K because the melting happens at 273.1 K. The equation given in the problem is now applied for each of the two amounts of water in the system, for 150 g to heat from the freezing point to 26.4^{0}C, and for 250 g of water to cool from 80^{0}C to 26.4^{0}C. Note that the heating leads to a positive entropy change and the cooling to a negative change; thus ΔS is written as:

$$\frac{150 g}{18 \, {}^{g}\!/_{mol}}\left(75.3\frac{J}{K \cdot mol}\right)\left(\ln\frac{299.5}{273.1} + \frac{2.5}{1.5}\ln\frac{299.5}{353.1}\right)$$

The factor before the last logarithm–term of this result recognizes that 250 g water are cooled, not just 150 g. Completing the calculation leads to ΔS = – 114.3 J/K. We combine both contributions to the entropy change of the system:

$$\Delta S_{system} = 182.6\frac{J}{K} - 114.3\frac{J}{K} = +68.3\frac{J}{K}$$

(c) For the process to be reversible, the change in the environment must be equal but opposite to the change in the system. Thus, $\Delta S_{environment}$ = – 68.3 J/K.

(d) Here we get ΔS_{system} = + 68.3 J/K and $\Delta S_{environment}$ = 0 J/K; i.e., the total entropy change is an increase of 68.3 J/K.

This is a thermodynamically possible process.

Problem 10.23

The standard entropy for 1 mol is determined from the definition:

$$\Delta S = S_{final} - S_{initial} = \sum_i \frac{Q_i}{T_i} \qquad (1)$$

We choose the initial state to be when the temperature is 0 K, at which $S = 0$ J/K. We choose the final state as the standard state at temperature 298 K. To obtain a value at constant pressure, the heat term in Eq. [1] is replaced by the term $Q = C_p \cdot \Delta T$:

$$S^0 = \sum_{T=0\,\mathrm{K}}^{298\,\mathrm{K}} \frac{C_p}{T} \Delta T$$

We obtain the standard entropy from the data in Table 10.7 plotting C_p/T versus the temperature. This plot is shown in Figure 7.

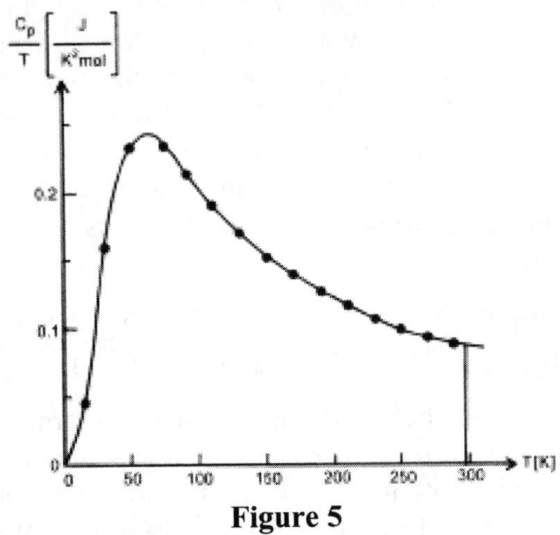

Figure 5

Problem 10.25

(a) The Gibbs free energy change of a chemical reaction, ΔG, is defined as:

$$\Delta G = \Delta H - T \cdot \Delta S$$

in which the given data are substituted:

$$\Delta G = -100\ \mathrm{kJ} - 298\ \mathrm{K}\left(-200\frac{\mathrm{J}}{\mathrm{K}}\right)$$

$$= -40.4\ \mathrm{kJ}$$

The reaction occurs spontaneously because ΔG is negative.

(b) $\Delta G = +\ 114.6$ kJ. Note that the change in temperature has a profound effect on this reaction; at 800°C it is no longer a spontaneous process.

Problem 10.27

(a) The gases are not yet mixed. Using the initial gas parameters, we find:

$$n_{\mathrm{I}} = \frac{p_{\mathrm{initial}} V_{\mathrm{I}}}{R T_{\mathrm{I}}} = 0.067\ \mathrm{mol}$$

$$n_{\mathrm{II}} = \frac{p_{\mathrm{initial}} V_{\mathrm{II}}}{R T_{\mathrm{II}}} = 0.102\ \mathrm{mol}$$

(b) Assuming that the gas mixture behaves ideally, we use Eq. [8.27] in the form:

$$p_{\mathrm{mix}}\left(V_{\mathrm{I}} + V_{\mathrm{II}}\right) = \left(n_{\mathrm{I}} + n_{\mathrm{II}}\right) R T_{\mathrm{mix}} \qquad (1)$$

This equation cannot be solved without further input because p_{mix} and T_{mix} are unknown. We know that the system does not exchange work or heat with the environment during mixing. Work is excluded because a valve is opened, and heat exchange is excluded since both containers are thermally insulated. Thus, the internal energy of the two gases must remain constant during mixing:

$$\Delta U_{\mathrm{I}} + \Delta U_{\mathrm{II}} = 0$$

This can be rewritten for the mixing process of ideal gases using $U = (3/2)\, n\, R\, T$:

$$n_{\mathrm{I}} R\left(T_{\mathrm{mix}} - T_{\mathrm{I}}\right) + n_{\mathrm{II}} R\left(T_{\mathrm{mix}} - T_{\mathrm{II}}\right) = 0$$

which yields after division by the universal gas constant R:

$$\left(n_{\mathrm{I}} + n_{\mathrm{II}}\right) T_{\mathrm{mix}} = n_{\mathrm{I}} \mathrm{T}_{\mathrm{I}} + n_{\mathrm{II}} \mathrm{T}_{\mathrm{II}} \qquad (2)$$

We combine Eq. [1] and Eq. [2] to obtain the final pressure:

$$p_{\mathrm{mix}} = \frac{\left(n_{\mathrm{I}} + n_{\mathrm{II}}\right) R T_{\mathrm{mix}}}{V_{\mathrm{I}} + V_{\mathrm{II}}}$$

$$= \frac{n_{\mathrm{I}} R T_{\mathrm{I}} + n_{\mathrm{II}} R T_{\mathrm{II}}}{V_{\mathrm{I}} + V_{\mathrm{II}}}$$

The two terms in the last numerator are rewritten with the results from part (a):

$$p_{\mathrm{mix}} = \frac{p_{\mathrm{initial}} \mathrm{V}_{\mathrm{I}} + p_{\mathrm{initial}} V_{\mathrm{II}}}{V_{\mathrm{I}} + V_{\mathrm{II}}} = p_{\mathrm{initial}}$$

The pressure in the system has not changed during mixing, as expected from Dalton's law for ideal gas components. The final temperature is the calculated from Eq. [1]:

$$T_{\text{mix}} = \frac{p_{\text{initial}}\left(V_{\text{I}} + V_{\text{II}}\right)}{R\left(n_{\text{I}} + n_{\text{II}}\right)} = 288\,\text{K}$$

which corresponds to +15°C.

(c) The molar fraction is defined in Eq. [8.28]:

$$x_{\text{I}} = \frac{n_{\text{I}}}{n_{\text{I}} + n_{\text{II}}} = 0.396$$

Note that this value is not equal to the ratio of 1.5 litres to 4.0 litres because the two gases are initially at different temperatures. The partial pressure of ideal gas I in the mixed gas is determined from Eq. [8.27]:

$$p_{\text{I}} = \frac{R\,T_{\text{mix}}}{V_{\text{total}}}\,n_{\text{I}} = 40.1\,\text{kPa}$$

We obtain this result alternatively from the molar fraction of gas I in Eq. [8.28]:

$$p_{\text{I}} = x_{\text{I}}\,p_{\text{mix}} = 40.1\,\text{kPa}$$

(d) If we study each gas component separately, the entropy of mixing has four contributions: each gas component changes its volume and, independently, its temperature. We assume that these contributions can be calculated separately, using Example 10.4 for the volume change and a further result that can be typically found in the physical chemistry literature for ΔS:

$$\Delta S = n\,C_p\,\ln\left(\frac{T_{\text{final}}}{T_{\text{initial}}}\right)$$

Furthermore, recall that C_p = (5/2) R for an ideal gas. Using all the previous results, Example 10.4 and the equation above, we obtain for ideal gas I:

$$\Delta S_{\Delta V} = n_{\text{I}}\,R\ln\left(\frac{V_{\text{final}}}{V_{\text{initial}}}\right) = +0.546\,\text{J/K}$$

$$\Delta S_{\Delta T} = n_{\text{I}}\,C_p\,\ln\left(\frac{T_{\text{final}}}{T_{\text{initial}}}\right) = +0.074\,\text{J/K}$$

and for ideal gas II:

$$\Delta S_{\Delta V} = n_{\text{II}}\,R\ln\left(\frac{V_{\text{final}}}{V_{\text{initial}}}\right) = +0.399\,\text{J/K}$$

$$\Delta S_{\Delta T} = n_{\text{II}}\,C_p\,\ln\left(\frac{T_{\text{final}}}{T_{\text{initial}}}\right) = -0.072\,\text{J/K}$$

The total change in entropy during mixing is ΔS = +0.947 J/K. The entropy of mixing is dominated by the volume contributions; the temperature effect is minor.

Problem 10.29

Since the molar mass of ethylene is 28.0 g/mol the provided sample of 1.0 kg contains:

$$n = \frac{1000\,\text{g}}{28\,\text{g/mol}} = 35.7\,\text{mol} \qquad \textbf{(1)}$$

Since the compression occurs at constant temperature, we use Eq. [10.6] for the work along with the number of moles in Eq. [1] and the given values for temperature, and initial and final volumes:

$$W = -n\,R\,T\ln\left(\frac{V_f}{V_i}\right) = 205\,\text{kJ}$$

CHAPTER ELEVEN

Transport of Energy and Matter

MULTIPLE CHOICE QUESTIONS

Multiple Choice 11.1

(a) Correct Answer (b). Fourier quantified the amount of heat transferred per second. This is expressed in Eq. [11.1] giving us the amount of heat per unit time, as a function of the cross-sectional area, the temperature difference between the ends of the rod, and the actual length of the rod.

(b) Correct Answer (d). To increase the effect observed, that is, the heat transferred per unit time, in Eq. [11.1] he could increase the cross-sectional area A, increase the temperature difference $T_{high} - T_{low}$, or decrease the length of the rod L. Note that (A) due to the inverse relationship decreases the effect, while (B) effectively reduces the cross-sectional area. Similarly, (D) and (E) reduce the temperature difference and thus weaken the effect.

(c) Correct Answer (B). Since iron has a lower thermal conductivity than aluminium (see Table 11.1), switching from aluminium to iron decreases the observed heat flow rate. In order to increase the hear flow rate to the initial state, from Eq. [11.1], he needs to increase the temperature difference. This can be accomplished by increasing the temperature of the hot reservoir, or by decreasing the temperature of the cold reservoir.

Multiple Choice 11.3

Correct Answer (a). From Table 1 we find that $\lambda_{window\ glass} = 0.8\ J/(m \cdot s \cdot K)$. This is a factor of ten more conductive than the wood panel that replaced the glass. Combined with the fact that the wood panel is one–quarter the thickness of the glass, the wood panel should provide 2.5 times the thermal insulation of the glass panel it replaces.

Table 1

Material	Thermal Conductivity λ ($J\ s^{-1}\ m^{-1}\ K^{-1}$)
1. Solid metals and alloys	
Silver (Ag)	420
Copper (Cu)	390
Gold (Au)	310
Aluminium (Al)	230
Iron (Fe)	80
Steel	50
2. Nonmetallic solids	
Ice	1.6
Quartz glass (SiO_2)	1.4
Window glass	0.8
Fat	0.24
Rubber	0.2
Wood	0.12 – 0.04
Felt, Silk	0.04
3. Liquids	
Mercury (Hg)	8.3
Water (H_2O)	0.6
Ethanol (C_2H_5OH)	0.18
4. Gases	
Air	0.026

Multiple Choice 11.5

Correct Answer (c).

Multiple Choice 11.7

Correct Answer (c). If we treat the entire setup as a single system, you could argue that internal energy flows from one section of the system to another. In that case you could also more specifically argue that the fraction of the internal energy that flows is thermal energy. Entropy also flows when heat flows, however, the more important observation with respect to entropy in this case is its production. In thermodynamic studies, however, the two heat reservoirs are treated as two separate systems. Then, as per the definition, heat flows out of one system and into the other.

Multiple Choice 11.9

Correct Answer (d).

Multiple Choice 11.11
Correct Answer (d). If the measurements you took are both accurate and precise, there is no doubt that there is a significant difference between the two diffusion coefficients. Though this author would likely ask the head if the purpose of running the experiment again was to check that the measurements were both accurate and precise.

Multiple Choice 11.13
Correct Answer (c). It takes four times as long to go twice the diffusion length. That means it will take four hours in total; since we have already waited one hour, we have an additional 3 hours to wait.

CONCEPTUAL QUESTIONS

Conceptual Question 11.1
Note that both surfaces are at the same temperature because they are in thermal equilibrium with their surroundings. However, your skin is at a higher temperature than either surface. Heat flows from your body through the floor surface; the rate of heat loss is governed by the thermal conductivity of the floor material. Inspecting Table 1, we estimate that the thermal conductivities for tile (use glass) and for carpet (use felt) differ by an order of magnitude.

Conceptual Question 11.3
The evaporation of the perspiration (sweat) is accompanied by the extraction of the latent heat of vaporization from the skin, which is about 580 cal/g at normal body temperature. The specific heat of the human body is somewhat less than 1 cal/g°C, and therefore the evaporation of one (1) gram of perspiration could cool over 580 grams of the body material by 1°C.

Conceptual Question 11.5
The metal base would feel colder because metal is a better heat conductor than wood, even though both objects have the same equilibrium temperature (the room temperature).

ANALYTICAL PROBLEMS

Problem 11.1
Fourier's law is used with the thermal conductivity for copper taken from Table 1:

$$\frac{Q}{t} = \lambda_{Cu} \cdot A\frac{\Delta T}{t}$$

$$= \frac{\left(390\frac{J}{m\,s\,K}\right)\left(4.8\times10^{-4}m^2\right)(100K)}{1.2m}$$

$$= 15.6\frac{J}{s}$$

Note that this is less than a tenth of the amount of heat that your body loses in the winter with dry clothing (see Example 11.1). Why would we compare these results? The answer is that we build an intuition for such numbers, as the loss of heat in winter is a process to which we can relate while the heat flowing in a metal rod is elusive.

Problem 11.3
(a) The requested equation is obtained by substituting $\lambda/l = 1/R$ into Fourier's law:

$$\frac{Q}{t} = \lambda \cdot A\frac{T_{high} - T_{low}}{l}$$

(b) We determine the units of R from the given equation:

$$unit(R) = \frac{unit(l)}{unit(\lambda)}$$

$$= \frac{m}{\frac{J}{m\cdot s\cdot K}} = \frac{s\cdot K\cdot m^2}{J}$$

Problem 11.5

We isolate the time in Eq. [11.1]:

$$t = \frac{Q}{\lambda \cdot A \frac{\Delta T}{l}}$$

i.e., the time for the process is proportional to the amount of heat required and inversely proportional to the temperature gradient in the meat.

The required heat is written with Joule's definition $Q = c \cdot m \cdot \Delta T$:

$$t = \frac{c \cdot m \cdot \Delta T}{\lambda \cdot A \frac{\Delta T}{l}} \quad \textbf{(1)}$$

The specific heat capacity and the thermal conductivity of turkey and mammoth are assumed to be the same.

To eliminate these terms, we rewrite Eq. [1] as a ratio:

$$\frac{t_{mammoth}}{t_{turkey}} = \frac{\dfrac{m_{mammoth}}{\left(\frac{A}{l}\right)_{mammoth}}}{\dfrac{m_{turkey}}{\left(\frac{A}{l}\right)_{turkey}}} \quad \textbf{(2)}$$

The mass scales with L^3 where L is the size (typical length) for an object of uniform density. This leads to $A/l \propto L \propto m^{1/3}$. Thus, we rewrite Eq. [2] in terms of the respective body masses:

$$\frac{t_{mammoth}}{t_{turkey}} = \frac{m_{mammoth}^{2/3}}{m_{turkey}^{2/3}} = \left(\frac{2000kg}{10kg}\right)^{2/3} = 34$$

Defrosting a mammoth takes 136 days.

Problem 11.7

(a) In this problem, the underlying assumption is that the heat transfer is a steady process, i.e., that (i) the temperature profile across the block and (ii) the rate of heat transfer do not change with time. Later in the textbook, we will define this as a distinguished state of the system called the *steady state*. In the steady state, the heat transferred through the two blocks per unit time must be the same. Otherwise, we would either have a depletion of heat at the interface between both blocks and the interface zone would have to cool down or we would have an accumulation of heat at the interface and that zone would become hotter and hotter. As a consequence, we can use Fourier's law twice, once for each block. The implication of the steady state requires $(Q/t)_1 = (Q/t)_2 = Q/t$, in which the indices 1 and 2 represent each of the blocks. Labelling the temperature at the interface T_x we obtain:

$$\frac{Q}{t} = \frac{\lambda_2 A(T_{high} - T_x)}{l_2} = \frac{\lambda_1 A(T_x - T_{low})}{l_1} \quad \textbf{(1)}$$

Note that Eq. [1] contains three formulas, as the first and second or first and third or second and third terms are equal. First, we use the equality of the second and third terms to derive a formula for the temperature at the interface, T_x. Multiplying both sides of the equation with $l_1 \cdot l_2$ and dividing both sides by the area A, we find:

$$\lambda_2 l_1 T_{high} - \lambda_2 l_1 T_x = \lambda_1 l_2 T_x - \lambda_1 l_2 T_{low}$$

Next we group together the terms containing T_x:

$$T_x(\lambda_1 l_2 + \lambda_2 l_1) = \lambda_2 l_1 T_{high} - \lambda_1 l_2 T_{low}$$

In a last step we isolate T_x:

$$T_x = \frac{\lambda_2 l_1 T_{high} + \lambda_1 l_2 T_{low}}{\lambda_1 l_2 + \lambda_2 l_1} \quad \textbf{(2)}$$

This result is substituted into either one of the other two formulas in Eq. [1]. Choosing the equality between the first and the second terms, the following calculation follows. For convenience, we do not substitute Eq. [2] into that equation right away since the formula would become very long and cumbersome. Instead, we initially substitute Eq. [2] only into the term $(T_{high} - T_x)$, which is a factor in the second term in Eq. [1]. Once this bracket has been simplified, we return to the full formula in Eq. [1] and determine the heat flow rate Q/t. For the bracket $(T_{high} - T_x)$ we find:

$$T_{high} - T_x = T_{high} - \frac{\lambda_2 l_1 T_{high} + \lambda_1 l_2 T_{low}}{\lambda_1 l_2 + \lambda_2 l_1}$$
$$= \frac{\lambda_1 l_2 T_{high} + \lambda_2 l_1 T_{high} - \lambda_2 l_1 T_{high} - \lambda_1 l_2 T_{low}}{\lambda_1 l_2 + \lambda_2 l_1}$$
$$= \frac{\lambda_1 l_2 (T_{high} - T_{low})}{\lambda_1 l_2 + \lambda_2 l_1} \quad (3)$$

The result in Eq. [3] is now substituted for the term ($T_{high} - T_x$) in the first equality of Eq. [1]:

$$\frac{Q}{t} = \frac{\lambda_2 A}{l_2} \frac{\lambda_1 l_2 (T_{high} - T_{low})}{\lambda_1 l_2 + \lambda_2 l_1}$$
$$= A \frac{\lambda_1 \lambda_2}{\lambda_1 l_2 + \lambda_2 l_1} (T_{high} - T_{low}) \quad (4)$$

Lastly, we divide both the numerator and the denominator of the right hand side of Eq. [4] by $\lambda_1 \cdot \lambda_2$, leading to:

$$\frac{Q}{t} = A \frac{(T_{high} - T_{low})}{\frac{l_2}{\lambda_2} + \frac{l_1}{\lambda_1}} \quad (5)$$

which is the result we sought.

(b) Eq. [5] is rewritten by applying the result from Problem 11.3 to each of the blocks, i.e., $R_1 = l_1/\lambda_1$ and $R_2 = l_2/\lambda_2$:

$$\frac{Q}{t} = A \frac{(T_{high} - T_{low})}{R_1 + R_2}$$

Thus, the R values, which are the thermal resistances, are added for blocks through which heat is passing in sequence. When we study fluid flow through tubes placed in sequence (Chapter 13), we will find that fluid flow resistances are also added; in Chapter 19 we will find the same to apply to electric resistances, which are added when electric charges flow through resistors in series. This illustrates that our finding is broadly applicable: resistances have to be added if the flow is through several components in sequence. We will also find that flow resistances have to be added inversely when the components are placed in parallel, i.e., such that the flow is divided and its parts pass through the components simultaneously.

Problem 11.9

We start with arrangement (a). After combining the two blocks we obtain an insulation layer of area $2 \cdot A$ with 50% of this area covered with material 1 of (combined) thickness $2 \cdot l$ where l is the thickness of a single piece of insulator. For this arrangement Fourier's law reads:

$$\frac{Q}{t}\Big|_{(a)} = \left(\frac{Q}{t}\right)_1 + \left(\frac{Q}{t}\right)_2$$
$$= \frac{A\lambda_1}{2l}(T_{high} - T_{low}) + \frac{A\lambda_2}{2l}(T_{high} - T_{low}) \quad (1)$$

We rewrite Eq. [1] for later comparison in the form:

$$\frac{Q}{t}\Big|_{(a)} = \frac{A}{2l}\lambda_{comb}^{(a)}(T_{high} - T_{low}) \quad (2)$$
$$with: \lambda_{comb}^{(a)} = \lambda_1 + \lambda_2$$

Now we consider arrangement (b). Both half–sides of the combined insulator consist of two layers with a 1–2 sequence of the two materials. To describe such an arrangement, we derived Eq. [5] from Problem 11.7. Using that formula for a total area of $2 \cdot A$ in the current problem, we write:

$$\frac{Q}{t}\Big|_{(b)} = \frac{2 \cdot A(T_{high} - T_{low})}{\frac{l}{\lambda_1} + \frac{l}{\lambda_2}} \quad (3)$$

which we rewrite in analogy to Eq. [2] above:

$$\frac{Q}{t}\Big|_{(b)} = \frac{A}{2l}\lambda_{comb}^{(b)}(T_{high} - T_{low}) \quad (4)$$
$$with: \lambda_{comb}^{(b)} = \frac{4 \cdot \lambda_1 \cdot \lambda_2}{\lambda_1 + \lambda_2}$$

in which the factor 4 in the last formula is due to the prefactor 2 moving from the numerator to the denominator between Eqs. [3] and [4]. The remaining factors in $\lambda^{(b)}_{comb}$ are due to the following mathematical step:

$$\frac{1}{\frac{1}{\lambda_1} + \frac{1}{\lambda_2}} = \frac{1}{\frac{\lambda_1 + \lambda_2}{\lambda_1 \cdot \lambda_2}} = \frac{\lambda_1 \cdot \lambda_2}{\lambda_1 + \lambda_2} \quad (39)$$

In order to compare Eqs. [2] and [4], we divide Eq. [2] by Eq. [4]. Since all other terms in both equations are equal, this corresponds to a division of the two combined λ factors:

$$\frac{\lambda_{comb}^{(a)}}{\lambda_{comb}^{(b)}} = \frac{(\lambda_1 + \lambda_2)^2}{4 \cdot \lambda_1 \cdot \lambda_2} \qquad \textbf{(5)}$$

We use a mathematical trick to determine whether the ratio in Eq. [5] is larger or smaller than 1: since we know that the square of any number is positive the following holds:

$$\begin{aligned}(\lambda_1 - \lambda_2)^2 &= \lambda_1^2 - 2 \cdot \lambda_1 \cdot \lambda_2 + \lambda_2^2 \\ &= \lambda_1^2 + 2\lambda_1\lambda_2 + \lambda_2^2 - 4\lambda_1\lambda_2 \\ &= (\lambda_1 + \lambda_2)^2 - 4 \cdot \lambda_1 \cdot \lambda_2 > 0\end{aligned}$$

which is true for any pair of values λ_1 and λ_2 if we assume $\lambda_1 \neq \lambda_2$. Note that the case $\lambda_1 = \lambda_2$ is trivial and not discussed further. Therefore, we find the following inequality: $(\lambda_1 + \lambda_2)^2 > 4 \cdot \lambda_1 \cdot \lambda_2$. From this we get:

$$\frac{\lambda_{comb}^{(a)}}{\lambda_{comb}^{(b)}} > 1 \Rightarrow \lambda_{comb}^{(a)} > \lambda_{comb}^{(b)}$$

The larger combined thermal conductivity for arrangement (a) leads to a larger amount of heat transported per time unit.

Problem 11.11

We assume that the bacterial putrefaction generates heat at a uniform rate, $(Q_{\text{putrefaction}}/t)/V = const = q^*$. Thus, the total amount of heat generated per second in a mound of radius R is:

$$\frac{Q_{putrefaction}}{t} = \frac{4}{3}\pi \cdot R^3 \cdot q^*$$

In the stationary case sought by the birds, this rate must be equal to the heat loss through the mound surface. Assuming that heat loss occurs uniformly across the surface of the sphere, we write:

$$\frac{4}{3}\pi \cdot R^3 \cdot q^* = -4 \cdot \pi \cdot R^2 \cdot \lambda \frac{\Delta T}{\Delta R} \qquad \textbf{(1)}$$

where the last term is Fourier's heat loss rate in which we rewrote the temperature step across the membrane of thickness l, $\Delta T/l$, as a temperature gradient $\Delta T/\Delta R$. From Eq. [1] we find the required temperature gradient:

$$\frac{\Delta T}{\Delta R} = -\frac{R \cdot q^*}{3 \cdot \lambda} \qquad \textbf{(2)}$$

If you want to avoid the use of calculus, you use a similar line of arguments from Eq. [2] as we use in the textbook in Section 14.4.1 to derive the elastic energy from the linear restoring force for an object attached to a spring. We find that a gradient that is linear in the position, $\Delta T/\Delta R \propto R$, yields a quadratic formula for the temperature profile with radius:

$$T - T_0 = -\frac{R^2 \cdot q^*}{6 \cdot \lambda}$$

The particular application for the Australian Brush–turkey reads as follows: the central temperature T_0 must be maintained at 35°C, but the external temperature T may vary. To compensate for variations of the external air temperature, the birds have only control over the radius of the mound; they must adjust the radius based on:

$$R = \sqrt{\frac{6 \cdot \lambda}{q^*}\left(T_{eggs} - T_{air}\right)}$$

which is consistent with the relationship we were seeking because λ and q^* are constant.

Problem 11.13

(a) A major heat loss mechanism at moderate environmental temperatures is convection. It requires that an air flow pass across the skin to carry the heat away. Clothes have air–filled pores of variable size in which the air cannot move. Thus, heat which would otherwise be lost from the bare skin by convection, must be conducted through air in the pores of the clothes. Heat conduction (Fourier's law) is a much less effective mechanism than convection, particularly since the thermal conductivity coefficient λ of air is very small.

(b) The algal blooms that one can observe in temperate lakes during the transitional seasons are caused by convective currents in the water of the lake. As illustrated in Fig. 11.20, the temperature profile of the lake during summer is layered with (i) a warm zone near the surface (since this zone is heated by the warm air and the sun's radiation), (ii) an intermediate layer called *thermocline*, and (iii) a cold layer near the bottom of the lake. During the transitional seasons the temperature change in the upper layer causes the thermocline layer to break down, which in turn causes convection to mix the water. The water currents associated with convection transport nutrients from the bottom of the lake to the surface. The nutrient–rich water brought that way to the surface can cause a rapid increase in the algae population as algae also need sunlight to grow.

Problem 11.15

We rewrite Fick's law with the diffusion coefficient as the dependent variable:

$$D = \frac{1}{A}\left(\frac{m}{t}\right)\frac{1}{\Delta\rho / l} \qquad \textbf{(1)}$$

where $\Delta\rho/l$ is the change of the density per unit length, i.e., the density gradient. In the last step, the given data are substituted into Eq. [1]:

$$D = \frac{5.7\times 10^{-15}\,\frac{kg}{s}}{(2\times 10^{-4} m^2)\left(3\times 10^{-2}\,\frac{kg}{m^4}\right)}$$

$$= 9.5\times 10^{-10}\,\frac{m^2}{s}$$

Problem 11.17

(a) Aerobic bacteria need to have oxygen present throughout their body in order for their metabolisms to function. Let us assume a spherical bacterium of average size, e.g. with a radius of 1 μm (although they are often not spherical, as their name implies). For this bacterium we calculate the time that it takes for oxygen to diffuse from the outer surface to the centre, using Eq. [11.6]. For the diffusion length we use $\Lambda = 1.0 \times 10^{-6}$ m.

We obtain a lower limit for the diffusion time by using the diffusion coefficient for oxygen in water at room temperature from Table 11.5:

$$t = \frac{\Lambda^2}{2D} = \frac{(1.0\times 10^{-6} m)^2}{2\left(1.0\times 10^{-9}\,\frac{m^2}{s}\right)} = 5\times 10^{-4} s$$

which is just half a millisecond.

In the same way, we use the diffusion coefficient of oxygen in tissue at room temperature from Table 11.5 and obtain an upper limit of $t = 5 \times 10^{-2}$ s, which is still less than a tenth of a second. Thus, an average sized bacterium at room temperature has no problem assimilating the oxygen it needs for its metabolism through passive diffusion.

(b) Now we focus on the human body with an oxygen consuming organ, such as the heart, at an assumed depth of 10 cm below the surface of the outer skin. This leads to a required diffusion length $\Lambda = 0.1$ m for this organ to be supplied with oxygen. We calculate the same two limiting cases as for the bacteria, assuming that oxygen is brought to the organ by passive diffusion. Note that a body temperature of endotherms of 37°C instead of 20°C improves the following result only insignificantly. For diffusion in water we find:

$$t = \frac{\Lambda^2}{2D} = \frac{(0.1m)^2}{2\left(1.0\times 10^{-9}\,\frac{m^2}{s}\right)}$$

$$= 5\times 10^{6} s \cong 58\,days$$

and for diffusion in tissue we obtain $t = 5 \times 10^{8}$ s, which is just less than 16 years. This result shows clearly that a larger organism cannot rely on passive diffusion to provide the oxygen required for its metabolism.

It is interesting to put this result in context with Table 11.4, which provides the history of life on Earth. When you read that table carefully, you notice that it took just over 500 million years for life to actually emerge after conditions that permit life to exist developed.

It took five times this long, a staggering 2.5 billion years, to have the first single–celled bacteria develop into a larger, multi–celled organisms. Once this had been achieved, a rapid diversification of life took place about 670 million years ago, called the Cambrian Explosion. Thus, Einstein's equation for the diffusion length can be considered to represent the single biggest hurdle in the development of life, not the occurrence of life itself. It is noteworthy that material transport within cells remains diffusion–limited, and thus, even the largest mammalian cells have diameters of no more than 20 μm.

(c) Hydras possess a central gastro–vascular cavity that is lined by a layer that is two cells thick to allow diffusive material exchange.

Problem 11.19

(a) We use Eq. [11.6]. The diffusion coefficient of the tobacco mosaic virus in water is taken from Table 11.8:

$$\Lambda = \sqrt{2\left(5\times10^{-12}\frac{m^2}{s}\right)3600s}$$

$$= 1.9\times10^{-4}m = 0.19mm$$

This performance of the tobacco mosaic virus isn't impressive. It takes 1 hour to travel about 0.2 mm, 4 days to travel about 2 mm and more than 13 months to travel a distance of 2 cm. Clearly, viruses choose other modes of transportation, such as drag effects in air or water, which allow them to spread more quickly.

(b) The two formulas for the diffusion lengths read:

$$\Lambda_{O_2} = \sqrt{2\cdot D_{O_2}\cdot t}$$

$$\Lambda_{CO_2} = \sqrt{2\cdot D_{CO_2}\cdot t}$$

and their ratio is given by:

$$\frac{\Lambda_{CO_2}}{\Lambda_{O_2}} = \sqrt{\frac{D_{CO_2}}{D_{O_2}}} = \sqrt{8.3} = 2.9$$

in which we have used the result of Problem 11.16 in the form:

$$D_{CO_2} \cong 8.3\cdot D_{O_2}$$

This means that carbon dioxide diffuses in tissue roughly three times farther than oxygen under the same conditions.

CHAPTER TWELVE

STATIC FLUIDS

MULTIPLE CHOICE QUESTIONS

Multiple Choice 12.1
Correct Answer (b).

Multiple Choice 12.3
Correct Answer (c). We write for the pressure change $\Delta p = \rho \cdot g \cdot h = (1.06 \times 10^3 \text{ kg/m}^3)$ (9.81 m/s^2) $(1.2 \text{ m}) = 12.5 \text{ kPa}$.

Multiple Choice 12.5
Correct Answer (a).

Multiple Choice 12.7
Correct Answer (a). Weight must be acting down, and a force must be acting in opposition to that force, otherwise the shark would be falling with an acceleration equal to *g*.
to the surface.

Multiple Choice 12.9
Correct Answer (c).

Multiple Choice 12.11
Correct Answer (a). Note ρ_{cheese} = (30 g)/(3 cm)(3 cm)(3 cm) = 1111 kg/m^3.

Multiple Choice 12.13
Correct Answer (e). The buoyant force is not responsible for the bird's ability to fly. The buoyant force plus a lift force is equal to the weight of the bird.

Multiple Choice 12.15
Correct Answer (d). It is the same as N/m.

Multiple Choice 12.17
Correct Answer (b). The pressure difference is greatest for the smaller radius of curvature.

Multiple Choice 12.19
Correct Answer (c).

Multiple Choice 12.21
Correct Answer (c). Any unbalanced force would cause the molecule to accelerate.

CONCEPTUAL QUESTIONS

Conceptual Question 12.1
The pressure of the water surrounding the bubbles decreases, allowing the gas (water vapour) to expand.

Conceptual Question 12.3
(a) The feet of geckos have enlarged overlapping plates on their undersurfaces, called *lamellae*. The lamellae in turn are covered by so–called *setae*, which are microscopic projections of the skin. These spatula–shaped prongs typically measure between 10 μm and 0.1 mm in length. The gecko brings the expanded tips of the setae in close contact with the underlying surface causing weak adhesive forces. These forces are sufficient to hold the gecko at a flat vertical surface because each toe has more than 1 million setae. The lamellae are pushed against the flat surface with an elaborate mechanism within the gecko's toes. An extensive capillary bed connects to a small blood reservoir beneath the bones in each toe. The gecko can shut off this system from its circulatory system with a set of valves. When the bone then pushes onto the filled blood reservoir, the capillaries are pressurized. The blood vessels expand and push onto the adjacent lamellae. This forces the lamellae tightly against the surface, following any of its irregularities closely. Since the surface energy of the substrate is a factor in the adhesive force, geckos find smooth glass surfaces with their large surface energy particularly easy to hold onto.
(b) The adhesion achieved in part (a) poses a problem when the gecko wants to walk. To lift the foot off the surface, the gecko must depressurize the capillary bed. To detach from the surface, the toe is rolled off from tip to base to not have to peel all setae off the surface at once. These attachment and detachment processes have to occur for every step taken.

ANALYTICAL PROBLEMS

Problem 12.1

We use a sphere of radius r, a cylinder of height h and radius r with $h = r$, a cube of side length h, a pyramid of base length h with four equilateral triangles, a tetrahedron of side length h, a cone with base radius r and height h with $r = h$, and an octahedron which is a double–pyramid. For these bodies, Table 1 shows a sketch, the formula for the volume, the value for r or h when the volume is $V = 1$ m³, the formula for the surface and the total surface area in unit m². Note that the sphere indeed has the smallest surface of all of these bodies of equal volume.

Body	Sketch	Volume Formula	r, h for V = 1	Surface Formula	Surface for V = 1
sphere		$\frac{4}{3}\pi r^3$	0.6204	$4\pi r^2$	4.8
cylinder (r = h)		$r^2\pi h$	0.6828	$2r\pi(r+h)$	5.9
cube		h^3	1.0	$6h^2$	6.0
pyramid		$\frac{h^3}{3\sqrt{2}}$	1.6189	$h^2(1+\sqrt{3})$	5.4
tetrahedron		$\frac{h^3}{12}\sqrt{2}$	2.0396	$h^2\sqrt{3}$	7.2
cone (r = h)		$\frac{r^2}{3}\pi h$	0.9847	$r\pi(r+\sqrt{r^2+h^2})$	7.4
octahedron		$\frac{h^3}{3}\sqrt{2}$	1.2849	$2h^2\sqrt{3}$	5.7

Table 1

Problem 12.3

This is an example of a possible diving accident when scuba diving. *Scuba* stands for *self–contained under water breathing apparatus*, a technique developed by Jacques–Yves Cousteau in 1943. When filling the lungs at depth d, the external pressure on the body and, correspondingly, the gas pressure in the lungs is given by Pascal's law, i.e., $p = p_{atm} + \rho \cdot g \cdot d$. As the diver ascends, the external pressure decreases until it reaches atmospheric pressure p_{atm} at the surface. At the same time the blood pressure decreases to its normal (out of the water) value. But the gas pressure in the lungs remains at the value it was at depth d since the diver doesn't exhale. Therefore, the pressure difference between the lungs and the outside pressure on the chest at the surface is:

$$\Delta p = p - p_{amt} = \rho \cdot g \cdot d$$

and the depth d is given by:

$$d = \frac{\Delta p}{\rho \cdot g} = \frac{(76\ \text{torr})\left(133.32\frac{\text{Pa}}{\text{torr}}\right)}{\left(1.0\times10^{3}\frac{\text{kg}}{\text{m}^{3}}\right)\left(9.8\frac{\text{m}}{\text{s}^{2}}\right)}$$
$$= 1.03\,\text{m}$$

in which we used the conversion for pressures of 1 torr = 133.32 Pa. Thus, surfacing from about a 1 m depth without exhaling in this case leads to 76 torr pressure difference, which is about 10% of the atmospheric pressure. It is still enough to rupture the lungs and force air from the higher pressure lungs into the lower pressure blood. This air may be carried to the heart and kill the diver. An ugly way to die!

Problem 12.5

This problem is solved using Pascal's law. Using the definition of the gauge pressure from the problem text, Pascal's law is rewritten in the form:

$$p_{gauge} = p - p_{atm} = -\rho \cdot g \cdot h \qquad \textbf{(1)}$$

in which the negative sign on the right hand side indicates that the pressure in the lungs is lower than the atmospheric pressure during the sucking.

We substitute the numerical values in Eq. [1]:

$$p_{gauge} = -\frac{\left(1.0\times10^{3}\frac{\text{kg}}{\text{m}^{3}}\right)\left(9.8\frac{\text{m}}{\text{s}^{2}}\right)(0.1\,\text{m})}{1.01\times10^{5}\frac{\text{Pa}}{\text{atm}}} \qquad \textbf{(2)}$$
$$= -9.7\times10^{-3}\,\text{atm}$$

The denominator in Eq. [2] allows us to convert to the non–standard unit atm. Of course, the best way to answer the question would be to provide an answer in the standard unit Pa; however, non–standard pressure units are still quite often used.

Problem 12.7

The gauge pressure needed is: $p = \rho$ g h, that is, p = (10^3 kg/m^3)(9.8 m/s^2)(365 m) which totals p = 3577 kPa.

Problem 12.9

For this problem we use the Archimedes principle. The magnitude of the weight of an iceberg of total volume V_{total} is:

$$W_{total} = m_{ice} \cdot g = \rho_{ice} \cdot V_{total} \cdot g$$

The magnitude of the weight of the displaced seawater is equal to the magnitude of the buoyant force acting on the iceberg, $F_{buoyant}$:

$$F_{buoyant} = m_{H_2O} \cdot g = \rho_{H_2O} \cdot V_{displaced\ water} \cdot g$$

in which $V_{displaced\ water}$ is equal to the volume of the iceberg below the surface of the sea. The iceberg is in mechanical equilibrium when it floats, i.e., the weight of the iceberg and the buoyant force must be equal, and a free-body diagram will have the buoyant force directed up balancing the weight directed down. Using Newton's first law we write for the balance of forces in the vertical direction:

$$\rho_{H_2O} \cdot V_{displaced\ water} \cdot g - \rho_{ice} \cdot V_{total} \cdot g = 0$$

which yields:

$$\frac{\rho_{ice}}{\rho_{H_2O}} = \frac{V_{displaced\ water}}{V_{total}} \qquad \textbf{(1)}$$

where in this case ρ_{H_2O} refers to the density of sea water. This provides us with a formula for the ratio of the volume of the displaced water to the total volume of the iceberg. We now express the quantity sought in the problem.

The question is about the fraction of the volume of the iceberg that reaches above the sea level:

$$\frac{V_{total} - V_{displaced\ water}}{V_{total}} = 1 - \frac{V_{displaced\ water}}{V_{total}}$$

We use Eq. [1] to replace the second term on the right hand side:

$$1 - \frac{V_{displaced\ water}}{V_{total}} = 1 - \frac{\rho_{ice}}{\rho_{H_2O}}$$

$$= 1 - \frac{0.92\frac{\text{kg}}{\text{L}}}{1.025\frac{\text{kg}}{\text{L}}} = 0.102$$

For icebergs off the coast of Newfoundland and Labrador, just over 10% of the iceberg volume extends beyond the surface of the water. Hence the expression "the tip of the iceberg", which is used to indicate that there is much more to something that is apparent.

Problem 12.11

(a) An object, which floats at a given depth below the surface of a fluid, must be in mechanical equilibrium. For the three cases we considered in the context of Figure 12.8, this was discussed as case (II). In Figure 12.8, such a mechanical equilibrium is based on two forces acting on the block B: the weight and the buoyant force. The situation in Figure 12.27 is different because in both cases an additional tension force acts on the object. Thus, without the string, neither case 12.27(a) nor case 12.27(b) would be in a mechanical equilibrium. It is the additional tension, which establishes this equilibrium. Consequently, the free–body diagram in each case must be based on three forces. The free–body diagram for the wooden sphere is shown in Figure 12.28(B). The buoyant force is drawn with a larger magnitude than the weight because we know from experience that the wooden sphere, if released, would buoy to the surface. To establish mechanical equilibrium a second downward directed force is needed. This force is provided by the tension in the string. For mechanical equilibrium, the free–body diagram must show the length of the tension force to be equal to the difference in length between the weight and the buoyant force (unlike in Figure 12.28(B)). Using Newton's first law, we write:

$$F_{buoyant} - T - W = 0 \quad \textbf{(1)}$$

Of the three forces in Eq. [1] we can quantify two:

- the weight: Use the volume of the wooden sphere and its density. Using the radius $r = d/2 = 5$ cm, we get:

$$W = m_{wood} \cdot g = V \cdot \rho_{wood} \cdot g = \frac{4}{3}\pi \cdot r^3 \cdot g \cdot \rho_{wood} \quad \textbf{(2)}$$

- the buoyant force:

$$F_{buoyant} = V_{H_2O} \cdot \rho_{H_2O} \cdot g = \frac{4}{3}\pi \cdot r^3 \cdot g \cdot \rho_{H_2O} \quad \textbf{(3)}$$

Now we substitute these two forces in Eq. [1] and solve for the magnitude of the tension **T**:

$$T = F_{buoyant} - W = \frac{4}{3}\pi \cdot r^3 \cdot g(\rho_{H_2O} - \rho_{wood})$$

Substituting the given values the right hand side reads:

$$\frac{4}{3}\pi(0.05\,\text{m})^3\left(9.8\frac{\text{m}}{\text{s}^2}\right)\left(1.0\frac{\text{g}}{\text{cm}^3} - 0.9\frac{\text{g}}{\text{cm}^3}\right)$$

This yields $T = 0.51$ N (remember to change the density into units of kg/m³).

(b) The free–body diagram for the heavy sphere from Figure 12.27(a) is shown in Figure 12.28(C). The string provides for a mechanical equilibrium. The tension associated with the sting is calculated from applying Newton's first law:

$$F_{buoyant} + T - W = 0 \quad \textbf{(4)}$$

Note that this equation differs from Eq. [1] for case (a) only in the sign of the tension as the string is now directed upward. Again, the buoyant force and the weight of the heavy sphere can be calculated; the formulas are identical to those shown in Eqs. [2] and [3] if we replace the label *wood* by *heavy sphere.* Note that the radius of the sphere is given in part (b) instead of its diameter.

Substituting Eqs. [2] and [3] in Eq. [4] and solving for the magnitude of the tension **T**, we obtain:

$$T = W - F_{buoyant} = \frac{4}{3}\pi \cdot r^3 \cdot g(\rho_{heavy} - \rho_{H_2O})$$

This yields $T = 41.05$ N.

Problem 12.13

According to Archimedes' principle, the weight of the displaced fluid is equal to the weight of the cargo and therefore:

$$\begin{aligned} m_{\text{cargo}} &= m_{\text{fluid}} \\ &= \rho_{\text{fluid}} V_{\text{object}} \end{aligned} \quad \textbf{(1)}$$

Assuming the fluid is fresh water, and given that the additional submerged volume can be calculated from the dimensions of the boat as well as the additional depth to which it sinks, Eq. [1] yields:

Problem 12.15

Given the low density of air when compared to all other fluids in the problem, we can ignore the buoyant force in air, and take the mass of the object in air as the real mass of the object. A free-body diagram for the object when immersed in oil or in water will involve three forces: the weight W directed down, and the tension T and the buoyant force F directed up. Therefore, with the positive axis directed up, Newton's First Law implies:

$$F = mg - T \quad \textbf{(1)}$$

Eq. [12.5] for the buoyant force can now be used into Eq. [1] to obtain:

$$\rho_{\text{fluid}} V = m - \frac{T}{g}, \quad \textbf{(2)}$$

where V is the submerged volume, in our case, the volume of the object since the entire object is immersed in the fluid.

(a) We use Eq. [2] for the situation when the object is immersed in water to find the volume of the object:

$$V = \frac{m - T_{\text{water}}/g}{\rho_{\text{water}}} \quad \textbf{(3)}$$

Since we know the mass of the object, we can use Eq. [3] to find its density:

$$\rho = \frac{m}{V} = \frac{\rho_{\text{water}}}{1 - T_{\text{water}}/mg} = 5400 \, \text{kg/m}^3$$

(b) We use Eq. [2] for the situation when the object is immersed in oil to find the oil's density:

$$\rho_{\text{oil}} = \frac{m - T_{\text{oil}}/g}{V} \quad \textbf{(4)}$$

We substitute the volume of the object from Eq. [3] into Eq. [4] to obtain:

$$\begin{aligned} \rho_{\text{oil}} &= \rho_{\text{water}} \left(\frac{m - T_{\text{oil}}/g}{m - T_{\text{water}}/g} \right) \\ &= \rho_{\text{water}} \left(\frac{mg - T_{\text{oil}}}{mg - T_{\text{water}}} \right) \end{aligned} \quad \textbf{(5)}$$

With the numerical values given in the problem Eq. [5] yields $\rho_{\text{oil}} = 680$ kg/m^3.

Problem 12.17

We use Jurin's law in Eq. [12.13] with a contact angle of $\theta = 0°$, and solve for the radius of the tube:

$$r = \frac{2\sigma_{\text{liquid}}}{\rho_{\text{liquid}}\, g} \cdot \frac{1}{h_{\text{liquid}}} = 347 \, \mu\text{m}$$

The diameter is then $d = 2r = 690$ μm.

Problem 12.19

The definition of surface tension used for this problem is given in Eq. [12.9]:

$$\sigma = \frac{F}{l_x} \qquad \textbf{(1)}$$

Note that the force in that formula is directed *tangential* to the depressed water surface, as properly indicated in Figure 12.32. The length l_x in Eq. [1] represents the length of the contact line along which the force of magnitude F acts. In the case of the insect's foot, this line is the circumference of the foot where it touches the surface of the water. This circumference is determined from the given diameter of the insect's foot by using Figure 1. The figure is a detailed view of the geometric relations of the force and spatial parameters relevant to this problem. We note that the circumference of the foot at the water line is given by $2 \cdot \pi \cdot r \cdot \cos\theta$ in which r is the radius of the foot. We label this circumference l_x. Using the value for l_x, we find from Eq. [1] the magnitude of the force **F** exerted by the water surface, as illustrated in Figure 12.32 and Figure 1:

$$F = \sigma \cdot l_x = \sigma \cdot 2 \cdot \pi \cdot r \cdot \cos\theta$$

Next we use Newton's first law to describe the mechanical equilibrium of the insect. Of interest is only the vertical direction as the symmetry of the foot provides automatically for a compensation of the x–directional components of the forces acting on the foot. The equilibrium must exist because the insect neither accelerates down (and drowns) nor accelerates up (while not intentionally flying away). Since an insect has six legs and usually rests with all of them on the water surface, Newton's law contains seven contributions: one force in the positive y–direction due to the force **F** acting on each leg, and one force down due to the weight of the insect:

$$-W_{insect} + 6(\sigma \cdot 2 \cdot \pi \cdot r \cdot \cos\theta)\cos\theta = 0$$

in which the extra $\cos\theta$ term is introduced by using the y–component of the force **F** in Figure 1.

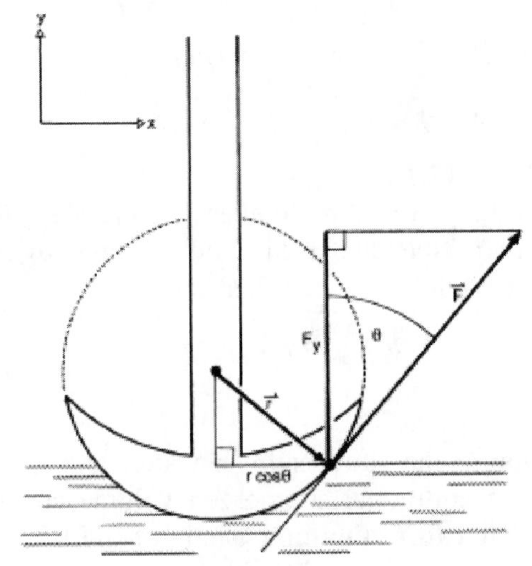

Figure 1

We solve Eq. [20] for $\cos^2\theta$:

$$\cos^2\theta = \frac{m \cdot g}{12 \cdot \pi \cdot r \cdot \sigma}$$

$$= \frac{1.5 \times 10^{-5}\,\text{kg}\left(9.8\,\frac{\text{m}}{\text{s}^2}\right)}{12 \cdot \pi \cdot (1.25 \times 10^{-4}\,\text{m})\left(0.073\,\frac{\text{N}}{\text{m}}\right)}$$

$$= 0.427$$

in which m is the mass of the insect. Thus, we obtain $\cos\theta = 0.653$ which corresponds to an angle $\theta = 49^0$. This illustrates that contrary to our intuition the depression of the water is rather steep, with a 41^0 angle between the flat-water surface and the edge of the foot.

CHAPTER THIRTEEN

Fluid Flow

MULTIPLE CHOICE QUESTIONS

Multiple Choice 13.1
Correct Answer (a).

Multiple Choice 13.3
Correct Answer (b).

Multiple Choice 13.5
Correct Answer (a).

Multiple Choice 13.7
Correct Answer (c).

Multiple Choice 13.9
Correct Answer (c).

Multiple Choice 13.11
Correct Answer (d).

Multiple Choice 13.13
Correct Answer (c).

Multiple Choice 13.15
Correct Answer (b).

Multiple Choice 13.17
Correct Answer (a). Note that profile (b) has a finite fluid speed at the wall surface.

CONCEPTUAL QUESTIONS

Conceptual Question 13.1
Air passing over the mound speeds up while passing over the hole. This lowers the air pressure above the hole, causing suction on the air in the burrow.

Conceptual Question 13.3
The fast-flowing gas inside the tube of the burner creates a difference in pressure with respect to the outside. This is expressed and quantified in Eq. [13.6] known as Bernoulli's Law. Due to the fast moving gas, the pressure inside the burner is lower than the pressure outside. Therefore if we make some holes in the cylinder of the burner, air will sucked into the burner with the gas to create a mixture suitable for effective combustion.

ANALYTICAL PROBLEMS

Problem 13.1
We use Bernoulli's law:

$$p + \frac{1}{2}\rho \cdot v^2 = const$$

at the top and bottom of the airplane wing in the form:

$$p_{top} + \frac{1}{2}\rho_{air} \cdot v_{top}^2 = p_{bottom} + \frac{1}{2}\rho_{air} \cdot v_{bottom}^2 \quad \textbf{(1)}$$

where $\rho_{air} = 1.2\ \text{kg/m}^3$ is the density of air. We re–arrange Eq. [1]:

$$\Delta p = p_{bottom} - p_{top} = \frac{1}{2}\rho_{air}(v_{top}^2 - v_{bottom}^2)$$

This yields:

$$\Delta p = \frac{1}{2}\left(1.2\frac{\text{kg}}{\text{m}^3}\right)\left\{\left(300\frac{\text{m}}{\text{s}}\right)^2 - \left(280\frac{\text{m}}{\text{s}}\right)^2\right\}$$

$$= 6960\frac{\text{N}}{\text{m}^2}$$

This pressure difference causes a net upward force on the wing of:

$$F_{net} = \Delta p \cdot A = \left(6960\frac{\text{N}}{\text{m}^2}\right)\cdot(20\text{m}^2)$$

$$= 1.4\times10^5\text{N}$$

Problem 13.3

(a) We use Bernoulli's law Eq. [13.5]. At the location of the small hole, both on the inside and the outside of the tank, we find:

$$p_{in} + \frac{1}{2}\rho \cdot v_{in}^2 = \rho_{out} + \frac{1}{2}\rho \cdot v_{out}^2 \qquad (1)$$

Since the tank is open to the air at the top, we further know from Pascal's law:

$$p_{in} = p_{atm} + \rho \cdot g \cdot h \qquad (2)$$

where h is the distance of the hole below the surface of the water. Inside the tank, the fluid speed is approximately zero.
Outside the tank we know that:

$$p_{out} = p_{atm} \qquad (3)$$

We substitute Eqs. [2] and [3] in Eq. [1]:

$$p_{atm} + \rho \cdot g \cdot h = p_{atm} + \frac{1}{2}\rho \cdot v_{out}^2$$

which simplifies and can be re–arranged as:

$$v_{out} = \sqrt{2gh} = \sqrt{2\left(9.8\frac{\text{m}}{\text{s}^2}\right)(16\,\text{m})} = 18\frac{\text{m}}{\text{s}}$$

(b) We use the definition of the volume flow rate:

$$\frac{\Delta V}{\Delta t} = A \cdot v$$

with v the speed of the fluid. Re–arranging and converting the units, we obtain:

$$A = \frac{1}{v}\frac{\Delta V}{\Delta t} = 2.3 \times 10^{-6}\,\text{m}^2$$

Since $A = \pi \cdot r^2 = \pi \cdot (d/2)^2$, we find that $d =$ 0.0017 m = 1.7 mm.

Problem 13.5

(a) We use the definition of the volume flow rate in Eq. [13.4]. The area of the faucet is calculated from its radius. We solve Eq. [13.4] for the fluid speed and substitute all values in SI units: $v = 2.7$ m/s.

(b) Since there are no other faucets open, the volume flow rate out of the faucet must be equal to the flow rate into the pipe. The cross–sectional area of the inflow pipe is determined from its radius. We can then find the speed of water into the pipe. In the final step, Bernoulli's law is used to find $p_{gauge} = 23$ kPa.

Problem 13.7

(a) The open end of the siphon is a distance h below the open surface of the tank. Therefore, the pressure in the fluid as it emerges from the siphon's open end is calculated with Pascal's law. We then use Bernoulli's law comparing the fluid at the surface of the tank and the fluid leaving the open end of the siphon. We note that the pressure at the surface of the tank is atmospheric, and that the fluid at the surface of the tank is essentially at rest.

Substituting these conditions into Bernoulli's law leads as an intermediate formula to:

$$p_{atm} = p_{atm} + \rho \cdot g \cdot h + \frac{1}{2}\rho \cdot v_{end}^2$$

(b) The device will work for all values of y up to $y_{max} = p_{atm}/(\rho \cdot g)$. This can be shown using again Bernoulli's law between the point of extraction of the water and the maximum point in the tube at height y if the water reaches this point with minimum speed.

Problem 13.9

Since the beaker is open to the atmosphere at the top, we could use Pascal's law to find the height of water in the beaker if we knew the pressure at the bottom. Bernoulli's law would allow us to find the pressure if we knew the speed of the water as it leaves the hole in the beaker. The speed of the water as it emerges from the hole in the beaker *can* be found because the water follows a projectile trajectory as it travels toward the floor. We use the kinematics relationships for two–dimensional motion in the x–y plane noting that $v_{initial,\,y} = 0$ since the initial velocity is only horizontal. We choose the origin of the system to be the location of the floor, directly below the hole in the beaker. Therefore the initial position of the water is (0.0 m, 1.0 m) and the final position as it hits the floor is (0.6 m, 0.0 m). Substituting the given values in the kinematics equation for the y–direction, we find for the time to the ground $t = 0.45$ s.
This time can be used in the kinematics equation for the x–direction, noting as always that the x–component of acceleration is zero

for a projectile. We find $v_{\text{initial, x}} = 1.33$ m/s.
We use Bernoulli's equation and Pascal's law together comparing the fluid inside and just outside the hole in the beaker, noting the fluid inside the beaker is approximately at rest. This yields $h = 0.09$ m = 9.0 cm.

Problem 13.11

Using Bernoulli's law we find that the pressure change in the constriction is $\Delta p = -17$ Pa. This is a very small decrease in pressure in the bronchus.

Problem 13.13

(a) We use the equation of continuity in the form of Eq. [13.2], where in the first section A1 = 8.0 cm2 and v1 = 250 cm/s, and in the second section A2 = 3.0 cm2. Solving for v2 we obtain:

$$v_2 = \frac{A_1}{A_2} v_1 = 670 \, \text{cm/s} \qquad (1)$$

(b) We use Bernoulli's Law in Eq. [13.5], where $p_1 = 1.1 \times 10^5$ Pa and $\rho = 1.5$ g/cm^3 is the density of the fluid with $\rho = \rho_1 = \rho_2$ since the liquid does not change densities. The fluid speeds are $v_1 = 2.5$ m/s in the first section and $v_2 = 6.7$ m/s from Eq. [1] in the second section. Solving for p_2 in Eq. [13.5] we find:

$$p_2 = p_1 + \frac{1}{2}\rho\left(v_1^2 - v_2^2\right) = 8.1 \times 10^4 \text{ Pa} \qquad (2)$$

The result from Eq. [2] is consistent with a qualitative analysis of Bernoulli's Law; if the speed increases the pressure must decrease.

Problem 13.15

We first calculate the pressure of the water in the syringe's barrel, p_1. This value is determined from the mechanical equilibrium of forces that act on the plunger. A mechanical equilibrium must exist since the question asks for a flow speed of the water, implying that there is no acceleration of the plunger involved. In the equilibrium the pressure inside the barrel is equal to the two components acting on the plunger from outside, the atmospheric pressure and the pressure caused by the exerted force:

$$p_1 = \frac{|F_{ext}|}{A_1} + p_{atm} = \frac{2.0\text{N}}{3 \times 10^{-5}\text{m}^2} + 1.01 \times 10^5 \text{Pa} = 1.68 \times 10^5 \text{Pa}$$

Now we apply Bernoulli's law across the needle of the syringe:

$$p_1 + \frac{\rho_{H_2O}}{2} v_{barrel}^2 = p_2 + \frac{\rho_{H_2O}}{2} v_2^2$$

in which we use for the speed of the water in the barrel $v_{\text{barrel}} \cong 0$ m/s as an approximation, and further that $p_2 = 1.0$ atm for the pressure in the needle. With these simplifications we write:

$$\frac{\rho_{H_2O}}{2} v_2^2 = p_1 - p_{atm}$$

From this equation the speed of the water in the needle is obtained:

$$v_2 = \sqrt{\frac{2(p_1 - p_{atm})}{\rho_{H_2O}}}$$

Substituting the given values, we find:

$$v_2 = \sqrt{\frac{2(1.68 \times 10^5 \text{Pa} - 1.01 \times 10^5 \text{Pa})}{1.0 \times 10^3 \frac{\text{kg}}{\text{m}^3}}} = 11.6 \frac{\text{m}}{\text{s}}$$

Problem 13.17

Poiseuille's law allows us to relate the volume flow rate of a Newtonian fluid through a tube to the pressure gradient in the tube. We start by changing the units of the volume flow rate to SI units. We then rewrite Poiseuille's law to solve for the change in pressure over the tube's length: $\Delta p = 2.08 \times 10^6$ Pa = 20.5 atm. If the pressure at the end of the tube is 1 atm, at its beginning we find $p = 2.08 \times 10^6$ Pa + 1.01×10^5 Pa = 2.18×10^6 Pa. But we are asked for the gauge pressure which is the pressure relative to atmospheric, so the gauge pressure is actually $p = 2.08 \times 10^6$ Pa = 20.5 atm.

Problem 13.19

$\Delta V/\Delta t_1 : \Delta V/\Delta t_2 = 8 : 1$, where we have used Poiseuille's law in Eq. [13.9]. With the same pressure difference for both tubes, halving the length doubles the volume flow rate. At the same time, halving the radius reduces the volume flow rate by a factor of sixteen. Thus the net effect is a reduction by a factor of eight in the volume flow rate.

CHAPTER FOURTEEN

Elasticity and Vibrations

MULTIPLE CHOICE QUESTIONS

Multiple Choice 14.1
Correct Answer (d).

Multiple Choice 14.3
Correct Answer (e).

Multiple Choice 14.5
Correct Answer (e).

Multiple Choice 14.7
Correct Answer (c).

Multiple Choice 14.9
Correct Answer (c).

Multiple Choice 14.11
Correct Answer (b).

Multiple Choice 14.13
Correct Answer (d).

Multiple Choice 14.15
Correct Answer (a).

Multiple Choice 14.17
Correct Answer (b). The first equation derived in Example 14.4 applies:

$$f=\frac{\omega}{2\cdot\pi}=\frac{1}{2\cdot\pi}\sqrt{\frac{k}{m}}$$

CONCEPTUAL QUESTIONS

Conceptual Question 14.1
The total energy is $E = ½\ k \cdot A^2$, and does therefore not change. The object will move with a smaller speed through the equilibrium position but with the same kinetic energy.

Conceptual Question 14.3
It travels a distance $4 \cdot A$ during a full cycle.

ANALYTICAL PROBLEMS

Problem 14.1
(a) The general mathematical formula to describe a linear dependence of y on x is:

$$y=a\cdot x+b$$

in which a (the slope) and b (the intercept of the y–axis) are constant. Two pairs of values for l and $F(l)$ are needed to identify the two constants. The two values for l should be chosen as far apart as possible to minimize the uncertainty in the values calculated for the constants. From the graph in Fig. 14.1 we choose for the segment in the interval $2.2\ \mu m \le l \le 3.2\ \mu m$ the data pairs $l_1 = 2.2\ \mu m$ with $F(l_1) = 100\%$ and $l_2 = 3.2\ \mu m$ with $F(l_2) = 32\%$. Writing the linear formula in the form

$$F=a\cdot l+b$$

with F in percent and l in μm, we find:

(I)	$100 = a \cdot 2.2 + b$
(II)	$32 = a \cdot 3.2 + b$
(I) – (II)	$68 = -1.0 \cdot a$

Thus, $a = -68\ \%/\mu m$. Substituting this result in either (I) or (II) we obtain $b = 250\%$.
(b) Since the line segment in the length interval of $2.0\ \mu m \le l \le 2.2\ \mu m$ is horizontal, we find without calculation that $a = 0\ \%/\mu m$ and $b = 100\%$.
(c) This part is solved in analogy to part (a). We find $a = +265\ \%/\mu m$ and $b = -344.5\%$.

Problem 14.3
The note at the end asks us to compare the pressure at ground level with the maximum stress with the condition $p \le \alpha$. The pressure is given by the force per unit area, with the force acting at the ground level of the building given by its weight. The weight in turn is given as the mass (obtained from the density and the volume), multiplied with g. Using h for the height of the building with $h = V/A$, in which V is the volume of the building and A its horizontal cross–sectional area, we find:

$$p=\frac{W}{A}=\frac{\rho\cdot V\cdot g}{A}=\rho\cdot h\cdot g\le\sigma$$

which yields for h with the given values:

$$h\le\frac{\sigma}{\rho\cdot g}=\frac{2\times10^{8}\text{Pa}}{\left(7.9\times10^{3}\frac{\text{kg}}{\text{m}^{3}}\right)\left(9.8\frac{\text{m}}{\text{s}^{2}}\right)}$$

$$=2580\text{m}$$

The tallest free–standing structure in the world is Burj Khalifa in Dubai, United Arab Emirates, which was opened in January 2010, and is 830 m in height.

Problem 14.5
The weight of the car is $W = 1.9 \times 10^4$ N.

Problem 14.7

(a) We obtain the total energy from the elastic energy at the amplitude point:

$$E_{total} = \frac{1}{2}k \cdot A^2 = \frac{1}{2}\left(80\frac{\text{N}}{\text{m}}\right)(0.1\text{m})^2$$
$$= 0.4\,\text{J}$$

(b) The elastic potential energy at any given displacement from the equilibrium position Δx follows from Eq. [14.10]:

$$E_{elast} = \frac{1}{2}k(x - x_{eq})^2$$

Substituting the position at the halfway point, $\Delta x = A/2$, we find:

$$E_{elast} = \frac{1}{2}k\left(\frac{A}{2}\right)^2 = \frac{k}{8}A^2 = 0.1\,\text{J}$$

The kinetic energy at the same point is the difference between the total energy and the elastic potential energy:

$$E_{kin} = E_{total} - E_{elast} = 0.3\,\text{J}$$

Problem 14.9

(a) We use the relations between angular frequency, frequency and period (Eqs. [14.18] and [14.19]) to relate the spring constant to the period of the vibrational motion:

$$T = \frac{1}{f} = \frac{2 \cdot \pi}{\omega} = 2 \cdot \pi\sqrt{\frac{m}{k}}$$

Isolating the parameter k we obtain:

$$k = m\left(\frac{2 \cdot \pi}{\text{T}}\right)^2 = 0.25kg\left(\frac{2 \cdot \pi}{0.5\text{s}}\right)^2 = 40\frac{\text{N}}{\text{m}}$$

(b) The maximum force acts on the object when it is at the largest displacement from the equilibrium position, i.e., when it is at $\Delta x = A$. At that point we find with the spring constant obtained in part (a):

$$F_{\max} = k \cdot A = \left(40\frac{\text{N}}{\text{m}}\right)0.1\text{m} = 4.0\text{N}$$

Problem 14.11
Conservation of energy implies:

$$m\,g\,d\sin\theta = \frac{1}{2}k\,A^2 - m\,g\,A\sin\theta\,, \qquad \textbf{(1)}$$

where A is the distance the spring is compressed with respect to its relaxed position. We rewrite Eq. [1] as a quadratic equation in A so that:

$$A^2 - b\,A - b\,d = 0\,, \qquad \textbf{(2)}$$

where:

$$b = \frac{2\,m\,g\sin\theta}{k} = 15\,\text{cm} \qquad \textbf{(3)}$$

The positive solution to Eq. [2] is:

$$A = \frac{b + \sqrt{b^2 + 4bd}}{2} \qquad \textbf{(4)}$$

With the value for d = 10 cm and Eq. [3] we find the result of Eq. [4] to be A = 22 cm.

Problem 14.13
Since the object–spring system is in equilibrium after the spring has been compressed, then we know from Newton's Second Law that the sum of the forces acting on the object equals zero. Following the examples solved in the text with tilted axis, we choose x– and y–axes such that the positive x–direction is uphill and the positive y– direction is upward perpendicular from the inclined surface. The spring force then acts in the positive x–direction, while a component of the object's weight acts in the negative x–direction. These two components must be equal:

$$k(x - x_{eq}) = m \cdot g \cdot \sin(\theta)$$

where $\theta = 30^0$ is the angle of the incline. We can find the spring constant as k = 98 N/m.

Problem 14.15

(a) The position of an object on a spring with time has the functional form given in Eq. [14.17]. Comparing that equation with the given equation yields $A = 0.25$ m.

(b) Again comparing the same two equations, which we can use along with the definition of the angular frequency in Eq. [14.18], we find $k = 0.47$ N/m.

(c) At the given time $\Delta x = 0.23$ m. Note here that you must multiply all three terms inside the brackets (a factor 0.4, π, and the time 0.3 s) before you take the cosine of that number. Also, you must have your calculator in "radians" mode because the argument of the cosine function is in radians. If your answer was 0.25 m, that is likely because your calculator is in "degrees" mode.

(d) We can use conservation of energy to find the speed of the object when we know its position. First, we know that the total energy of the system is given by Eq. [14.19]. Recall that at $t = 0.3$ s we know Δx from part (c). At that instant the total energy has a kinetic and an elastic potential contributions with the speed the only variable. We solve to find the speed to be $v = 0.14$ m/s.

Problem 14.17

(a) The motion of the wing is described as a simple harmonic motion. We use the first equation found in Example 14.4 to calculate the frequency:

$$f = \frac{1}{2\cdot\pi}\sqrt{\frac{k}{m}} - \frac{1}{2\cdot\pi}\sqrt{\frac{0.74\,/}{0.3\cdot 10^{-6}}} \qquad \textbf{(38)}$$
$$= 250$$

This value is a good approximation for many insects, e.g. honeybees flap their wings with a frequency of about 250 Hz and mosquitoes with a frequency higher than 500 Hz. The range of frequencies observed in nature is rather wide, with 4 Hz for butterflies and up to 1000 Hz for some gnats.

(b) Using Eq. [14.16] we find for the maximum speed of the tip of the inner end of the wing, which has a vertical amplitude of 0.3 mm:

$$v_{\max} = \sqrt{\frac{k}{m}}A = \sqrt{\frac{0.74\,\mathrm{N/m}}{0.3\times 10^{-6}\,\mathrm{kg}}}0.3\times 10^{-3}\,\mathrm{m}$$
$$= 0.5\frac{\mathrm{m}}{\mathrm{s}}$$

(c) We treat the wing as a rigid body rotating about the pivot point. Fig. 1 allows us to relate geometrically the maximum speed of the inner end of the wing with the maximum speed at the outer tip:

$$\frac{v_{\max,in}}{v_{\max,out}} = \frac{l_1}{l_2} = \frac{0.5\,\mathrm{mm}}{14\,\mathrm{mm}} = 0.035$$

which yields:

$$v_{\max,out} = 28\cdot v_{\max,in} = 14\frac{\mathrm{m}}{\mathrm{s}}$$

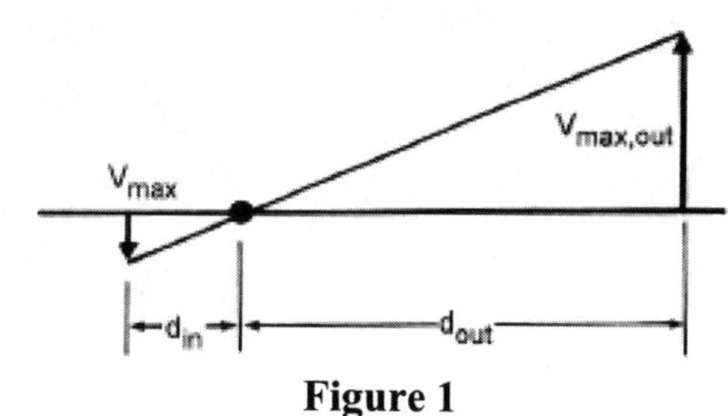

Figure 1

Problem 14.19

(a) If we choose the gravitational potential energy to be zero at $d = 0$, then the total energy of the system will be the sum of the spring elastic and gravitational potential energy, $E_{total} = 101$ J. Note that the kinetic energy of the system is zero because it is momentarily at rest at the pogo stick's maximum compression.

(b) At the highest point of the child's jump the spring is completely uncompressed and no energy is stored in elastic potential energy. Also, the system is again momentarily at rest so it has no kinetic energy. This means the total energy, which is the same value as in part (a) due to conservation of energy, is equal to the gravitation potential energy. This leads to the result of $d_2 = 41$ cm.

(c) At $d = 0$, the speed of the child can again be found through conservation of energy. At this equilibrium position, the elastic potential energy is zero and the gravitational potential energy is also zero by our original definition in part (a). Therefore all the energy is kinetic energy, which yields $v = 2.9$ m/s.

(d) The acceleration of the child at d_1 can be found by examining the forces acting on him. There will be a gravitational force acting downward which is equal to the child's weight and a spring force acting upward which follows Hooke's law. Together these forces sum to give the upward acceleration experienced by the child. We use Newton's second law to find this acceleration as $a = 90.2$ m/s^2.

(e) The child is momentarily exposed to more than nine times the gravitational acceleration!

CHAPTER FIFTEEN

Sound I

MULTIPLE CHOICE QUESTIONS

Multiple Choice 15.1
Correct Answer (b).

Multiple Choice 15.3
Correct Answer (b).

Multiple Choice 15.5
Correct Answer (a).

Multiple Choice 15.7
Correct Answer (e).

Multiple Choice 15.9
Correct Answer (c).

Multiple Choice 15.11
Correct Answer (c).

CONCEPTUAL QUESTIONS

Conceptual Question 15.1
A wave on a massless string would have an infinite speed because the mass per length unit of the string is zero.

Conceptual Question 15.3
When a sound wave travels through a medium, the particles move backwards and forwards along the direction of propagation of the wave, like the compressions on a slinky.

Conceptual Question 15.5
When an object vibrates in a given medium, it creates compressions and rarefactions in the medium: these are the sound waves. The frequency of the waves generated is identical to the vibration frequency of the object. The wave propagation speed depends on the density of the medium.

ANALYTICAL PROBLEMS

Problem 15.1
(a) The wavelength is obtained from the relation of the speed of the wave, the wavelength and the frequency $v_{\text{wave}} = \lambda \cdot f$:

$$\lambda = \frac{v_{wave}}{f} = \frac{6.5\,\text{m/s}}{5.0\,\text{Hz}} = 1.3\,\text{m}$$

(b) The relation between period and frequency of a vibration is applicable to waves:

$$T = \frac{1}{f} = \frac{1}{5.0\,\text{Hz}} = 0.20\,\text{s}$$

(c) The relation between frequency and angular frequency remains unchanged as introduced for vibrations:

$$\omega = 2 \cdot \pi \cdot f = 2 \cdot \pi \cdot 5.0\,\text{Hz} = 31\frac{\text{rad}}{\text{s}}$$

(d) The harmonic wave is given in Eq. [15.9]:

$$D = A\sin(\omega \cdot t - \kappa \cdot x)$$

The amplitude is given in the problem text. The angular frequency has been calculated in part (c). Thus, we are missing the wave number, which we determine from $\kappa = 2 \cdot \pi / \lambda$ with the wavelength taken from part (a):

$$\kappa = \frac{2 \cdot \pi}{\lambda} = \frac{2 \cdot \pi}{1.3\,\text{m}} = 4.8\,\text{m}^{-1}$$

This allows us to write the wave function:

$$D = (0.04\,\text{m})\sin\left(\left\{31.4\frac{\text{rad}}{\text{s}}\right\} \cdot t - \left\{4.84\frac{1}{\text{m}}\right\} \cdot x\right)$$

Problem 15.3

The problem contains an implicit assumption that the hearing process takes place in air of typical environmental conditions. Using T = 20^0C, we obtain the speed of sound from Table 15.1 as c = 343 m/s. We use this value to analyse the lower frequency of 16 Hz first:

$$\lambda = \frac{c}{f} = \frac{343\text{m/s}}{16\text{Hz}} = 21.5\text{m}$$

The wavelength at the higher frequency is λ = 1.72 cm.

Problem 15.5

(a) Based on the given diagram, the amplitude is half the distance between the maximum and minimum of the wave, $A = ½ \cdot L_1 = 9$ cm.

(b) Based on the given diagram, the wavelength is the distance between successive maxima of the wave, $\lambda = 2 \cdot L_2 =$ 20 cm.

(c) Since we have the frequency of the wave, we can calculate the period as $T = 0.04$ s.

(d) The wave speed is $v = 5.0$ m/s.

Problem 15.7

The limits of the range of frequencies 28 Hz $< f <$ 4200 Hz correspond to wavelengths based on Eq. [1]. We find 8.2 cm $\leq \lambda \leq$ 12.3 m. Note that the lowest frequency has the largest wavelength and vice versa due to the inverse relationship between wavelength and frequency.

Problem 15.9

At a temperature of 22^0C, the speed of sound is c = 344 m/s. If it takes 3.0 s for a sound wave to travel to a wall and back again (to create an echo) then it must take just 1.5 s for the wave to travel to the wall. Since the wave speed is constant, the distance to the wall must be d = 516 m away.

Problem 15.11

The angle can be calculated according to $\sin\theta = 2/3$ so that $\theta = 42^0$

Problem 15.13

(a) The intensity is defined as the amount of energy transported by a wave per time interval through a plane of unit area, which is placed perpendicular to the wave's propagation direction. If we label the intensity I, the energy ΔE, the time interval Δt and the area A, then:

$$I = \frac{1}{A} \cdot \frac{\Delta E}{\Delta t}$$

Using the given values, we find:

$$I = \frac{2 \times 10^{-11}\text{J}}{(5 \times 10^{-4}\text{m}^2)(4\text{s})} = 1 \times 10^{-8}\frac{\text{J}}{\text{m}^2 \cdot \text{s}}$$

(b) The pressure variation Δp in the wave is calculated from Eq. [15.11]:

$$\Delta p_{\text{max}} = c \cdot \rho \cdot \omega \cdot A \qquad \textbf{(1)}$$

So far, we are not given a value for the amplitude; we find it from re–arranging Eq. [15.14] with the amplitude as the dependent variable, which is then substituted in Eq. [1]:

$$\Delta p = \frac{c \cdot \rho \cdot \omega}{\omega}\sqrt{\frac{2 \cdot I}{c \cdot \rho}} = \sqrt{2 \cdot I \cdot c \cdot \rho} \qquad \textbf{(2)}$$

Eq. [2] allows us now to substitute the given values. The square–root on the right hand side of Eq. [2] reads:

$$\sqrt{2\left(1 \times 10^{-6}\frac{\text{J}}{\text{m}^2\text{s}}\right)\left(343\frac{\text{m}}{\text{s}}\right)\left(1.2\frac{\text{kg}}{\text{m}^3}\right)}$$

which leads to:

$$\Delta p = 2.9 \times 10^{-2}\,\text{Pa} \qquad \textbf{(3)}$$

The speed of sound was taken from Table 15.1, using the given temperature. Note how small these pressure variations in sound waves usually are; the value in Eq. [3] corresponds to 29 mPa!

Problem 15.15

(a) We use the relation between sound intensity and intensity level, IL. Identifying the sound of interest with index 1 and the reference sound with index 2, we write I_1/I_2 = 4. This leads to a difference in the intensity levels of the two sounds:

$$IL_1 - IL_2 = 10\left(\log_{10}\frac{I_1}{I_0} - \log_{10}\frac{I_2}{I_0}\right)$$

$$= 10\left(\log_{10}\frac{I_1}{I_2}\right) = 10\log_{10}4 = 6.0 \text{ dB}$$

Thus, the difference between the two sounds is 6 dB, regardless of the absolute intensity of the sounds.

(b) Answering this question is straightforward for a sound of 1 kHz, i.e., at the only frequency where the decibel scale and the phon scale are equal. At that frequency the louder sound has 66 phon. Figure 15.29 indicates that this relation is approximately correct in the range from 200 Hz to 2000 Hz, i.e., essentially across the frequency range of the human voice during a conversation. At other frequencies, the sound perception would have to be converted to an intensity level using Figure 15.29, and the louder sound has to be converted back to the phon scale at the same frequency.

Problem 15.17

The difference in intensity levels may be written as:

$$IL_2 - IL_1 = 10\ \log_{10}\left(\frac{I_2}{I_0}\right) - 10\log_{10}\left(\frac{I_1}{I_0}\right)$$

which we rewrite using the properties of logarithms as:

$$IL_2 - IL_1 = 10\ \log_{10}\left(\frac{I_2}{I_0}\cdot\frac{I_1}{I_0}\right) = 10\log_{10}\left(\frac{I_1}{I_1}\right)$$

Therefore the difference between the intensity levels of the two sounds is 3.01 dB.

Problem 15.19

We use the relation of speed of sound, wavelength and frequency. With the given frequency, the diameter of the eardrum can be determined using the speed of sound. Since the speed of sound depends on the temperature of air, we need to make an assumption regarding the temperature of the air in the outer ear. The value lies somewhere between the environmental temperature and the body temperature. The respective speed of sound is then determined from Table 15.1 and Eq. [15.7], with the latter requiring the assumption that air is an ideal gas:

$$c = c_0\sqrt{1+\alpha\cdot T}$$

Depending on your pick of temperature, you will use a value of c between 343 m/s (20^0C) and 353 m/s (37^0C). In the calculation below the speed of sound at 20^0C is used.

For the calculation we note that the problem asks for the radius of the eardrum, while the diameter is linked to the wavelength. Thus, we use $2 \cdot r_{eardrum} = \lambda_{max}$:

$$r_{eardrum} = \frac{1}{2}\cdot\frac{c}{f_{max}} = \frac{0.5\left(343\frac{m}{s}\right)}{1.85\times10^4 s^{-1}}$$

$$= 9.3\times10^{-3} m = 9.3\ mm$$

CHAPTER SIXTEEN

SOUND II

MULTIPLE CHOICE QUESTIONS

Multiple Choice 16.1
Correct Answer (b).

Multiple Choices 16.3
Correct Answer (e).

Multiple Choice 16.5
Correct Answer (b).

CONCEPTUAL QUESTIONS

Conceptual Question 16.1
The energy is carried in the kinetic energy of the gas elements.

Conceptual Question 16.3
This corresponds to the case in which source and receiver move, with Eq. [16.17] applying.

Conceptual Question 16.5
The "echo" of a sound wave is nothing but the reflected sound wave off a given object. Some objects have a high efficiency of reflection while others have a high efficiency of absorption. Sound proofing a room requires the use of highly sound absorbing materials or the use of architecture that enables destructive interference.

ANALYTICAL PROBLEMS

Problem 16.1
(a) We use Eq. [16.12] to find the intensity reflection R_I alongside with the impedance values from Table 16.2:

$$R_I = \left(\frac{Z_{\text{muscle}} - Z_{\text{air}}}{Z_{\text{muscle}} + Z_{\text{air}}}\right)^2 = \left(\frac{1.6\times10^6 - 414}{1.6\times10^6 + 414}\right)^2 = 0.9990$$

(b) Since $R_I + T_I = 1$ we find:

$$T_I = 0.0010$$

(c) The result from part (b) is also equal to the ratio I_t / I_i which can be converted to dB:

$$\Delta\text{IL} = 10\log_{10}\left(\frac{I_t}{I_i}\right) = -30\,\text{dB}$$

(d) No useful images are obtained because almost none of the ultrasound waves penetrate the muscle tissue to give meaningful information. The wave gets reflected almost in its entirety at the interface. The jelly-like fluid eliminates air from the problem allowing for the wave to go directly from the instrument to the fluid and from the fluid to the body without having to be transported through air. The fluid effectively eliminates the air gap allowing for better transmission.

Problem 16.3
(a) We calculate the acoustic impedance according to Eq. [16.10]:

$$\begin{aligned} Z_1 &= \rho_1 c_1 = \left(1100\,\tfrac{\text{kg}}{\text{m}^3}\right)\left(1450\,\tfrac{\text{m}}{\text{s}}\right) \\ &= 1.60\times10^6\ \text{rayl} \\ Z_2 &= \rho_2 c_2 = \left(1210\,\tfrac{\text{kg}}{\text{m}^3}\right)\left(1678\,\tfrac{\text{m}}{\text{s}}\right) \\ &= 2.03\times10^6\ \text{rayl} \end{aligned} \qquad \textbf{(1)}$$

(b) The fraction of the wave that gets reflected is given by Eq. [16.12] as R_I with the values calculated in Eq. [1] for the impedances:

$$R_I = \left(\frac{Z_2 - Z_1}{Z_1 + Z_2}\right)^2 = 0.014 \qquad \textbf{(2)}$$

That is, about 1.4% of the incident intensity is reflected. Similarly, we can use Eq. [16.11] along with the values in Eq. [1] to calculate the fraction of the wave that gets transmitted as TI:

$$T_I = \frac{4\,Z_1 Z_2}{(Z_1 + Z_2)^2} = 0.986$$

That is, about 98.6% of the incident intensity is transmitted. Given that Eq. [2] represents the ratio of the reflected intensity to the incident intensity we can use it to calculate the intensity loss at the reflection in dB:

$$\Delta IL_R = 10\log_{10}(I_r/I_i) = -18.41\,\text{dB} \quad \textbf{(3)}$$

That is, at each interface the intensity level decreases by about 18 dB.

(c) The attenuation at each layer can be calculated using Eq. [16.4]:

$$\Delta IL_A = -\alpha f x = -1.3\,\text{dB} \quad \textbf{(4)}$$

Just before reaching the final air interface, the sound wave would have passed through 19 interfaces and 20 layers so the total attenuation is calculated using the results from Eq. [3] and Eq. [4] as:

$$\begin{aligned}\Delta IL_{\text{total}} &= 19\,\Delta IL_R + 20\,\Delta IL_A \\ &= -380\,\text{dB}\end{aligned}$$

The first echo, which is a reflection at the first interface, is attenuated by:

$$\Delta IL_1 = \Delta IL_R + 2\,\Delta IL_A = -21.0\,\text{dB} \quad \textbf{(5)}$$

The second echo, which is a reflection at the second interface, is attenuated by:

$$\Delta IL_2 = 3\Delta IL_R + 4\,\Delta IL_A = -60.4\,\text{dB} \quad \textbf{(6)}$$

Given the values found in Eq. [5] and Eq. [6], the first echo is clearly detected; the second echo lies at the threshold of detection and the third echo will not be detected.

Problem 16.5

Because both the bat and the insect move, we have to combine the two separate Doppler effect cases:

$$f_{reciever} = f_0 \pm \frac{v_{reciever}}{\lambda} = f_0\left(1 \pm \frac{v_{reciever}}{c}\right)$$

which is Eq. [16.14]. We use Eq. [17.84] as well:

$$f_{source} = f_0 \frac{1}{1 \pm \dfrac{v_{source}}{c}}$$

Different from the application of Doppler ultrasound in medicine (as discussed in the textbook), we have to use different speeds of the source (insect) and the receiver (bat). The combined formula is called the general Doppler effect. With v_{source} the speed of the source and v_{receiver} the speed of the receiver we find:

$$f_{received} = f_{emitted}\left(\frac{1 + v_{receiver}/c}{1 - v_{source}/c}\right) \quad \textbf{(1)}$$

in which f_{emitted} is the frequency emitted by the bat and f_{received} is the frequency received by the bat after reflection off the insect. The + sign in the numerator of Eq. [1] is due to the motion of the receiver *toward* the source and the – sign in the denominator is due to the motion of the source *toward* the receiver. Either of the signs can change if the respective animal moves away from the other; however, the ultrasound emission of bats is focused in the forward direction and thus, Eq. [1] is meaningless if the bat moves away from the insect. We substitute the given data in Eq. [1]:

$$\begin{aligned}f_{received} &= 9\times10^4\ \text{Hz}\left(\frac{1+\dfrac{10\ \text{m/s}}{343\ \text{m/s}}}{1+\dfrac{3\ \text{m/s}}{343\ \text{m/s}}}\right) \\ &= 93.4\ \text{kHz}\end{aligned}$$

in which we used 343 m/s for the speed of sound in air.

Problem 16.7

The difference in sound levels is:

$$dbs = db_1 - db_2 = 10\times\log\left(\frac{I_1}{I_2}\right)$$

Using the given values we find:

$$\begin{aligned}dbs &= 10\times\log\left(\frac{900}{100}\right) = 10\times\log(9) \\ &= 20\times\log(3) = 9.5\,\text{dB}\end{aligned}$$

Problem 16.9
Light, from the lightning source, propagates at the speed $c = 3\times10^8$ m/s; it travels so fast that the observer almost instantaneously perceives it. On the other hand sound waves propagate at a speed c_s = 330 m/s ≅ 1/3 km/s. The distance d to the source of lightning and thunder can then be expressed as:

$$d = c_s T = \frac{T}{3}\text{km}$$

Problem 16.11
(a) The ratio of the sound speeds in two media at different temperatures is given by:

$$\frac{c_{s1}}{c_{s2}} = \sqrt{\frac{T_1}{T_2}}$$

The refraction law gives:

$$\frac{c_{s1}}{c_{s2}} = \frac{\sin 40°}{\sin r}$$

which allows us to calculate the refraction angle r:

$$r = \arcsin\left(\sin 40° \sqrt{\frac{90+273}{15+273}}\right) = 46.2°$$

(b) For total reflection r=90°, so this would require a temperature that obeys:

$$\frac{\sin 40°}{\sin 90°} = \sqrt{\frac{T_1}{T_2}}$$

Therefore, solving for T_2 we find:

$$T_2 = \frac{T_1}{\sin^2 40°} = 424°\text{C}$$

Problem 16.13
(a) Due to Doppler effect, when the aircraft is flying towards the observer, the frequency of the sound heard increases (compressed wavelength), as opposed to a decrease in frequency when the aircraft is flying away. The aircraft is rotating and consequently the frequency increases and decreases periodically.
(b) The minimum observed frequency is detected when the aircraft is at a point in the circumference moving straight away from the observer:

$$f_{\min} = \left(\frac{c_s}{c_s + v}\right) f$$

The maximum frequency is detected when the aircraft is moving straight towards the observer:

$$f_{\max} = \left(\frac{c_s}{c_s - v}\right) f$$

The speed of the aircraft can be calculated from the data about its motion:

$$v = \frac{d}{t} = \frac{2\pi R}{T} = 18.85\,\text{m/s}$$

This speed yields minimum and maximum frequencies:

$$f_{\min} = 473.74\,\text{Hz}$$
$$f_{\max} = 529.35\,\text{Hz}$$

It takes half a revolution between the detection of the minimum and the maximum frequency, so the time interval is 2.5 s.

Problem 16.15

(a) Frequency is the number of occurrences of a periodic event per unit time. Intensity, on the other hand, is the power or time rate of change of energy per unit area. The units of frequency are s^{-1} or Hertz (Hz), and the units of intensity are Watts per square meter ($W\ m^{-2}$).

(b) See Figure 1. The loudness and sensitivity are proportional. The maximum loudness is perceived around 2000 Hz. Below 100 Hz and above 10000 Hz the perceived loudness falls rapidly with frequency, and therefore sound waves at these frequencies needs to be emitted with high intensity in order to be perceived by a human being.

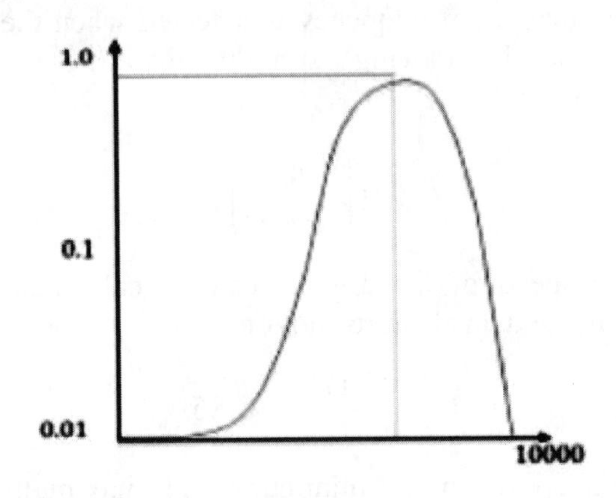

Figure 1

(c) The response of the ear to sound waves depends on frequency and intensity. The human ear is most sensitive to frequencies close to 1000 Hz; this intensity level has been chosen as a reference that defines a zero dB or $10^{-12}\ Wm^2$. The level of the intensity:

$$L = k \log\left(\frac{I}{I_0}\right)$$

where I is the intensity of level L, I_0 the threshold intensity of $10^{-12}\ W\ m^2$, and k is an arbitrary constant chosen to be 10 for the decibel dB scale.

CHAPTER SEVENTEEN

Electric Force and Field

MULTIPLE CHOICE QUESTIONS

Multiple Choice 17.1
Correct Answer (e).

Multiple Choice 17.3
Correct Answer (a). A single positive charge remains unbalanced even after shielding due to a hydration shell.

Multiple Choice 17.5
Correct Answer (d).

Multiple Choice 17.7
Correct Answer (e).

Multiple Choice 17.9
Correct Answer (d).

Multiple Choice 17.11
Correct Answer (c) or (e). Mathematically, answer (c) is correct; physically it may well be (e) because a unified theory including both forces has not yet been found.

Multiple Choice 17.13
Correct Answer (c).

Multiple Choice 17.15
Correct Answer (c).

Multiple Choice 17.17
Correct Answer (b).

CONCEPTUAL QUESTIONS

Conceptual Question 17.1
The field points to the left. Since both charges have the same magnitude and are at the same distance from point P, the magnitude of the electric fields caused by each charge at P is identical. The field caused by the positive charge points up and to the left, while the field caused by the negative charge points down and to the left. Furthermore, the geometry implies that the angles for both fields with respect to the vertical are identical. Therefore, the vertical components are of the same magnitude and opposite directions; they cancel out. This leaves the horizontal contribution of both fields pointing to the left, so the net field at P points to the left.

Conceptual Question 17.3
Under static conditions, the charge resides on the surface of a charged conductor, so the electric field intensity E inside the surface is zero. It is therefore possible for E to be zero at a point where the electric potential is not zero.

Conceptual Question 17.5
The gravitational force is given by:

$$F_g = G\frac{m_p^2}{R^2}$$

The electrostatic force is given by:

$$F_g = \frac{1}{4\pi\varepsilon_0}\frac{e^2}{R^2}$$

This leads to the following ratio

$$r = \frac{F_e}{F_g} = \frac{e^2}{4\pi\varepsilon_0 G m_p^2} = 1.24\times10^{36}$$

ANALYTICAL PROBLEMS

Problem 17.1
The force on point charge q_3 is the superposition of the forces due to point charges q_1 and q_2, i.e., $\mathbf{F}_{13}$ and $\mathbf{F}_{23}$. We calculate each of these two force vectors separately using Coulomb's law. Then we add them to obtain the net force. Starting with the magnitude of the force exerted by q_1 on q_3, $|\mathbf{F}_{13}|$, we find:

$$\begin{aligned}|F_{13}| &= \frac{1}{4\cdot\pi\cdot\varepsilon_0}\cdot\frac{|q_1||q_3|}{r_{13}^2}\\ &= \left(9\times10^9\frac{\text{N}\cdot\text{m}^2}{\text{C}^2}\right)\frac{(5\times10^{-9}\text{C})(2.5\times10^{-9}\text{C})}{(6.0\text{m})^2} \quad \textbf{(1)}\\ &= 3.1\times10^{-9}\text{N}\end{aligned}$$

The direction of this force is along the line connecting point charges q_1 and q_3 and is directed away from point charge q_1 since the two charges repel each other. This leads to a vector which forms an angle θ with the positive x–axis, as illustrated in Figure 1. The angle θ is obtained from geometric analysis of Figure 1.

We find, $\sin\theta = 4.0\ \text{m}/6.0\ \text{m} = 0.667$ which corresponds to $\theta = 41.8^0$. This allows us to express the x– and y–components of the force in the form:

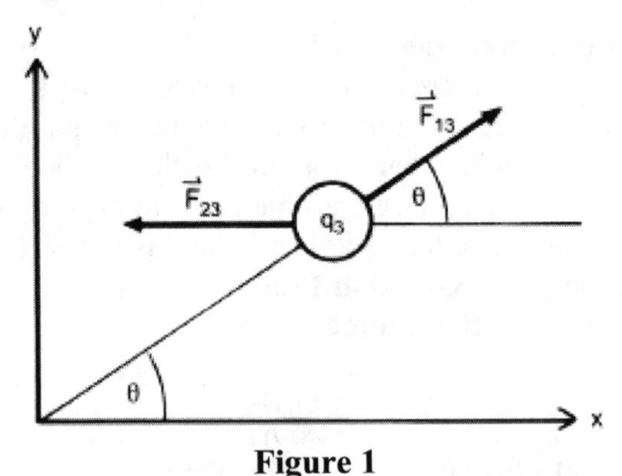

Figure 1

$$F_{13,x} = |F_{13}|\cos\theta = 2.31\times10^{-9}\,\text{N}$$
$$F_{13,y} = |F_{13}|\sin\theta = 2.07\times10^{-9}\,\text{N} \qquad \textbf{(2)}$$

We apply again Coulomb's law to obtain the magnitude of the second force, $\mathbf{F_{23}}$. Figure 1 is used for the required distance between the two point charges q_2 and q_3. Applying trigonometry we find:

$$l_{23}^2 + l_{12}^2 = l_{13}^2 \qquad \textbf{(3)}$$

which leads to:

$$l_{23} = \sqrt{l_{13}^2 - l_{12}^2} = \sqrt{(6\text{m})^2 - (4\text{m})^2} = 4.47\,\text{m} \qquad \textbf{(4)}$$

Now the given data and the value from Eq. [4] are combined in Coulomb's law:

$$\begin{aligned} |F_{23}| &= \frac{1}{4\cdot\pi\cdot\varepsilon_0}\cdot\frac{|q_2||q_3|}{r_{23}^2} \\ &= \left(9\times10^9\,\frac{\text{N}\cdot\text{m}^2}{C^2}\right)\frac{(4\times10^{-9}\,\text{C})(2.5\times10^{-9}\,\text{C})}{(4.47\text{m})^2} \\ &= 4.50\times10^{-9}\,\text{N} \end{aligned} \qquad \textbf{(5)}$$

The direction of this force is along the connecting line between the point charges q_2 and q_3 and is directed toward q_2 since the two charges attract each other. This is illustrated in Figure 1.

With the two individual forces identified, we now calculate the net force acting on q_3. For the x–component we find:

$$\begin{aligned} F_{net,x} &= F_{13,x} - |F_{23}| \\ &= 2.31\times10^{-9}\,\text{N} - 4.50\times10^{-9}\,\text{N} \\ &= -2.19\times10^{-9}\,\text{N} \end{aligned} \qquad \textbf{(6)}$$

for the y–component we get:

$$F_{net,y} = F_{13,y} = +2.07\times10^{-9}\,\text{N} \qquad \textbf{(7)}$$

Providing the Cartesian components of a vector in Eqs. [6] and [7] is one way to express it. Alternatively, you can calculate the magnitude of the vector, $|\mathbf{F_{net}}|$, and its angle with the positive x–axis, φ (which is the polar coordinate representation). For the vector in Eqs. [6] and [7], this yields:

$$|F_{net}| = \sqrt{F_{net,x}^2 + F_{net,y}^2} = 3.01\times10^{-9}\,\text{N} \qquad \textbf{(8)}$$

and:

$$\tan\varphi = \frac{F_{net,y}}{F_{net,x}} = \frac{+2.07\times10^{-9}\,\text{N}}{-2.19\times10^{-9}\,\text{N}} \qquad \textbf{(9)}$$

which yields:

$$\varphi = 136.6^0$$

Problem 17.3

In this problem we are given the formula:

$$r = 1.2\times10^{-15}\cdot A^{1/3} \qquad \textbf{(1)}$$

(a) Density is defined as $\rho = m/V$. For the material in the nucleus, the mass is the atomic mass, A. The volume of the nucleus is proportional to the cube of the radius of the nucleus, $V \propto r^3$. Substituting Eq. [1] into this relation, we find for the volume $V \propto (A^{1/3})^3 = A$. Thus, the density is independent of the atomic mass because $\rho = m/V \propto A/A$.

Note that we made an implicit assumption when using the density: $\rho = m/V$ can only be written if the density is constant across the entire volume. Is this assumption justified for a nucleus? Surprisingly, the assumption of a constant density is a very good one for the nuclei of heavier atoms.

This is illustrated in Figure 2 showing the charge density in the nucleus. Only close to the edge does the nuclear density tail off.

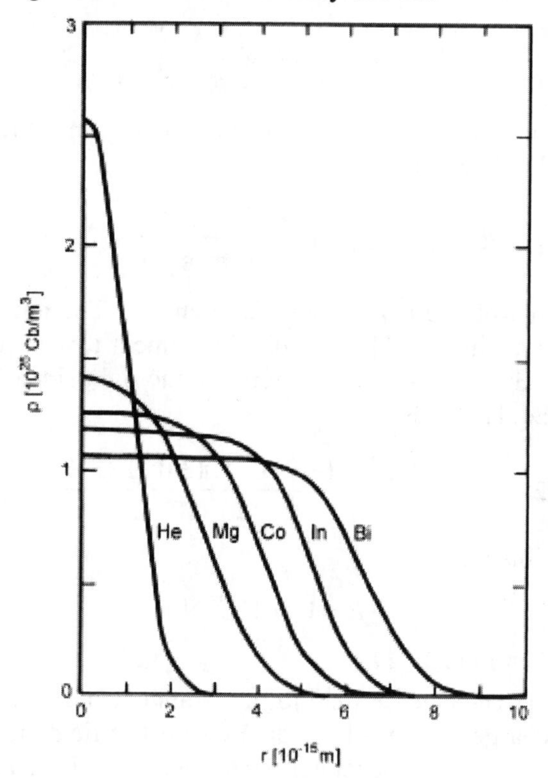

Figure 2

(b) Substituting the given atomic mass of bismuth in Eq. [1], we find for the radius of the Bi nucleus:

$$r = 1.2\times10^{-15}\cdot 209^{1/3} = 7.1\times10^{-15}\,\text{m} \qquad \textbf{(2)}$$

The diameter of the nucleus is twice its radius. The charge of a proton is equal in magnitude to the elementary charge e, with $e = 1.6 \times 10^{-19}$ C. Therefore, the Coulomb force between two protons equals:

$$|F| = \frac{1}{4\cdot\pi\cdot\varepsilon_0}\cdot\frac{e^2}{(2\cdot r)^2}$$
$$= \left(9\times10^9\,\frac{\text{N}\cdot\text{m}^2}{\text{C}^2}\right)\frac{(1.6\times10^{-19}\,\text{C})^2}{(14.2\times10^{-15}\,\text{m})^2} \qquad \textbf{(3)}$$
$$= 1.1\,\text{N}$$

This is a small force when acting on a macroscopic object, but it is a tremendous force when acting at an atomic length scale. It should lead to the explosion of this and any other nucleus, except for the hydrogen nucleus with only one proton. Luckily, an even stronger attractive force acts between the protons and neutrons in a nucleus, which is the nuclear force.

However, the nuclear force falls off much more steeply than the Coulomb force and the latter starts to dominate at about the distance used in this problem. Therefore, no stable nuclei larger than bismuth's nucleus exist, with two heavier elements only coming close: the thorium isotope Th–232 with a half–life of 14 billion years and the uranium isotope U–238 with a half–life of 4.5 billion years. Note that the latter is not the uranium isotope used in nuclear reactors!

Problem 17.5

(a) Each of the eight Cl^- ions at the corners of the unit cell of the CsCl crystal exerts the same magnitude of electrostatic force on the Cs^+ ion at the centre of the unit cell. All of these pair–wise forces are attractive since they act between a positive Cs ion and a negative Cl ion. Since, therefore, there are four pairs of equal but opposite forces, the net force on the central Cs ion is zero. *Note*: The same is true for the chlorine ions because each Cl^- ion lies in the same fashion at the centre of eight Cs^+ ions. This becomes evident when you keep in mind that the unit cell of the CsCl crystal is repeated in all three Cartesian directions.

(b) From an electric point of view, removing a Cl^- ion from one of the corners of the unit cell is the same as adding in Figure 17.25 a positive elementary charge to that same chlorine ion. Thus, the change from part (a) is one additional force component between that additional positive charge and the central charge of the Cs^+ ion.

We determine first the distance between the added charge and the centre of the unit cell. The distance is half of the length of a line drawn through the cube of side length a. From trigonometry we know that the diagonal line in such a cube has the length $\sqrt{3}\cdot a$. Thus, the additional force is:

$$|F| = \frac{1}{4\cdot\pi\cdot\varepsilon_0}\cdot\frac{e^2}{\left(\frac{\sqrt{3}\cdot a}{2}\right)^2}$$

$$= \left(9\times10^9\,\frac{\text{N}\cdot\text{m}^2}{\text{C}^2}\right)\frac{(1.6\times10^{-19}\,\text{C})^2}{\frac{3}{4}(0.4\times10^{-9}\,\text{m})^2}$$

$$= 1.9\times10^{-9}\,\text{N}$$

This is a repulsive force, i.e., it acts on the central ion in the direction pointing away from the missing ion at the corner of the unit cell. It is interesting to compare this force with the force we calculated in Problem 17.3, showing the significant difference between electrostatic forces at the length scale of a nucleus and at atomic length scales.

Problem 17.7

The charge of the alpha particle is $q_\alpha = +2e$, while $q_{Au} = +79e$ is the charge of the gold nucleus. As the two charges are positive, the force on the alpha particle will be repulsive. With a separation distance of $r = 2.0\times10^{-17}$ m, we can use Eq. [17.1] known as Coulomb's Law to find the magnitude of the force:

$$F = \frac{1}{4\pi\varepsilon_0}\frac{|q_\alpha|\cdot|q_{Au}|}{r^2}$$

$$= 9.1\times10^7\,\text{N} \quad ,$$

where we have used $e = 1.6\times10^{-19}$ C for the elementary charge and the permittivity of vacuum is $\varepsilon_0 = 8.85\times10^{-12}\,\text{C}^2/(\text{N}\cdot\text{m}^2)$.

Problem 17.9

We use Eq. [17.10], which gives us the electric field far from a dipole in the axial direction:

$$\lim_{x\gg d} E_{net} = \frac{q}{2\cdot\pi\cdot\varepsilon_0}\cdot\frac{d}{x^3}$$

For the force between the charge and the dipole we find:

$$F = q_{electron}\,|E| = \frac{e\cdot q\cdot d}{2\cdot\pi\cdot\varepsilon_0\cdot x^3} \qquad (1)$$

in which e is the elementary charge. The term $q\cdot d$ in Eq. [1] is the dipole moment μ with $\mu = 3\times10^{-29}$ C · m. The term on the right side of Eq. [1] reads:

$$2\left(9\times10^9\,\frac{\text{N m}^2}{\text{C}^2}\right)\frac{(1.6\times10^{19}\,\text{C})(3.0\times10^{-29}\,\text{C m})}{(20\times10^{-9}\,\text{m})^3}$$

This yields:

$$F = 1.1\times10^{-14}\,\text{N}$$

Problem 17.11

(a) The electric field for an arrangement of two charges is the sum of the two electric fields for each charge separately. The two electric field vectors at the point halfway between the two charges are sketched in Figure 3. Note that $l_1 = l_2 = r$. The respective directions of the two vectors are determined from the convention introduced in Figure 17.17.

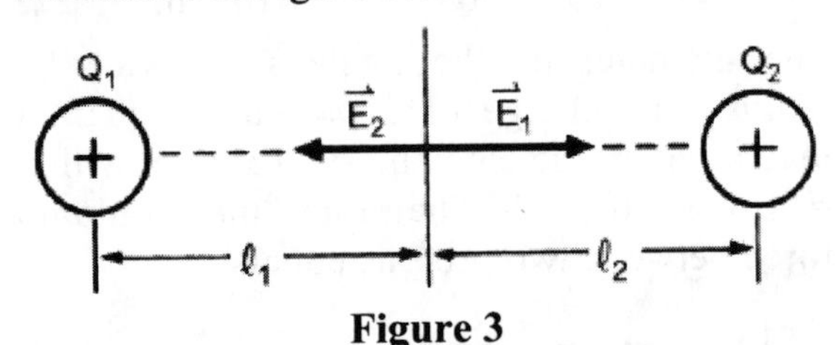

Figure 3

The first charge we consider has the value of $+10.0\times10^{-9}$ C and is shown at left in Figure 3. The distance to the halfway point is $r = 0.1$ m, and thus, the field contribution at that point is:

$$|E_1| = \frac{1}{4\cdot\pi\cdot\varepsilon_0}\cdot\frac{q_1}{r^2}$$

$$= \left(9\times10^9\,\frac{\text{N}\cdot\text{m}^2}{\text{C}^2}\right)\cdot\frac{1\times10^{-8}\,\text{C}}{(0.1\,\text{m})^2} \qquad (1)$$

$$= 9\times10^3\,\frac{\text{N}}{\text{C}}$$

The field contribution due to the second charge at the same point is:

$$\begin{aligned} |E_2| &= \frac{1}{4\cdot\pi\cdot\varepsilon_0}\cdot\frac{q_2}{r^2} \\ &= \left(9\times10^9\,\frac{\mathrm{N\cdot m^2}}{\mathrm{C^2}}\right)\cdot\frac{5\times10^{-9}\,\mathrm{C}}{(0.1\ \mathrm{m})^2} \qquad \textbf{(2)} \\ &= 4.5\times10^3\,\frac{\mathrm{N}}{\mathrm{C}} \end{aligned}$$

Both fields, given as magnitudes in Eqs. [1] and [2], have only *x*–components, as shown in Figure 3.

The net field has, therefore, also only an *x*–component which is given by:

$$\begin{aligned} E_{net,x} &= E_{1,x} + E_{2,x} = |E_1| - |E_2| \\ &= +4.5\times10^3\,\frac{\mathrm{N}}{\mathrm{C}} \qquad \textbf{(3)} \end{aligned}$$

with the *y*–component zero.

(b) The only change in comparison to part (a) is the sign of the second charge, causing a 180^0 change in the direction of field vector $\mathbf{E_2}$ in Figure 3. This changes the corresponding sign in Eq. [3], leading to:

$$\begin{aligned} E_{net,x} &= E_{1,x} + E_{2,x} = |E_1| + |E_2| \\ &= +1.35\times10^4\,\frac{\mathrm{N}}{\mathrm{C}} \end{aligned}$$

The *y*–component of the net field vanishes again.

Problem 17.13

The magnitude of the force acting on the electron is given by $F = e\cdot|\mathbf{E}|$ in which e is the elementary charge, carried by an electron. $|\mathbf{E}|$ is the magnitude of the electric field at the actual location of the electron. Thus, the present problem would be mathematically challenging for any other arrangement of fixed charges than a parallel plate capacitor because it is a constant only for that device.

The acceleration of the electron in the electric field is determined from Newton's second law:

$$\sum_i F_i = q\,|E| = m\cdot a$$

which yields:

$$\begin{aligned} a &= \frac{e\,|E|}{m} \\ &= \frac{(1.6\times10^{-19}\,\mathrm{C})(1.5\times10^3\,\mathrm{N/C})}{9.11\times10^{-31}\,\mathrm{kg}} \qquad \textbf{(1)} \\ &= 2.6\times10^{14}\,\mathrm{m/s^2} \end{aligned}$$

in which the mass of the electron was taken from Table 1. The tremendous acceleration found in Eq. [1] is attributed to (i) the very small mass of the electron and (ii) the strength of the electric force.

Table 1

Particle	Mass (kg)	Charge (C)
Electron	9.11×10^{-31}	-1.6×10^{-19}
Proton	1.673×10^{-27}	$+1.6\times10^{-19}$
Neutron	1.675×10^{-27}	0

Problem 17.15

The electric field in this setup is uniform (except near the edges of the metal plates where fringe effects have to be included):

$$V_B - V_A = +|E|\,d$$

We substitute the given values in this equation:

$$|E| = \frac{\Delta V}{d} = \frac{12\ \mathrm{V}}{0.25\times10^{-2}\,\mathrm{m}} = 4.8\times10^3\,\frac{\mathrm{V}}{\mathrm{m}}$$

The direction of the electric field is toward the negatively charged plate.

Problem 17.17

Given that the proton is a positive charge, the electric field at the location of the electron will be directed away from the proton. In a pictorial representation, we see this in Figure [17.17]; the electric field points outwards. To find the magnitude of the field E, we use Eq. [17.6]:

$$E = \frac{1}{4\pi\varepsilon_0}\frac{|q|}{r^2}, \quad \textbf{(1)}$$

where $q = +1.6 \times 10^{-19}$ C is the charge of the proton and $r = 5.0 \times 10^{-11}$ m is the distance between the proton and the point of interest in our calculation of the electric field. Substituting these values and the electric permittivity constant ε_0 in Eq. [1] we obtain:

$$E = 5.8 \times 10^{11}\ \mathrm{N/C},$$

for the magnitude of the electric field caused by the proton in the hydrogen atom, at the location of the electron.

Problem 17.19

In a free body diagram of the problem we would have the tension T directed up, the gravitational force mg directed down, and the electric force F_e directed up. We know that the electric force will be directed up because the electric field is directed up and the charge suspended is positive. Since the piece of aluminium foil is in equilibrium, Newton's Second Law implies:

$$T + F_e - mg = 0, \quad \textbf{(1)}$$

where we have set the positive direction to be upwards. If the tension is reduced to zero by adjusting the field strength, then Eq. [1] becomes:

$$F_e = mg \quad \textbf{(2)}$$

We can now use Eq. [17.4] to relate the electric field with the electric force and substitute in Eq. [2]:

$$qE = mg \quad \textbf{(3)}$$

Solving Eq. [3] for the field strength E, with the given values of $q = 2.5\ \mu$C, and $m = 50$ g, we find:

$$E = \frac{mg}{q} = 2.0 \times 10^5\ \mathrm{N/C}$$

Problem 17.21

(a) Consider Figure 17.17 with the point P located at an arbitrary position (x,y), not along any of the coordinate axes. Without loss of generality, consider the point in the first quadrant at a position farther to the right than the location of the positive charge. At that point, there are two contributions to the electric field due to the dipole, a contribution we label $\mathbf{E}_1$ due to the positive charge and a contribution $\mathbf{E}_2$. Note that $\mathbf{E}_1$ points up and to the right, while $\mathbf{E}_2$ points down and to the left. Identify the distance between the positive charge and P as r_1, and the distance between the negative charge and P as r_2. Furthermore, note that the angle θ_1 that $\mathbf{E}_1$ makes with respect to the horizontal is the same as the angle that r_1 makes with respect to the horizontal, so that:

$$\cos\theta_1 = \frac{x - d/2}{r_1} \quad \text{and} \quad \sin\theta_1 = \frac{y}{r_1} \quad \textbf{(1)}$$

Similarly, the angle θ_2 that $\mathbf{E}_2$ makes with respect to the horizontal is the same as the angle that r_2 makes with respect to the horizontal, so that:

$$\cos\theta_2 = \frac{x + d/2}{r_2} \quad \text{and} \quad \sin\theta_2 = \frac{y}{r_2} \quad \textbf{(2)}$$

In addition, using the Pythagorean Theorem, we can write:

$$r_1^2 = (x - d/2)^2 + y^2 \quad \textbf{(3)}$$

and

$$r_2^2 = (x + d/2)^2 + y^2$$

Now, from Eq. [17.6] for the field of a point charge the magnitudes of the fields $\mathbf{E}_1$ and $\mathbf{E}_2$ are respectively:

$$E_1 = \frac{1}{4\pi\varepsilon_0}\frac{q}{r_1^2} \quad \text{and} \quad E_2 = \frac{1}{4\pi\varepsilon_0}\frac{q}{r_2^2} \quad \textbf{(4)}$$

Since $\mathbf{E}_1$ points to the right while $\mathbf{E}_2$ points to the left, the horizontal components of these fields are:

$$E_{1;x} = E_1 \cos\theta_1 \quad \textbf{(5)}$$

and

$$E_{2;x} = -E_2 \cos\theta_2$$

In similar fashion, since $\mathbf{E}_1$ points up while $\mathbf{E}_2$ points down, the vertical components of these fields are:

$$E_{1;y} = E_1 \sin\theta_1 \quad \textbf{(6)}$$

and

$$E_{2;y} = -E_2 \sin\theta_2$$

The net field $\mathbf{E}$ at P will be the superposition of fields $\mathbf{E}_1$ and $\mathbf{E}_2$. We can find E_x and E_y, the components of $\mathbf{E}$:

$$E_x = E_{1;x} + E_{2;x} \quad ; \quad E_y = E_{1;y} + E_{2;y} \quad \textbf{(7)}$$

Substituting Eq. [1], Eq. [2], Eq. [4], Eq. [5], and Eq. [6] into Eq. [7] we obtain for E_x:

$$E_x = \frac{q}{4\pi\varepsilon_0}\left(\frac{x - d/2}{r_1^3} - \frac{x + d/2}{r_2^3}\right) \quad \textbf{(8)}$$

while for E_y we find:

$$E_y = \frac{q}{4\pi\varepsilon_0}\left(\frac{y}{r_1^3} - \frac{y}{r_2^3}\right) \quad \textbf{(9)}$$

Note that in Eq. [8] and Eq. [9] the values of r_1 and r_2 are found from Eq. [3] as:

$$r_1 = \sqrt{\left(x - d/2\right)^2 + y^2} \quad \textbf{(10)}$$

and

$$r_2 = \sqrt{\left(x + d/2\right)^2 + y^2}$$

Therefore, Eq. [8], Eq. [9], and Eq. [10] completely determine the value of the electric field $\mathbf{E} = (E_x, E_y)$ due to the electric dipole in Figure [17.17] when observed at a point P in an arbitrary position in the (x,y)-plane.

(b) In the far field regime, where the point P is far enough from the dipole so that:

$$x \gg d \quad \text{and} \quad y \gg d, \quad \textbf{(11)}$$

then the values of r_1 and r_2 in Eq. [10] will obey:

$$r_1 \cong r_2 \cong r, \quad \textbf{(12)}$$

where r is given by:

$$r = \sqrt{x^2 + y^2} \quad \textbf{(13)}$$

It is important to note that the approximation described in Eq. [12] is not found by simply making $d = 0$ in Eq. [10], but by properly using the mathematical information from Eq. [11]. We illustrate the case of r_1. First expanding the square inside the square-root:

$$r_1 = \sqrt{x^2 - xd + \left(d/2\right)^2 + y^2}$$
$$= \sqrt{r^2 - xd + \left(d/2\right)^2} \quad \textbf{(14)}$$

Factoring r^2 out of the square-root in Eq. [14] we find:

$$r_1 = r\sqrt{1 - \left(\frac{xd}{r^2}\right) + \left(\frac{d}{2r}\right)^2} \quad \textbf{(15)}$$

Given Eq. [11] and Eq. [13]:

$$\frac{d}{r} \ll 1 \quad \text{and} \quad \left(\frac{d}{r}\right)^2 \to 0 \quad \textbf{(16)}$$

Thus, Eq. [16] justifies the approximation we made for $r_1 \cong r$. A similar argument leads to the equivalent approximation $r_1 \cong r$. Back to the problem at hand, substituting Eq. [12] into Eq. [8] we obtain:

$$E_x \cong \frac{q}{4\pi\varepsilon_0}\left(\frac{x - d/2}{r^3} - \frac{x + d/2}{r^3}\right)$$
$$= -\frac{qd}{4\pi\varepsilon_0}\cdot\frac{1}{r^3} \quad \textbf{(17)}$$

Substituting Eq. [12] into Eq. [9] we obtain:

$$E_y \cong \frac{q}{4\pi\varepsilon_0}\left(\frac{y}{r^3} - \frac{y}{r^3}\right)$$
$$= 0 \quad \textbf{(18)}$$

We can interpret Eq. [17] and Eq. [18] so that the far field of the electric dipole in Figure 17.17 obeys and inverse-cube law, has no vertical component, and its horizontal component always points to the left.

CHAPTER EIGHTEEN

Electric Energy and Potential

MULTIPLE CHOICE QUESTIONS

Multiple Choice 18.1
Correct Answer (c).

Multiple Choice 18.3
Correct Answer (c).

Multiple Choice 18.5
Correct Answer (e)

Multiple Choice 18.7
Correct Answer (c).

Multiple Choice 18.9
Correct Answer (c).

Multiple Choice 18.11
Correct Answer (b).

Multiple Choice 18.13
Correct Answer (e). To the upper left.

Multiple Choice 18.15
Correct Answer (c).

Multiple Choice 18.17
Correct Answer (a).

CONCEPTUAL QUESTIONS

Conceptual Question 18.1
The potential is $V = E\,s = 50$ mV.

Conceptual Question 18.3
It decreases.

Conceptual Question 18.5
Two options: you can use a dielectric with a large dielectric constant, and/or you can use a small plate separation distance. Recall, however, that air breaks electrically down when an electric field of 3×10^6 N/C is reached (called its dielectric strength), with air molecules ionizing and the gas becoming a conductor. These are the conditions that occur in the atmosphere during a lightening storm. The same applies to other dielectrics, except a vacuum.

Conceptual Question 18.7
Doubling the potential causes a doubling of the charge because the capacitance is constant.

ANALYTICAL PROBLEMS

Problem 18.1
The electric energy of a test charge between two uniformly charged parallel plates is given in Eq. [18.2]:

$$E_{el} = q_{mobile}\frac{\sigma}{\varepsilon_0}y \qquad \textbf{(1)}$$

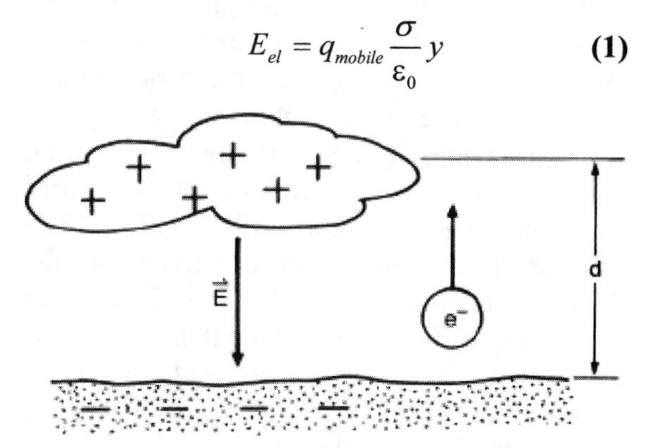

Figure 1

Can we apply this formula to the charge distribution causing the processes shown in Figure 18.29? Yes, in an approximate sense: Eq. [1] holds if we identify the origin of the motion of charges in Figure 18.29 in the form done in Figure 1. In this figure, we treat the cloud cover as one plate and Earth's surface as the other plate of a parallel plate capacitor. The surface of Earth is charged negative and the cloud is charged positive since the electric field is pointing down. As shown in Figure 1, a free electron accelerates toward the cloud since negative charges free to move accelerate always toward the region of positive charges. The motion of the electron is accompanied by a reduction in its electric potential energy. The change in the electric potential energy is:

$$\Delta E_{el} = -e\,|\,E\,|\,\Delta y$$

$$= \left(-1.6\times10^{-19}\,\text{C}\right)\left(150\frac{\text{N}}{\text{C}}\right)(650\text{ m})$$

$$= -1.56\times10^{-14}\,\text{J}$$

in which the negative sign on the right hand side of the first formula is the result of a decreasing potential energy in the direction of increasing height y.

Problem 18.3

(a) Note that we have chosen the same arrangement of charges as in Problem 17.10 to illustrate the difference in calculation procedure for the potential, which is a scalar, and the electric field, which is a vector. It is useful to compare both problems once the current one is done. The potential at a given point P in the vicinity of a single point charge is given in Eq. [18.8]. If there is more than one fixed-point charge, the potential is calculated as the sum of all potential contributions due to the single point charges in the arrangement. We used this approach in Example 18.5 for two fixed point charges (forming a dipole) and we will use it in the current case for the three point charges in Figure 18.30. Eq. [18.8] indicates that we need not to worry about the direction in which the fixed charges lie relative to the point P because it contains only the distance between the point and the point charge. The distance from each of the three charges to P in Figure 18.30 is $d/\sqrt{2}$, as we already discussed in Problem 17.10. Thus, we find:

$$V = \frac{1}{4 \cdot \pi \cdot \varepsilon_0} \sum_{i=1}^{3} \frac{q_i}{|r_i|}$$

$$= \frac{1}{4 \cdot \pi \cdot \varepsilon_0} \left(\frac{q}{\frac{d}{\sqrt{2}}} + \frac{q}{\frac{d}{\sqrt{2}}} + \frac{2 \cdot q}{\frac{d}{\sqrt{2}}} \right) \quad \textbf{(1)}$$

$$= \frac{\sqrt{2} \cdot q}{\pi \cdot \varepsilon_0 \cdot d}$$

Substitution of the given numerical values in Eq. [1] yields:

$$V = \frac{\sqrt{2}\left(1 \times 10^{-9}\,\mathrm{C}\right)}{\pi\left(8.85 \times 10^{-12} \frac{\mathrm{C}}{\mathrm{V \cdot m}}\right)(1.0\ \mathrm{m})} = 50.9\ \mathrm{V}$$

(b) Once the potential is known at a given point, the potential energy for a specific charge brought to that point is obtained from:

$$E_{el} = q_{test} \cdot V = \left(-2 \times 10^{-9}\,\mathrm{C}\right)(50.9\ \mathrm{V})$$

which yields:

$$E_{el} = -1.02 \times 10^{-7}\ \mathrm{J}$$

in which we note that the unit volt V is equal to the unit J/C.

Problem 18.5

We use the equation for the electric potential energy of the mobile charge (the ion) with $E_{el} = q \cdot V$, which means the change in energy must be written as $\Delta E_{el} = q \cdot \Delta V$. We rearrange this equation to find the charge on the ion:

$$q = \frac{\Delta E_{el}}{\Delta V} = \frac{1.92 \times 10^{-17}\ \mathrm{J}}{60\ \mathrm{V}} = 3.2 \times 10^{-19}\ \mathrm{J}$$

which is twice the elementary charge.

Problem 18.7

(a) Note that only the displacement in the direction of the electric field contributes to the change in potential energy of the point charge. We use Eq. [18.1] to find the work done by the electric field. Note that since the electric force and the displacement both point in the $+x$ direction the work is positive. This implies that the change in electric potential energy will be negative:

$$\Delta E_{\mathrm{el}} = -q_{\mathrm{mobile}} |E| \Delta y$$

$$= -\left(10 \times 10^{-6}\,\mathrm{C}\right)\left(300\,{}^{\mathrm{N}}\!/\!_{\mathrm{m}}\right)(0.30\,\mathrm{m}) \quad \textbf{(1)}$$

$$= -0.90\,\mathrm{mJ}$$

(b) We use Eq. [18.6] along with the result from Eq. [1] to find the potential difference:

$$\Delta V = \frac{\Delta E_{\mathrm{el}}}{q_{\mathrm{mobile}}} = -90\,\mathrm{V}$$

Problem 18.9

Since the potential is fixed, the work required is equal to the change in electric potential energy. We calculate this using Eq. [18.6] with the potential difference of 9 V and a mobile charge of 270 kC:

$$W = q_{\text{mobile}} \Delta V = 2.43\,\text{MJ}$$

Problem 18.11

(a) The formula for the capacitance in Eq. [18.12] is modified for a dielectric material with dielectric constant $\kappa_{\text{dielectric}}$ in the form:

$$C_{dielectric} = \frac{\kappa_{dielectric} \cdot \varepsilon_0 \cdot A}{b} = \kappa_{dielectric} \cdot C_{vacuum}$$

With the dielectric constant of paper κ_{paper} = 3.5 (see Table 18.2), we obtain:

$$\begin{aligned} C &= \kappa_{paper} \cdot \varepsilon_0 \frac{A}{b} \\ &= 3.5\left(8.85 \times 10^{-12} \frac{\text{C}^2}{\text{N m}^2}\right) \frac{12 \times 10^{-4}\,\text{m}^2}{1.5 \times 10^{-3}\ \text{m}} \\ &= 2.5 \times 10^{-11}\,\text{F} = 25\ \text{pF} \end{aligned}$$

(b) We calculate first the maximum potential difference from the given dielectric strength:

$$\begin{aligned} \Delta V_{\max} &= |E_{\max}|\, b \\ &= \left(15 \times 10^6 \frac{\text{V}}{\text{m}}\right)(1.5 \times 10^{-3}\text{m}) \\ &= 2.3 \times 10^4\,\text{V} \end{aligned}$$

This is the maximum potential, which can be applied before an electric breakdown occurs. The maximum charge, which can be placed on the capacitor plates, is then calculated:

$$\begin{aligned} q_{\max} &= C \cdot \Delta V_{\max} \\ &= (2.5 \times 10^{-11}\text{F})(2.3 \times 10^4\,\text{V}) \\ &= 5.8 \times 10^{-7}\text{C} = 0.58\ \mu\text{C} \end{aligned}$$

Problem 18.13

In order to find the charged stored on the capacitor, we first need its capacitance and we can use it and the potential difference to solve for the stored charge. To find the capacitance of the air–filled capacitor we need the area in square metres ($A = 2.0 \times 10^{-4}$ m²) and the plate separation in unit metres ($b = 2.0 \times 10^{-3}$ m). The capacitance is then $C = 8.9 \times 10^{-13}$ F. We can then use the definition of the capacitance in Eq. [18.11] to find $Q = 5.3 \times 10^{-12}$ C.

Problem 18.15

(a) In order to find the potential difference across the plates of a capacitor, we first need its capacitance and we can use it and the stored charge to solve for the potential difference. To find the capacitance of the air–filled capacitor we first express the area in square metres and the plate separation in metres. Finally we re–arrange the capacitance definition to calculate the potential difference: $\Delta V = 90.3$ V.

(b) The magnitude of the electric field is constant for a parallel-plate capacitor and equal to the potential difference between two points divided by the distance between those points. Here the potential difference was found in part (a), and the distance is the plate separation so that we find: $|\mathbf{E}| = 9.03 \times 10^4$ V/m.

Problem 18.17

(a) The magnitude of the electric field between the plates of a capacitor is the potential difference between the plates divided by their separation $|\mathbf{E}| = 3000$ V/m.

(b) The charge stored on each plate may be found by re–arranging the definition of the capacitance, but first we need to find the capacitance. In the case of a water–filled capacitor, we must use the equation that takes into account the dielectric constant of water: $C = 6.9 \times 10^{-11}$ F. Then we solve for the stored charge: $Q_{\text{water}} = 4.1 \times 10^{-10}$ C = 0.41 nC.

(c) If water is replaced by air, then the capacitance changes since the dielectric constant becomes approximately equal to 1. Instead of determining the new capacitance, let's solve this using ratios. Since $Q = C \cdot \Delta V$ for each of the air–filled and water–filled cases, and the potential difference and physical size of the capacitor don't change, then:

$$\frac{Q_{air}}{Q_{water}} = \frac{C_{air}}{C_{water}}$$

From this we find $Q_{\text{air}} = 5.2 \times 10^{-12}$ C.

Problem 18.19

This problem becomes possible to solve when you realize that the electric field is uniform between the plates of the capacitor and therefore the electron feels a constant force and thus experiences a constant acceleration. This becomes a problem projectile motion except that the electric force provides the acceleration in the y–direction instead of gravity. We start by finding the electric field inside the plates, which relates directly to the electric force on the electron: $F_{\text{el}} = 8.0 \times 10^{-15}$ N. The acceleration of the electron comes from Newton's second law. In order to treat this as a projectile motion we need to calculate the vertical component of the initial velocity. We further need to realize the point of closest approach to the bottom plate will be when the vertical velocity of the electron becomes zero, i.e. where the electron turns around and heads back to the top plate. Therefore we can use the kinematics equations, taking the final vertical velocity to be zero, which yields $\Delta y = 9.1 \times 10^{-4}$ m as the total vertical distance the electron will travel before it turns around. Since the electron started out 1.0 mm from the bottom plate it will come close to the bottom plate by a distance of $d = 0.11$ mm.

CHAPTER NINETEEN

The Flow of Charges

MULTIPLE CHOICE QUESTIONS

Multiple Choice 19.1
Correct Answer (b).

Multiple Choice 19.3
Correct Answer (a).

Multiple Choice 19.5
Correct Answer (e).

Multiple Choice 19.7
Correct Answer (e). The unit of drift velocity is m/s; it has nothing to do with buoyancy.

Multiple Choice 19.9
Correct Answer (e).

CONCEPTUAL QUESTIONS

Conceptual Question 19.1
Potential differences cause the flow of charges in a conductor. This would cause non–stationary conditions.

Conceptual Question 19.3
(a) Because their electric interaction is many orders of magnitude greater than the gravitational pull on an electron. Thus, gravity effects can be neglected and the electric electron/core ion interaction keeps them uniformly distributed.
(b) Because the immobile core ion to which the respective electron belongs carries a positive charge. Electrons cannot move far from their respective core ion unless another electron moves into the vicinity of the core ion, as happens when a current flows. Note that *excess* electrons brought into the metal do indeed drift to the surface as stated in the question.

ANALYTICAL PROBLEMS

Problem 19.1
Use Ohm's law, in the form of Eq. [19.5]:

$$R = \frac{\Delta V}{I} = \frac{120V}{6A} = 20\Omega$$

Problem 19.3
From Eq. [19.1], when an electric charge of $\Delta Q = 8.0$ mC flows through a wire in a time of $\Delta t = 4$ s, we are able to find the current I given by:

$$I = \frac{\Delta Q}{\Delta t} = 2.0\,\text{mA}$$

Problem 19.5
We use Ohm's Law (Eq. [19.5]) to find the resistance R of the resistor:

$$R = \frac{\Delta V}{I} = \frac{120\text{ V}}{0.6\text{ A}} = 200\Omega \quad (1)$$

With the potential difference being reduced to $\Delta V_2 = 70$ V, and the previously calculated resistance from Eq. [1], we use Ohm's Law once more to find the new current I_2:

$$I_2 = \frac{\Delta V_2}{R} = 0.4\,\text{A}$$

Problem 19.7
(a) We can use Eq. [19.5], also known as Ohm's Law, with $\Delta V = 12$ V and $I = 0.4$ A to find the resistance R of the wire:

$$R = \frac{\Delta V}{I} = 30\Omega \quad (1)$$

(b) From Eq. [19.6] we can find the resistivity of the wire as:

$$\rho = \frac{AR}{l} = \frac{\pi r^2 R}{l} \quad (2)$$

If we use the value from Eq. [1], the given radius of the wire of $r = 4.0$ mm, and its length $l = 3.2$ m into Eq. [2] we find:

$$\rho = 5 \times 10^{-4}\, \Omega \cdot \text{m}$$

Problem 19.9

(a) We use Eq. [19.6] to relate the resistance and resistivity:

$$R = \frac{\rho \cdot l}{A} \quad \textbf{(1)}$$

Each square end of the copper block has an area of $A_a = (2 \times 10^{-2}\text{ m})^2 = 4 \times 10^{-4}\text{ m}^2$. With a length of the block of $l_a = 0.1$ m, we get:

$$R = \frac{(1.7 \times 10^{-8}\Omega)(0.01)}{4 \times 10^{-4\;2}}$$
$$= 4.25 \times 10^{-6}\Omega = 4.25 \mu\Omega$$

(b) All 4 rectangular faces of the copper block have the same area, $A_b = 2 \times 10^{-2}\text{ m} \cdot 0.1\text{ m} = 2 \times 10^{-3}\text{ m}^2$. Using Eq. [1] with the length of the block now $l_b = 2 \times 10^{-2}$ m we find $R = 1.7 \times 10^{-7}\ \Omega = 0.17\ \mu\Omega$. Note that the difference between the resistances in parts (a) and (b) is entirely due to the change in geometry.

Problem 19.11

We use Eq. [19.6] to determine the resistivity of the wire material. Its cross–sectional area is $A = r^2 \cdot \pi = \pi\ (0.5 \times 10^{-3}\text{ m})^2 = 7.85 \times 10^{-7}\text{ m}^2$, where we converted the given diameter to a radius. Thus:

$$\rho = \frac{R \cdot A}{l} = \frac{(50 \times 10^{-3}\Omega)(7.85 \times 10^{-7\;2})}{1.67}$$
$$= 2.35 \times 10^{-8}\Omega \cdot$$

Comparing with the tabulated values of resistivities, this value comes closest to the value of gold (Au).

Problem 19.13

We need to look at the potential difference between two points in a copper wire of cross–sectional area $A = \pi \cdot (1.1 \times 10^{-2}\text{ m})^2 = 3.8 \times 10^{-4}\text{ m}^2$ and the length $l = 0.04$ m. Using Ohm's law we find $\Delta V = 89\ \mu$V.

Problem 19.15

The current across the membrane, I_m, and the time the current flows combine to the charge that is separated across the membrane. This charge is used in the definition of the capacitance to calculate the potential difference:

$$\Delta V = \frac{|I_m|\Delta t}{C} = \frac{J_m \cdot A \cdot \Delta t}{C} \quad \textbf{(1)}$$

In Eq. [1] the current is replaced by the current density because this quantity is given in the problem text. Next we substitute the capacitance from Eq. [18.12] with a dielectric constant (see the discussion on Section 18.6.2), and enter the numerical values, including the dielectric constant of the nerve membrane from Table 18.2 and the current density $J_m = 0.8 \times 10^{-4}\text{ A/cm}^2$, which is the same as 0.8 A/m^2:

$$\Delta V = \frac{J_m \cdot A \cdot \Delta t}{\kappa \cdot \varepsilon_0 \, A/b} = \frac{J_m \cdot b \cdot \Delta t}{\kappa \cdot \varepsilon_0}$$
$$= \frac{(0.8\,\text{A}/\text{m}^2)(6 \times 10^{-9})(150 \times 10^{-6})}{7.0(8.85 \times 10^{-12}\,\text{C}^2/\text{N·m}^2)}$$
$$= -0.012 = 12$$

Problem 19.17

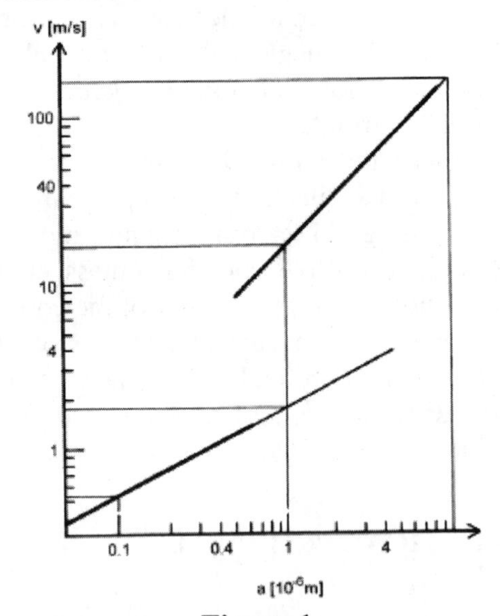

Figure 1

We start with the unmyelinated nerves. Figure 1 shows a particular choice of two points in the double–logarithmic graph of Figure 19.17 for the data analysis. The data read off the figure are shown in Table 1. We write the general power law relation between the radius of the axon and the impulse speed (with speed v given in unit m/s and parameter a given in unit μm):

$$v = c_2 \cdot a^{c_1}$$

with c_1 and c_2 constants. This yields:

$$\ln v = \ln c_2 + c_1 \cdot \ln a \qquad \textbf{(1)}$$

In this formula we need only to evaluate c_1 because the proportionality relationships predict a power law coefficient, but no prefactor.

Table 1

a (μm)	Lna	v (m/s)	lnv
0.1	– 2.303	0.51	– 0.67
1.0	0.0	1.75	+ 0.56

For the data in Table 1 we find:

$$c_1 = \frac{\Delta \ln v}{\Delta \ln a} = \frac{1.23}{2.303} = 0.53$$

Next we analyse the data for the myelinated nerve in Figure 19.17. Figure 2 shows again a choice of data points to quantify the power–law behaviour. The data are listed in Table 2.

Table 2

a (μm)	lna	v (m/s)	lnv
1.0	0.0	16.1	+ 2.78
10.0	+ 2.303	160.0	+ 5.08

Using again Eq. [1], we find for the power law coefficient for myelinated nerves:

$$c_1 = \frac{\Delta \ln v}{\Delta \ln a} = \frac{2.3}{2.303} = 1.0$$

Both exponents are consistent with the proportionalities sought.

Problem 19.19

(a) The first part of the question serves as a preparation step to obtain some necessary parameters to quantify later the electric properties.

The volume of the blood cell is estimated from the mass of the blood cell and the density of blood. The density of blood is a sufficiently good approximation of the density of the blood cell as blood cells float in whole blood. We find for the volume:

$$V = \frac{1 \times 10^{-12}}{1.06 \times 10^{3}\ \overline{\ 3\ }} = 9.4 \times 10^{-16\ 3} \qquad \textbf{(1)}$$

The volume of a spherical blood cell is $V = 4 \cdot \pi \cdot r^3/3$ and its surface is $A = 4 \cdot \pi \cdot r^2$. From Eq. [1], we obtain $r = 6.1 \times 10^{-6}$ m = 6.1 μm. This yields:

$$A = 4.7 \times 10^{-10\ 2} \qquad \textbf{(2)}$$

(b) Treating the membrane as a parallel plate capacitor we find using Eq. [2] and Eq. [18.12] with a dielectric constant:

$$C = 5.0\left(8.85 \times 10^{-12}\,\text{-}\right)\frac{4.7 \times 10^{-10\ 2}}{100 \times 10^{-9}}$$

$$= 2.08 \times 10^{-13}$$

(c) Using $q = C \cdot \Delta V$ we find from part (b) for the charge:

$$q = (2.08 \times 10^{-13})(100 \times 10^{-3})$$

$$= 2.08 \times 10^{-14}$$

Dividing this charge by the elementary charge e allows us to calculate the number of elementary charges on the surface membrane of the blood cell:

$$N = \frac{q}{e} = \frac{2.08 \times 10^{-14}}{1.6 \times 10^{-19}} = 130000$$

Problem 19.21

(a) There is no change, since the time constant τ does not depend on $\rho_{axoplasm}$, the resistivity of the axoplasm.

(b) The potential difference of the resting nerve is –70 mV. The change to –60 mV is a perturbation of 10 mV that decays toward the resting nerve value. This decay occurs as a function of the distance from the perturbation according to Eq. [19.20]. We are interested in a point x_0 along the nerve with axoplasm resistivity 1.1 Ω·m, where:

$$\Delta V(x_0) = 0.2\,\Delta V_{max} = 2\,\text{mV}$$

For the nerve with the higher axoplasm resistivity, ρ_{high} = 1.1 Ω·m. So that substituting λ, we find from Eq. [19.20] and Eq. [19.21]:

$$\Delta V(x_0) = \Delta V_{max}\exp\left(-\frac{x_0}{\lambda}\right)$$

$$= \Delta V_{max}\exp\left(-\frac{x_0}{\sqrt{\dfrac{ab}{2}\dfrac{\rho_{membrane}}{\rho_{high}}}}\right) \quad \textbf{(1)}$$

Reorganizing Eq. [1]:

$$\ln\left[\frac{\Delta V(x_0)}{\Delta V_{max}}\right] = \ln 0.2 = -1.609 = -\frac{x_0}{\lambda} \quad \textbf{(2)}$$

Solving Eq. [2] for x_0:

$$x_0 = 1.609\sqrt{\frac{ab}{2}\frac{\rho_{membrane}}{\rho_{high}}} \quad \textbf{(3)}$$

In the second step, the potential difference remaining from the 10 mV perturbation is calculated at a distance x_0 from the perturbation for a nerve with the lower axoplasm resistivity of ρ_{low} = 0.5 Ω·m. This is done by substituting the value we obtained for x_0 in Eq. [3], as well as the new resistivity ρ_{low} into Eq. [19.20] and Eq. [19.21]:

$$\Delta V(x_0) = \Delta V_{max}\exp\left(-\frac{x_0}{\lambda}\right)$$

$$= (10\,\text{mV})\exp\left(-\frac{1.609\sqrt{\dfrac{ab}{2}\dfrac{\rho_{membrane}}{\rho_{high}}}}{\sqrt{\dfrac{ab}{2}\dfrac{\rho_{membrane}}{\rho_{low}}}}\right) \quad \textbf{(4)}$$

The argument inside the exponential of Eq. [4] simplifies so that:

$$\Delta V(x_0) = (10\,\text{mV})\exp\left(-1.609\sqrt{\frac{\rho_{low}}{\rho_{high}}}\right)$$

$$= 3.4\,\text{mV}$$

That is, the potential difference perturbation has not decayed to a value of 2 mV as before, but only to 3.4 mV at the same distance from the 10 mV perturbation.

CHAPTER TWENTY

Atomic, Electromagnetic, and Optical Phenomena

MULTIPLE CHOICE QUESTIONS

Multiple Choice 20.1
Correct Answer (e).

Multiple Choice 20.3
Correct Answer (b). Otherwise it would lose energy continuously (i.e., it would be a closed system and not an isolated system).

Multiple Choice 20.5
Correct Answer (e).

Multiple Choice 20.7
Correct Answer (e). The electron absorbs energy in the form of an external photon.

Multiple Choice 20.9
Correct Answer (e).

Multiple Choice 20.11
Correct Answer (e).

Multiple Choice 20.13
Correct Answer (b). Lithium, sodium, and potassium have a single valence electron. From the list, only oxygen misses a single electron to obtain a noble gas configuration, so it is the one that should vary chemically the most from the others.

CONCEPTUAL QUESTIONS

Conceptual Question 20.1
Smaller helicopters have a second, smaller rotor turned 90^0 at the tail. Large helicopters have two rotors that spin in opposite directions.

Conceptual Question 20.3
In Eq. [20.12] we defined the angular momentum L as:

$$L = r \cdot m \cdot v \cdot \sin\varphi$$

The angular momentum is conserved during a jump. To achieve a maximum speed of rotation v, the mass distribution of the rotating object must be as close as possible to the axis of rotation; i.e., the product $m \cdot r$ has to be a minimum.

Conceptual Question 20.5
No, because the energy of the electron in the hydrogen atom is proportional to $1/n^2$.

Conceptual Question 20.7
No. It can absorb energy in the ground state to transfer into any of its excited states, then emit light of the corresponding frequency.

ANALYTICAL PROBLEMS

Problem 20.1
The magnitude of the angular momentum of an object in circular motion is given in Eq. [20.12], but taking the angle as 90° because the velocity of the object is always perpendicular to the radial direction. For Earth moving around the Sun we know that the average distance between Earth and the Sun is 1.5×10^{11} m and that the time for one orbit is a year which is equal to 3.15×10^7 s. Thus, the average speed of Earth is 3.0×10^4 m/s. The angular momentum of Earth as it moves about the Sun is then $L = 2.69 \times 10^{40}$ kg · m²/s.

Problem 20.3
The angular speed is $\omega = 8.0$ revolutions/s. A collapsing star rotates faster and faster.

Problem 20.5
(a) The radius of the lowest orbit is called the Bohr radius. The radii of the excited states of the hydrogen atom are related in a simple fashion to the Bohr radius: $r(n) = n^2 \cdot r_{\text{Bohr}}$. Thus, we find for $n = 2$ a radius of $r = 2.12 \times 10^{-10}$ m = 0.212 nm.
(b) The only form of potential energy relevant in the atomic shell is the electric potential energy. For $n = 2$ we find:

$$E_{el} = -\frac{e^2}{4 \cdot \pi \cdot \varepsilon_0 \cdot r}$$

$$= -\left(9 \times 10^9 \frac{\text{N} \cdot \text{m}^2}{\text{C}^2}\right) \frac{(1.6 \times 10^{-19}\,\text{C})^2}{2.12 \times 10^{-10}\,\text{m}}$$

$$= -1.09 \times 10^{-18}\,\text{J} = -6.8\ \text{eV}$$

(c) There are two ways to calculate the total energy. Calculating the kinetic energy and adding the kinetic energy and the result of part (b) requires a longer calculation. A shorter approach is to use the formula that preceeds Eq. [20.14]:

$$-E_{el} = 2 \cdot E_{kin}$$

Thus, $E_{total} = -5.5 \times 10^{-19}$ J, or – 3.4 eV.

Problem 20.7

The force acting on the electron is the Coulomb force. Using for the distance between electron and proton the Bohr radius, we find:

$$\begin{aligned} || &= \frac{1}{4 \cdot \pi \cdot \varepsilon_0} \cdot \frac{e^2}{r_{Bohr}^2} \\ &= \left(9 \times 10^9 \frac{\mathrm{N \cdot m^2}}{\mathrm{C^2}}\right) \frac{\left(1.6 \times 10^{-19}\,\mathrm{C}\right)^2}{\left(5.29 \times 10^{-11}\,\mathrm{m}\right)^2} \\ &= 8.2 \times 10^{-8}\,\mathrm{N} \end{aligned}$$

Problem 20.9

We convert the given wavelength into a photon energy using $E = h \cdot f$ and using $c = \lambda \cdot f$:

$$E_{trans} = \frac{h \cdot c}{\lambda} = \frac{(6.6 \times 10^{-34}\,\mathrm{J\,s})\left(3 \times 10^8 \,\frac{\mathrm{m}}{\mathrm{s}}\right)}{6.56 \times 10^{-7}\,\mathrm{m}} \quad \textbf{(1)}$$

$$= 3.02 \times 10^{-19}\,\mathrm{J} = 1.89\ \mathrm{eV}$$

In the next step we search for a combination of hydrogen levels as calculated preceding Example 20.2, which corresponds to this energy. We find the transition between $n = 2$ and $n = 3$. We know further that the hydrogen atom has emitted the photon with the energy calculated in Eq. [1]. Emission corresponds to a loss of energy, thus, the transition occurred from $n = 3$ to $n = 2$, i.e., the atom was excited prior to the transition.

Problem 20.11

(a) The only force that acts on the electron in orbit around the proton is Coulomb's force. This force provides the centripetal acceleration of the electron that causes it to travel in uniform circular motion around the proton. We write:

$$\frac{e^2}{4\pi\varepsilon_0 r^2} = m_{electron} \frac{v^2}{r} \quad \textbf{(1)}$$

We re-arrange Eq. [1] for the velocity to find the value $v = 1.6 \times 10^6$ m/s.

(b) The de Broglie wavelength is calculated from Eq. [20.19] as $\lambda = h/(m \cdot v) = 0.45$ nm.

Problem 20.13

When hydrogen is in the state with $n = 3$, we can find the energy it takes to be ionized by using Eq. [20.15], after substituting the value of the Rydberg constant. We take $n_{initial} = 3$ and $n_{final} = 4$ because the final state is for the atom to be ionized. The energy to ionize this already excited atom is $\Delta E_{ionization} = 1.51$ eV.

CHAPTER TWENTY-ONE

Magnetism and Electromagnetic Waves

MULTIPLE CHOICE QUESTIONS

Multiple Choice 21.1
Correct Answer (d).

Multiple Choice 21.3
Correct Answer (b).

Multiple Choice 21.5
Correct Answer (b).

Multiple Choice 21.7
Correct Answer (d).

Multiple Choice 21.9
Correct Answer (d).

Multiple Choice 21.11
Correct Answer (d).

CONCEPTUAL QUESTIONS

Conceptual Question 21.1
A current flows parallel or anti–parallel to the magnetic field vector.

Conceptual Question 21.3
No. The metal's positive core ions appear to move with the drift speed in the opposite direction. Thus, the same magnetic field is observed.

Conceptual Question 21.5
There is no net force but a torque acting on the conductors.

Conceptual Question 21.7
The same that would happen if the point charge were moving with the opposite velocity vector past the stationary magnet. For example, this case occurs in Faraday's experiment when a magnet moves through a conductor loop.

Conceptual Question 21.9
The magnet causes a force on the electrons that move inside the Brownian tube toward the screen.

Conceptual Question 21.11
None, because the force and the displacement are perpendicular.

Conceptual Question 21.13
No. For an acceleration, you need a changing magnetic field or a charge that already moves at an angle to the magnetic field.

Conceptual Question 21.15
The stoichiometric formula of the molecule is $C_8H_8O_2$ causing the peak at m/Z = 136 (136 mass units). The fragment at m/Z = 105 has lost 31 units, which corresponds to the ligand –OCH_3; the fragment at m/Z = 77 has lost 59 units, or an additional 28 units, which corresponds to an additional loss of the carbonyl group (–CO–); and the fragment at m/Z = 51 has lost 85 units, or an additional 26 units, which corresponds to a break– up of the benzene ring with a loss of two –CH– units.

Conceptual Question 21.17
A moving charge, for example, a radio station causing the vibration of charges in an antenna. An electron transferring from one atomic state to another causes light, which is a particular example of electromagnetic radiation. Classically, this is described by the oscillation of the electron between the two states.

Conceptual Question 21.19
Surfaces that radiate more heat than others would be brighter. If these objects can be described as blackbodies, the ones with the highest temperature are brightest. (Stefan's Law)

Conceptual Question 21.21
If a green street light would emit green light (e.g. in the 500 to 550 nm wavelength range) and a red street light would emit red light (e.g. in the 650 to 700 nm wavelength range) then, indeed, the green light were about twenty times brighter than the red light. However, actual street lights function in a different fashion. The colour of a streetlight is the result of elimination of certain wavelengths: The light bulb in the streetlight emits white light and a filter eliminates part of the spectrum to create the final colour impression. As an example, if molecules embedded in the filter absorb in the green part of the spectrum then you see the complementary colour, in this case red. Thus, you see all streetlight colours about equally intensive as only minor fractions of the white light are removed.

Conceptual Question 21.23
Water and ice particles in the atmosphere refract sunlight toward your eye in the same fashion as a prism. Blue (and violet) light are refracted more strongly than red light.

Conceptual Question 21.25
The colour travelling more slowly is bent more.

ANALYTICAL PROBLEMS

Problem 21.1
We quantify the magnetic field for each of the two wires before answering the three questions. The magnetic field as a function of distance from a current– carrying wire is given in Eq. [21.2]:

$$|\,| = \frac{\mu_0}{2 \cdot \pi} \cdot \frac{I}{d}$$

For the wire carrying I_1 we find:

$$|{}_1| = \frac{\left(1.26 \times 10^{-6} \frac{\text{N}}{\text{A}^2}\right)(4\ \text{A})}{2 \cdot \pi \cdot d_1} = \frac{8.0 \times 10^{-7}\,\text{T} \cdot \text{m}}{d_1} \qquad \textbf{(1)}$$

in which d_1 is the distance from wire 1. For the wire carrying I_2 we find in the same fashion:

$$|{}_2| = \frac{6.0 \times 10^{-7}\,\text{T} \cdot \text{m}}{d_2} \qquad \textbf{(2)}$$

in which d_2 is the distance from wire 2.
(a) We determine the net magnetic field at point P_1 as the sum of two contributions: the magnetic field at P_1 due to wire 1 and the magnetic field at P_1 due to wire 2. Even if we were not asked for the direction of the net magnetic field, the direction of each of the two contributions must be determined since we need to know whether the two contributions should be added or subtracted from each other. The contribution at point P_1 due to wire 1 is calculated with $d_1 = l_1$:

$$|{}_1|(P_1) = \frac{8.0 \times 10^{-7}\,\text{T} \cdot \text{m}}{0.06\ \text{m}} = 1.33 \times 10^{-5}\,\text{T}$$

This contribution is directed out of the paper in Figure 21.40 due to the right hand rule. The contribution at the same point due to wire 2 is calculated with $d_2 = l_1 + l_2$:

$$|{}_2|(P_1) = \frac{6.0 \times 10^{-7}\,\text{T} \cdot \text{m}}{0.11\ \text{m}} = 5.5 \times 10^{-6}\,\text{T}$$

This contribution is directed into the plane of the paper in Figure 21.40. Therefore, the net magnetic field at P_1 is $|\mathbf{B}|(P_1) = 7.8 \times 10^{-6}$ T, pointing out of the plane of the paper in Figure 21.40.
(b) We determine the net magnetic field at point P_2 in the same fashion as in part (a). We find with $d_1 = l_2 + l_3$:

$$|{}_1|(P_2) = 8.0 \times 10^{-6}\,\text{T}$$

This contribution is directed into the plane of the paper in Figure 21.40. Also with $d_2 = l_3$:

$$|{}_2|(P_2) = 1.20 \times 10^{-5}\,\text{T}$$

This contribution is directed out of the paper in Figure 21.40. Therefore, the net magnetic field at P_2 is $|\mathbf{B}|(P_2) = 4.0 \times 10^{-6}$ T pointing out of the plane of the paper in Figure 21.40.
(c) From parts (a) and (b) we know that the contributions due to the two wires have to be subtracted from each other for all points to the left or to the right of the arrangement. Thus, on either side there could be a point where the net magnetic field is indeed vanishing.

To set the problem properly up for this, we have to define two conventions:

- We assign a positive sign to the magnetic field value at a point where that field points out of the plane of paper in Figure 21.40, and we assign a negative sign if the magnetic field points into the plane of the paper.
- We define an x–axis perpendicular to the two wires in the plane of Figure 21.40. The positive x–axis points toward the right and the origin ($x = 0$) is chosen at the position of wire 1.

With these conventions, we combine the two equations for the magnitudes of the magnetic field for wire 1 and wire 2, i.e., Eqns. [1] and [2]:

$$|_1|(x) = \frac{-8\times10^{-7}\,\mathrm{T\cdot m}}{x} + \frac{6\times10^{-7}\,\mathrm{T\cdot m}}{x - l_2} \qquad \mathbf{(3)}$$

We find the x–position at which the magnetic field becomes zero by setting Eq. [3] equal to zero:

$$\frac{-8\times10^{-7}(x - l_2) + 6\times10^{-7}x}{x\cdot(x - l_2)} = 0$$

This simplifies to:

$$x = +4\cdot l_2$$

Thus, the point with zero magnetic field lies 20 cm to the right of wire 1 or 15 cm to the right of wire 2.

Problem 21.3

To establish mechanical equilibrium, the magnetic force per unit length of the wire, acting on the top wire, must be equal to the weight per unit length of the wire. Thus, the free–body diagram of the system (e.g. choosing 1 metre as the unit length of the wire) contains two vertical force vectors, the weight downward and the magnetic force upward.

The weight per unit length is labelled |**W**|/L and its value for the wire in the present problem is given by:

$$\frac{||}{L} = \frac{m\cdot g}{L} = \frac{10\ \mathrm{g}}{1\ \mathrm{m}}\left(9.8\frac{\mathrm{m}}{\mathrm{s}^2}\right) = 0.098\frac{\mathrm{N}}{\mathrm{m}}$$

Now we use Eq. [21.1] for the magnetic force per unit length of a wire:

$$\frac{|\ |}{l} \propto \frac{I_1\cdot I_2}{d}$$

Thus, we require:

$$\frac{\mu_0\cdot I_1\cdot I_2}{2\cdot\pi\cdot d} = \frac{||}{L} \qquad \mathbf{(1)}$$

Isolating the unknown variable d in Eq. [1], we find:

$$d = \frac{\mu_0\cdot I_1\cdot I_2}{2\cdot\pi\left(||/L\right)}$$

This yields:

$$d = \frac{\left(1.26\times10^{-6}\frac{\mathrm{N}}{\mathrm{A}^2}\right)(20\ \mathrm{A})(35\ \mathrm{A})}{2\cdot\pi\left(0.098\frac{\mathrm{N}}{\mathrm{m}}\right)} = 1.4\ \mathrm{mm}$$

The distance between the wires is 1.4 mm.

Problem 21.5

The magnetic force exerted on the lower wire by the upper wire is directed upward since their currents flow in the same direction. In mechanical equilibrium, we write for a piece of the lower wire of length L:

$$\sum_i F_{i,y} = 0 = \frac{\mu_0\cdot I_1\cdot I_2\cdot L}{2\cdot\pi\cdot d} - m\cdot g \qquad \mathbf{(1)}$$

in which the upward force component is the magnetic force taken from Eq. [21.1] and the downward force is the weight. d is the distance between the two wires in mechanical equilibrium, and m is the mass of a wire segment of length L. We determine the current in the lower wire, I_2, from Eq. [1]:

$$I_2 = \frac{2\cdot\pi\cdot d}{\mu_0\cdot I_1}\cdot\frac{m}{L}\cdot g$$

$$= \frac{2\cdot\pi(0.04\ \mathrm{m})\left(0.01\frac{\mathrm{kg}}{\mathrm{m}}\right)\left(9.8\frac{\mathrm{m}}{\mathrm{s}^2}\right)}{\left(1.26\times10^{-6}\frac{\mathrm{N}}{\mathrm{A}^2}\right)(100\ \mathrm{A})}$$

This yields:

$$I_2 = 195\ \mathrm{A}$$

Problem 21.7
We use the magnetic force on a length l of conductor, Eq. [21.3], but since we have been asked to find the magnitude of the magnetic force we can use Eq. [21.4] where the given quantities are the magnitudes of the relevant vector quantities and the angle θ is the angle between the magnetic field direction and the direction of the current. We can now find the magnetic force as $F_{mag} = 7.5$ N.

Problem 21.9
First of all we must consider the directions of the fields created by each conductor at the location of point P. Using the right–hand rule where the thumb points in the direction of current and the field curls in the direction of the fingers, the directions of each magnetic field contribution are: B_A up and to the right, B_B up and to the left, B_C up and to the left and B_D up and to the right. Note that all angles are at 45^0 above horizontal. The magnitude of each magnetic field is equal since the currents are all equal and the distances between each conductor and point P are the same. This distance may be found as the hypotenuse of the triangle that makes up a quarter of the square configuration: d = 0.141 m. Each magnetic field is then:

$$B = \frac{\mu_0 \cdot I}{2 \cdot \pi \cdot d} = \frac{1.26\times10^{-6}\,\frac{\text{N}}{\text{A}^2}}{2\pi}\,\frac{4.0\text{ A}}{0.141\text{ m}}$$
$$= 5.69\times10^{-6}\text{T}$$

The total magnetic field in each direction is then twice this value, once directed up and right, and once directed up and left, as shown in Figure 1:

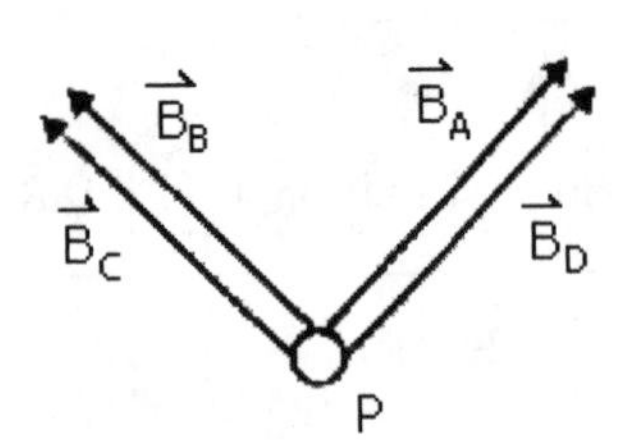

Figure 1

The total magnetic field may be calculated using the Pythagorean theorem as B_P = 1.6 × 10^{-5} T. This field is directed upward because the left and right component cancel, leaving us with only upward components from each contribution.

Problem 21.11
(a) The problem is illustrated in Figure 2. The figure indicates the direction of the magnetic field **B** due to the current in the wire.

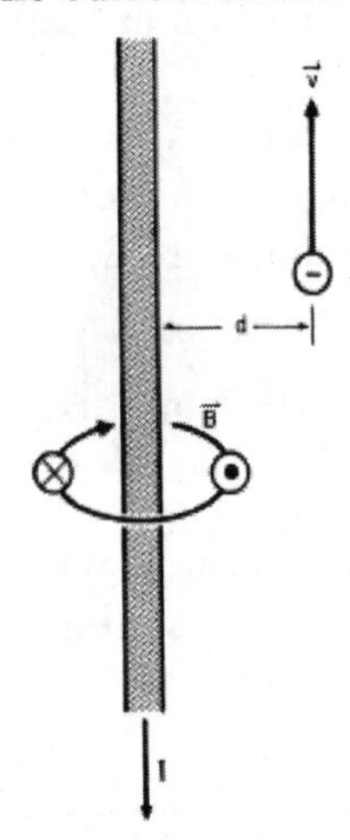

Figure 2

As shown, the magnetic field at the position of the electron beam points out of the plane of the paper. We first use Eq. [21.2]:

$$\| = \frac{\mu_0}{2\cdot\pi}\cdot\frac{I}{d} \quad \textbf{(1)}$$

and Eq. [21.11]

$$f_{mag} = q\cdot v\cdot B \quad \textbf{(2)}$$

to determine the magnitude of the force acting on each electron. Eq. [1] allows us to calculate the magnitude of the magnetic field of the current at a given distance d from the wire:

$$B = \frac{\left(1.26\times10^{-6}\,\frac{\text{N}}{\text{A}^2}\right)1.5\text{ A}}{2\cdot\pi(5\times10^{-3}\text{m})} = 6\times10^{-5}\text{T} \quad \textbf{(3)}$$

With this result, we use Eq. [2] to determine the magnitude of the magnetic force on each electron in the beam. Eq. [2] contains the speed of the electrons, which we calculate, from the given kinetic energy of 20 eV:

$$E_{kin} = 20\ \text{eV}\left(1.6\times10^{-19}\frac{\text{J}}{\text{eV}}\right) = 3.2\times10^{-18}\ \text{J} = \frac{1}{2}m_{electron}\cdot v^2 \qquad \textbf{(4)}$$

which leads to $v = 2.65 \times 10^6$ m/s when the mass of the electron is taken from Table 13.1. Note that it is always useful to check such a speed, calculated from an energy for an atomic or sub–atomic particle, against the speed of light. In the current case we find that the speed is just below 1% of the speed of light; thus, our classical calculation (using $E_{\text{kin}} = ½ \cdot m \cdot v^2$) is valid. If the speed exceeds a few percent of the speed of light a relativistic correction would have to be used. The values from Eqs. [3] and [4] are substituted into Eq. [2]:

$$f_{mag} = (1.6\times10^{-19}\text{C})\left(2650\frac{\text{km}}{\text{s}}\right)(6\times10^{-5}\text{T}) = 2.5\times10^{-17}\text{N}$$

(b) The direction of the force is determined with the right hand rule as illustrated in Figure 3 for both positively and negatively charged particles. We apply Figure 3(b) to the directions shown in the sketch of Figure 2. With the velocity vector directed upward and the magnetic field at the position of the electron pointing out of the plane of the paper, the force is directed toward the wire. Thus, the electron is attracted toward the wire.

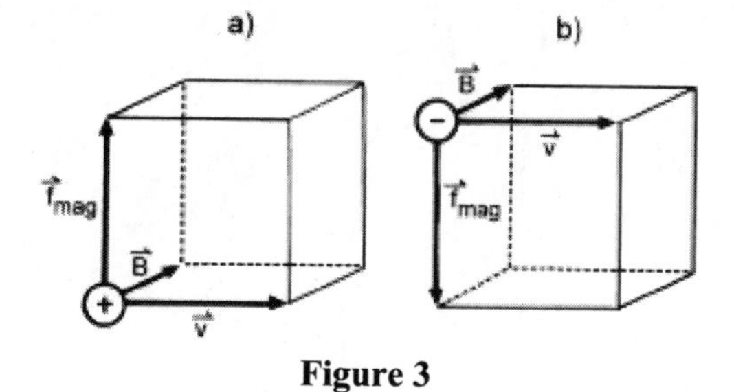

Figure 3

Problem 21.13

This problem requires us to first calculate the number of sodium ions and then find the magnetic force acting on all the ions at once since they travel together in the blood vessel. The number of sodium ions is found from the volume, the molar concentration and Avogadro's number as $N_{\text{Na+}} = 4.2 \times 10^{21}$ ions. The magnetic force on the blood vessel is the total force on all the ions. We can find the magnitude of this force from Eq. [21.11]: $F_{\text{net}} = 240$ N.

Problem 21.15

The radius of the proton's circular path is given in Eq. [21.15]. From Eq. [21.16] we see that the period of this circular motion is related to the speed and radius by $v/r = 2 \cdot \pi/T$. With this is mind we rearrange the equation for the radius of the path in the form:

$$\frac{v}{r} = \frac{q\cdot B}{m} = \frac{2\cdot\pi}{T}$$

which we re–arrange and find that the period is given by: $T = 8.2 \times 10^{-8}$ s.

Problem 21.17

(a) We need not to quantify the properties of the Wien filter in this case because the speed of the selected ions is given. We quantify Eq. [21.15] for each isotope separately and then calculate the difference in position for the collector. Note from Figure 21.15 that this distance is twice the difference in radii as calculated from Eq. [21.15] because both isotopes enter the 180^0 sector field. The isotope labels allow us to determine the mass of each isotope: ^{235}U has a mass of 235 · *u* in which *u* is the atomic unit (1 $u = 1.6605677 \times 10^{-27}$ kg). Therefore, the mass of ^{235}U is 3.902×10^{-25} kg. ^{238}U has a mass of 238 · *u*, which is 3.952×10^{-25} kg. This leads to:

$$r_{U-235} = \frac{(3.902 \times 10^{-25}\, kg)\left(2.5 \times 10^5 \frac{m}{s}\right)}{(1.6 \times 10^{-19}\, C)(2.0\, T)}$$
$$= 0.305\, m$$

and $r_{U-238} = 0.309$ m. Thus, their separation is 8 mm.

(b) The analogous calculation for the two carbon isotopes leads to $r_{C-12} = 0.0156$ m and $r_{C-14} = 0.0182$ m. i.e., a separation of 5 mm. Note that a smaller magnetic field leads to a larger separation.

CHAPTER TWENTY-TWO

Geometric Optics

MULTIPLE CHOICE QUESTIONS

Multiple Choice 22.1
Correct Answer (c).

Multiple Choice 22.3
Correct Answer (a).

Multiple Choice 22.5
Correct Answer (a).

Multiple Choice 22.7
Correct Answer (b).

Multiple Choice 22.9
Correct Answer (d).

Multiple Choice 22.11
Correct Answer (d).

Multiple Choice 22.13
Correct Answer (c).

Multiple Choice 22.15
Correct Answer (c).

Multiple Choice 22.17
Correct Answer (a). Note that choices (c) to (e) can immediately be excluded based on a dimensional analysis.

Multiple Choice 22.19
Correct Answer (d).

Multiple Choice 22.21
Correct Answer (b).

Multiple Choice 22.23
Correct Answer (c).

Multiple Choice 22.25
Correct Answer (e). Note in particular that choice (d) is not correct because we use the near point of the standard man (s_0 = 25 cm) in the calculation of the angular magnification.

Multiple Choice 22.27
Correct Answer (b).

Multiple Choice 22.29
Correct Answer (d).

Multiple Choice 22.31
Correct Answer (e).

Multiple Choice 22.33
Correct Answer (d).

CONCEPTUAL QUESTIONS

Conceptual Question 22.1
Let's go over the image you see in the mirror in detail. Note that what is at your left side remains at the left side in the image. Further, your head is at the top in the image as it is at the top of the object. Thus, two of the three axis which define a Cartesian coordinate system did not change. The mirror image still does not represent the object in its three–dimensional form as the third direction, the direction toward the mirror, is inverted. What is in front of you toward the mirror is located in the image closer to the mirror than your image. At this point our brain is unwilling to contemplate the physical facts; it goes beyond comprehension to mirror a person front to back. Instead, the brain interprets the image in a conceptually more acceptable way: because our body has a left–right symmetry the brain concludes that the image is left–right switched.

Conceptual Question 22.3
A distance of 20 to 25 cm places the object at the near point of the person (reading distance). The image of the person in the mirror is then apparently 40 to 50 cm from the eye. Both images require different accommodations of the eye that are not possible at the same time.

Conceptual Question 22.5
The optical definition; due to refraction you see the Sun just below the horizon. The same physics applies at dusk; thus, the optical day is longer than the geometrical day.

Conceptual Question 22.7

(a) Figure 1 illustrates a spherical droplet of radius R on a flat leaf surface.

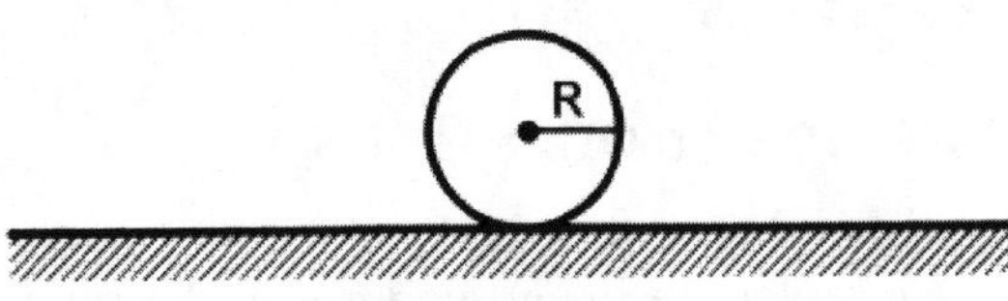

Figure 1

We treat the droplet as a thin lens, and thus, use the thin–lens formula, Eq. [22.12]:

$$\frac{1}{p}+\frac{1}{q}=\frac{1}{f}$$

Then we combine it with the lens maker's equation, Eq. [22.14]:

$$\frac{1}{p}+\frac{1}{q}=(n-1)\left(\frac{1}{R_1}-\frac{1}{R_2}\right)$$

Together they state:

$$\frac{1}{f}=(n-1)\left(\frac{1}{R_1}-\frac{1}{R_2}\right)$$

Using Figure 1 we note that $-R_1=R_2$ due to the symmetry of the two water–air interfaces of the droplet, i.e., one radius is measured behind the interface and one radius is measured in front of the interface (as defined in Table 22.4). Defining $-R_1=R_2=R$ and with the indices of refraction of water and air from Table 22.2, we obtain:

$$\frac{1}{f}=(1.33-1.00)\left(\frac{2}{R}\right) \quad\Rightarrow\quad f=1.5\cdot R$$

Since we treat the sphere as a thin lens in this calculation, the focal length f is measured from the centre of the spherical droplet. Thus, sunlight would only be focused deep in the leaf with no noticeable focusing at the surface, i.e., at distance R from the centre of the droplet. Thus, the suggested burning cannot take place.

(b) Plant cells, like all other living cells, can get undercooled, i.e., plants can get a chill. The undercooling results when the water droplets on the leaf evaporate, removing for this process the latent heat of evaporation locally from the leaf beneath. You can test this effect by spraying water on your skin and blowing over the skin to let the water evaporate; this is also the reason why children shiver when they come out of a pool despite intense sunshine in summer.

Conceptual Question 22.9

Because the image is inverted on the retina due to the geometric optics occurring at the lens. Thus, the brain's inversion is the needed correction.

ANALYTICAL PROBLEMS

Problem 22.1

The given distance is the object distance p = 0.4 m. The mirror is a spherical mirror since the only other type of mirrors we discuss in the textbook is the flat mirror, and flat mirrors don't generate magnified images. We can use the mirror equation (Eq. [22.3]) to determine the focal length f if we can first identify the image length q. To obtain q we use the information about the magnification of the mirror: M = + 2.0 since an upright image is associated with a positive magnification (based on the sign conventions in Table 22.1). Therefore, the equation for the magnification of the mirror (Eq. [22.5]) reads:

$$M=-\frac{q}{p}=2$$

and yields for the image distance:

$$q=-2\cdot p=-0.8\text{ m}$$

With this value for q, the mirror equation reads:

$$\frac{1}{f}=\frac{1}{p}+\frac{1}{q}=\frac{1}{0.4\text{ m}}-\frac{1}{0.8\text{ m}}$$

and yields for the focal length:

$$f=+0.8\text{ m}$$

The mirror is concave since f is positive. Note that 80 cm focal length corresponds to a radius of curvature of the mirror of R = 1.6 m.

Problem 22.3

The three sketches are shown in Figure 2.

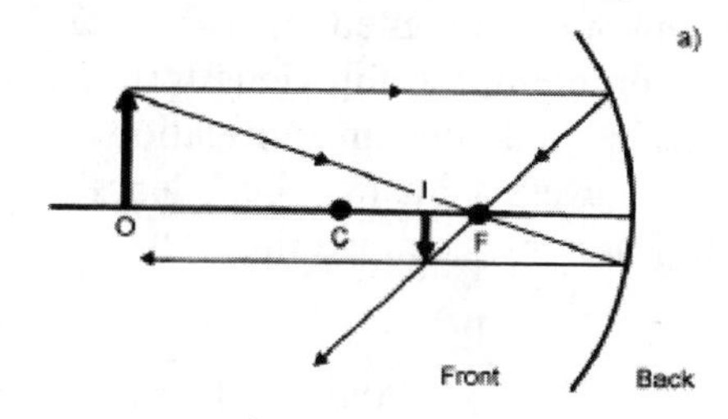

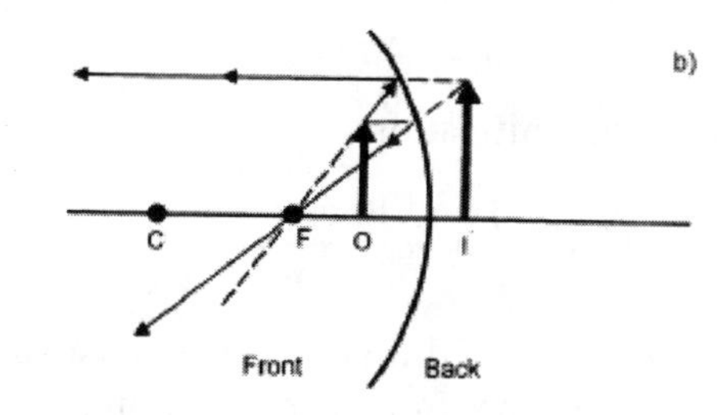

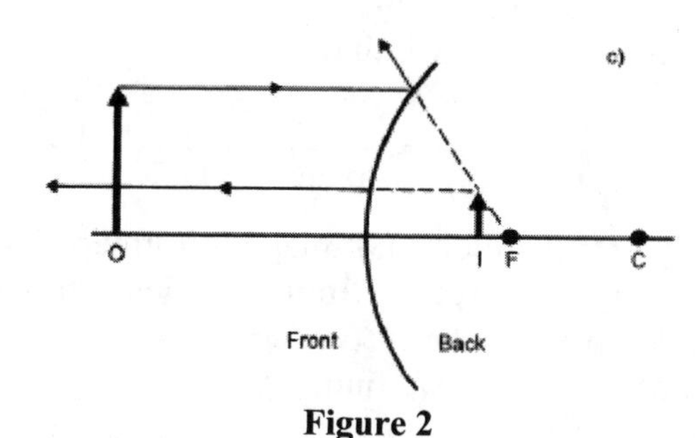

Figure 2

Problem 22.5

(a) We use the law of refraction at the first interface from air to glass, labeling the angles of incidence and refraction θ:

$$\sin\theta_{glass} = \frac{n_{air}}{n_{glass}}\sin\theta_{air} = \frac{1.0}{1.5}\sin 30^0$$

which yields:

$$\theta_{glass} = 19.5^0$$

For the second interface from glass to air, we have to read the law of refraction in the opposite direction, finding θ_{air} = 30^0. This result is expected as the interface and all the parameters of the light ray exactly mirror the conditions at the first interface.

(b) The distance the light ray travels through the glass is obtained geometrically. Figure 3 illustrates the incident beam (which is extended through the glass slab for geometric construction purposes resulting in line AD), the refracted beam (line AC) and the direction across the glass slab perpendicular to the two parallel glass surfaces (line AB, with a given length of 2.0 cm). The distance h we seek is equal to the distance between points A and C. We introduce further the label α for the angle between lines AC and AD, which defines it as $\alpha = \theta_1 - \theta_2$.

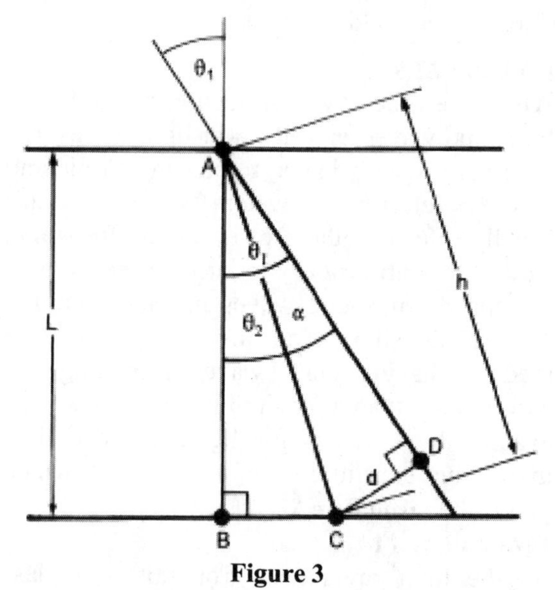

Figure 3

Now we use Figure 3 to quantify the length h based on the triangle ABC:

$$\cos\theta_2 = \frac{AB}{AC} = \frac{2\text{ cm}}{h}$$

which yields:

$$h = \frac{2\text{ cm}}{\cos 19.5^0} = 2.12\text{ cm}$$

This does not answer the question, however, because the lateral shift is sought. The lateral shift d is shown in Figure 3 as well. The length d is obtained from the triangle ACD. With $\alpha = \theta_1 - \theta_2 = 30^0 - 19.5^0 = 10.5^0$ we find:

$$d = h\cdot\sin\alpha = (2.12\text{ cm})\sin 10.5^\circ = 0.39\text{ cm}$$

Problem 22.7

The law of refraction is given in the following form, $n_1 \cdot \sin\theta_1 = n_2 \cdot \sin\theta_2$, where medium 1 will be air and medium 2 will be mineral oil. We can rewrite this for the angle in mineral oil by isolating $\sin\theta_2$. Since the index of refraction for any given medium may be calculated as $n = c/v_{light}$, the ratio of the indices of refraction, n_1/n_2, is equal to the inverse ratio of the speeds of light in each medium, v_2/v_1. The speed of light in mineral oil is given and the speed of light in air is approximately equal to the speed of light in vacuum, c. Now we can calculate $\sin\theta_2$, which yields $\theta_2 = 16.5^0$.

Problem 22.9

We can use the law of refraction in Eq. [22.8] for sound waves as well as for light waves, re–arranging it with index 1 referring to air and index 2 referring to water. While we don't usually refer to indices of refraction for sound waves, the ratio n_1/n_2 is related to the ratio of the speeds of sound waves in each medium. The relationship is an inverse one, with a medium having slow waves refracting the waves more than a medium having fast waves, exactly the same as for light. We can then make the substitution $n_1/n_2 = v_2/v_1$, which yields the result $\theta_2 = 67.4^0$.

Problem 22.11

As the light ray passes from air into glass Snell's law (Eq. [22.6]) applies. We are given the fact that the angle of refraction is one–half the angle of incidence, or the angle of incidence is twice the angle of refraction, which we can write as $\alpha = 2 \cdot \beta$. We then refer to the Math Review on Trigonometry found after Chapter 27, which has the theorem:

$$\sin(\alpha + \beta) = \sin\alpha \cdot \cos\beta + \cos\alpha \cdot \sin\beta$$

If we use this theorem as it applies to our problem and let α and β both be equal, then we can write this theorem as $\sin(2 \cdot \alpha) = 2 \cdot \sin\alpha \cdot \cos\alpha$. We can use this formula, often referred to as a double–angle formula, in Snell's law; we find $\beta = 38.7^0$, and $\alpha = 77.4^0$.

Problem 22.13

(a) The focal length f is positive for a converging lens as stated in Table 22.4. To solve the problem, the thin–lens formula from Eq. [22.12] and the magnification in Eq. [22.11] are used, with the focal length $f = +20.0$ cm. For $p = 40$ cm, we find:

$$\frac{1}{q} = \frac{1}{f} - \frac{1}{p} = \frac{1}{20\ \text{cm}} - \frac{1}{40\ \text{cm}}$$

which yields for the image distance:

$$q = +40\ \text{cm}$$

and for the magnification:

$$M = -\frac{q}{p} = -\frac{40\ \text{cm}}{40\ \text{cm}} = -1.0$$

The image is real and inverted. It is located 40 cm behind the lens. In this case, the image has the same size as the object.

(b) For $p = 20$ cm, we find:

$$\frac{1}{q} = \frac{1}{f} - \frac{1}{p} = \frac{1}{20\ \text{cm}} - \frac{1}{20\ \text{cm}}$$

i.e., $q = \infty$; therefore, no image is formed. The light rays emerging from the lens travel parallel to each other.

(c) For $p = 10$ cm, we find:

$$\frac{1}{q} = \frac{1}{f} - \frac{1}{p} = \frac{1}{20\ \text{cm}} - \frac{1}{10\ \text{cm}}$$

which yields for the image distance:

$$q = -20\ \text{cm}$$

and for the magnification:

$$M = -\frac{q}{p} = -\left(\frac{-20\ \text{cm}}{10\ \text{cm}}\right) = +2.0$$

The image is upright and virtual. It is located 20 cm in front of the lens. The image is twice as large as the object.

Problem 22.15

Complete the drawing using Figure 22.43. Remember that the image created by the lens is then treated as the object for the mirror.

Problem 22.17

This problem requires the combination of thin–lens formula (Eq. [22.12]) and lens maker's equation (Eq. [22.14]) in the form:

$$\frac{1}{f}=(n-1)\left(\frac{1}{R_1}-\frac{1}{R_2}\right) \quad \textbf{(1)}$$

Note that we consider the same medium on both sides of the lens. We isolate the radius R_1 in Eq. [1]:

$$\frac{1}{n-1}\left(\frac{1}{f}+(n-1)\frac{1}{R_2}\right)=\frac{1}{R_1}$$

which yields:

$$R_1=\frac{(n-1)\cdot f\cdot R_2}{(n-1)\cdot f+R_2} \quad \textbf{(2)}$$

Substituting the given values in Eq. [21] yields:

$$R_1=+1.6\text{ cm}=+16\text{ cm}$$

Problem 22.19

(a) We use the thin–lens formula to determine the focal length of the prescription lens. The text identifies the distance to the object as p = 25 cm. The prescription lens must form a virtual image at a distance q = – 100 cm since the image of the prescription lens serves as the object for the eye's lens. We find therefore:

$$\frac{1}{f}=\frac{1}{p}+\frac{1}{q}=\frac{1}{25\text{ cm}}+\frac{1}{-100\text{ cm}}$$

which yields f = 33.3 cm.

(b) The corresponding refractive power is:

$$\mathfrak{R}=\frac{1}{f}=\frac{1}{0.333\text{ m}}=+3.0\text{ dpt}$$

Problem 22.21

(a) The near point at 75.0 cm means that the patient cannot see objects clearly which are closer than that distance from the eye. Reading is therefore a problem, which is likely the reason why the patient came to see an optometrist. The optometrist prescribes corrective glasses such that the patient can clearly see (e.g. read a text) at a distance of 25 cm. Thus, for an object placed at object distance p = + 25.0 cm the prescribed lens must form a virtual image at q = – 75.0 cm at which the patient's eye then can look. We calculate for this situation the focal length of the prescribed lens from the thin–lens formula:

$$\frac{1}{f}=\frac{1}{p}+\frac{1}{q}=\frac{1}{25\text{ cm}}+\frac{1}{-75\text{ cm}} \quad \textbf{(1)}$$

so f = 37.5 cm and $\mathfrak{R}$ = 1/f = 2.67 dpt.

(b) We repeat the calculation of part (a) except that we use p = 26.0 cm for the object distance for the prescription lens. Substituting this value in Eq. [1] we find for the actual focal length f = 39.8 cm and for the actual refractive power $\mathfrak{R}$ = 2.51 dpt. Thus, the error is 0.16 dpt.

Problem 22.23

(a) Two possible paths exist to solve problems with combinations of two (or more) lenses: depending on the way the question is asked we start either with the first or with the last lens. Although this may sound trivial, it is important to keep this in mind when trying to work on problems like the one in this question, since it means that we have to be open to reversing the chosen approach if a solution isn't easily found. In the current problem it is necessary to start with the second lens and work backward. One may anticipate this as the question asks for the position of the object in relation to the position of the first lens. The value of the focal length of the second lens is f_2 = 20.0 cm. The image distance follows with the given values of L and l:

$$q_2=-(L-l)=-\ (50\text{ cm}-31\text{ cm})$$
$$=-19.0\text{ cm}$$

where the negative sign is due to the sign convention in Table 22.4. The term "in front of the lens" in Figure 22.44 is any position to the left of lens 2, as shown. We calculate with these values the object distance relative to lens 2, i.e., the position of the object, which forms the image, I at the position shown. Note that this is not the position of the object O shown in Figure 22.44 since we are still working only with the second lens. The object position p_2 is found with the thin–lens formula, which yields:

$$\frac{1}{p_2}=\frac{1}{f_2}-\frac{1}{q_2}=\frac{1}{20\text{ cm}}-\frac{1}{-19\text{ cm}} \quad \textbf{(1)}$$

from Eq. [1] we find $p_2 = +9.74$ cm. Now we consider the first lens. We can do this next as we now have enough information to determine the object distance p_1 sought in the problem: Besides the focal length of the first lens, given as $f_1 = 10$ cm, we also know the image position for the first lens since it follows from the object distance for the second lens, i.e., $q_1 = L - p_2 = (50 \text{ cm}) - (9.74 \text{ cm}) = 40.26$ cm. Using again the thin–lens formula we find:

$$\frac{1}{p_1} = \frac{1}{f_1} - \frac{1}{q_1} = \frac{1}{10 \text{ cm}} - \frac{1}{40.26 \text{ cm}}$$

which yields $p_1 = +13.3$ cm.

(b) We consider both lenses separately since each may contribute to the overall magnification:

$$M_1 = -\frac{q_1}{p_1} = -\frac{40.26 \text{ cm}}{13.3 \text{ cm}} = -3.03$$

$$M_2 = -\frac{q_2}{p_2} = -\frac{-19 \text{ cm}}{9.74 \text{ cm}} = +1.95$$

The overall magnification is the product of the magnifications of the single lenses, i.e., $M_{total} = M_1 \cdot M_2 = -5.91$. The final image is inverted since M_{total} is negative, it is also virtual, i.e., it is located in front of the last lens.

Problem 22.25

(a) The simplest way to treat this system of two converging lenses is to deal with the lenses one at a time. We will find the location and magnification of the image created by the first lens, and that image will act as the object for the second lens. Relative to the first lens, the object distance is $p = 30$ cm. We use the thin–lens equation in Eq. [22.12], which yields $q_1 = 15$ cm. This real object will be 15 cm behind the first lens, which is 5 cm in front of the second lens (the lenses are 20 cm apart). We can use the thin–lens equation again using the focal length of the second lens and an object distance of 5 cm; this yields $q_2 = -6.67$ cm. This negative image distance means the final image is virtual and is located 6.67 cm in front of the second lens, i.e. between the two lenses.

(b) The total magnification can be calculated by taking the magnification of each lens separately before combining them. The magnification of the first lens is $M_1 = -q_1/p_1 = -0.5$. The magnification of the second lens is $M_2 = -q_2/p_2 = +1.33$. Together there will be a combined magnification which is a product of both magnifications: $M_{combined} = M_1 \cdot M_2 = -667$.

Problem 22.27

Let ϕ represent the angle of the refracted ray, so that the law of refraction is written as:

$$n_1 \sin\theta = n_2 \sin\phi \qquad \textbf{(1)}$$

From the geometry of the problem we have:

$$\beta = \pi - \theta - \phi$$

Thus we find:

$$\begin{aligned} \sin\phi &= \sin(\pi - (\theta + \beta)) = \sin(\theta + \beta) \\ &= \sin\theta\cos\beta + \cos\theta\sin\beta \end{aligned} \qquad \textbf{(2)}$$

Substituting the value from Eq. [2] into Eq. [1] and dividing all terms by $\cos\theta$ we find:

$$n_1 \tan\theta = n_2 \tan\theta\cos\beta + n_2 \sin\beta$$

The result follows from this equation by reorganizing the terms and solving for $\tan\theta$.

Problem 22.29

We use $n_{acrylic} = 1.507$ from Figure 22.46. The same index of refraction must apply, which isn't the case anywhere for fused quartz in Figure 22.46. If there is a solution, we expect it to be at a wavelength that lies below 400 nm.

Problem 22.31

We use the law of refraction for each of the indices of refraction yielding: $\theta_{blue} = 17.6^0$ and $\theta_{red} = 18.0^0$. The difference between these two angles is $\Delta\theta = 0.4^0$.

CHAPTER TWENTY-THREE

The Atomic Nucleus

CONCEPTUAL QUESTIONS

Conceptual Question 23.1

(a) Two nuclides are described as isotopes if they have the same proton number or chemical nature.

(b) The number of neutrons in the nucleus of $^{14}_{6}C$ is 14–6 = 8. The number of protons in the nucleus of $^{14}_{6}C$ is 6.

(c) Another isotope of carbon is $^{12}_{6}C$.

Conceptual Question 23.3

It is measured by its Half-Life. The Half-life is defined at the time during which half of any large amount of identical nuclei decay.

Conceptual Question 23.5

A paramagnetic material in the presence of an external magnetic field is magnetized parallel to the field. In contrast, a diamagnetic material in the presence of an external magnetic field is magnetized anti-parallel to the field. For more details see the discussion in Section 23.6.2.

ANALYTICAL PROBLEMS

Problem 23.1

(a) First, the decay chain from ^{232}Th to ^{208}Pb is part of the *Thorium Series* and it contains a total of six α decays if we only count events with 10% or higher branching ratio. Next, the decay chain from ^{235}U to ^{207}Pb is part of the *Actinium Series* and it contains a total of seven α decays if we only count events with 10% or higher branching ratio. Lastly, the decay chain from ^{238}U to ^{206}Pb is part of the *Radium Series* and it contains a total of eight α decays if we only count events with 10% or higher branching ratio.

(b) In terms of the half-life $T_{1/2}$ the number of radioactive nuclei remaining in a sample after time t will be given by:

$$N(t) = N_0 2^{-\frac{t}{T_{1/2}}} \quad (1)$$

You can verify Eq. [1] using Eq. [23.10] and substituting into Eq. [23.8]. Since the half-life of ^{238}U is 4.47 billion years, after 4.60 billion years, using Eq. [1] we find:

$$N = N_0 2^{-\frac{4.60}{4.47}} = 0.49\,N_0$$

That is, after 4.6 billion years about 49% of the original ^{238}U remains on Earth.

With the half-life of ^{235}U at 0.704 billion years, after 4.60 billion years we find using again Eq. [1]:

$$N = N_0 2^{-\frac{4.60}{0.704}} = 0.011\,N_0$$

Thus, after 4.6 billion years about 1.1% of the original ^{235}U remains on Earth.

Problem 23.3

We calculate the decay constant from the half–life of the plutonium isotope:

$$\lambda = \frac{\ln 2}{T_{1/2}} = \frac{\ln 2}{24000 \text{ yrs}} = 2.89 \times 10^{-5} \text{yrs}^{-1}$$

Note that the value is given in unit 1/yrs. Although it is always advisable to convert to SI units (here 1/s), we will find that it is not necessary for the current problem. Now we apply Eq. [23.8] with $N(t) = 0.1 \cdot N_0$ which corresponds to 10% of the initial amount of radioactive plutonium. This leads to:

$$t = -\frac{\ln(0.1)}{2.89 \times 10^{-5} \text{yrs}^{-1}} = 79700 \text{ yrs}$$

Just waiting isn't good enough when it comes to dealing with nuclear waste!

Problem 23.5

In the conventional 5-day procedure, the residual number of atoms would be:

$$N_r = N_0 e^{-\lambda T_5}$$
$$= N_0 e^{-0.9075}$$

The number of disintegrations is then:

$$N_0 - N_r = N_0\left(1 - e^{-0.9075}\right) \qquad \textbf{(1)}$$

A delay of 1-day leads to a residual number of atoms:

$$\tilde{N}_r = N_0 e^{-\lambda T_1}$$
$$= N_0 e^{-0.1815}$$

The number of disintegrations a time t after the delay is:

$$\tilde{N}_r - \tilde{N}_r e^{-\lambda t} = \tilde{N}_r\left(1 - e^{-\lambda t}\right)$$
$$= N_0 e^{-0.1815}\left(1 - e^{-\lambda t}\right) \qquad \textbf{(2)}$$

Since the treatment must achieve the same number of disintegrations, Eq. [1] must be equal to Eq. [2], so that:

$$\cancel{N_0}\left(1 - e^{-0.9075}\right) = \cancel{N_0} e^{-0.1815}\left(1 - e^{-\lambda t}\right)$$

Solving for the time yields $t = 6.89$ days.

Problem 23.7

The difference between the combined energies of nitrogen and neutron, and that of the α particle is:

$$(2.139 + 3.260 - 5.350)\,\text{MeV} = 0.149\,\text{MeV}$$

Since 1 amu is equivalent to 931 MeV, the decrease in energy found is equivalent to:

$$\Delta m = \frac{\Delta E}{931\,\text{MeV}} = 0.00016\,\text{amu}$$

The mass of the initial particles of Boron and α particle is 15.01667 amu. Therefore, the combined mass of the final particles is (15.01667 – 0.00016) amu = 15.01651 amu. The mass of the neutron is therefore given by (15.01651 – 14.00752) amu = 1.00899 amu.

Problem 23.9

The magnitude of the torque τ is related to the magnitude of the dipole moment μ, the magnitude of the external magnetic field B, and the angle θ between the dipole moment and the external magnetic field according to:

$$\tau = \mu B \sin\theta$$

Therefore, the sine of the angle is:

$$\sin\theta = \frac{\tau}{\mu B}$$

Using the Pythagorean trigonometric identity we find the cosine of the angle, which will be needed to calculate the energy:

$$\cos\theta = \pm\sqrt{1 - \left(\frac{\tau}{\mu B}\right)^2} \qquad \textbf{(1)}$$

The interaction energy torque is given by:

$$E = \mu B \cos\theta \qquad \textbf{(2)}$$

Substituting Eq. [1] into Eq. [2] we obtain:

$$E = \pm\mu B\sqrt{1 - \left(\frac{\tau}{\mu B}\right)^2} \qquad \textbf{(3)}$$

Eq. [3] can be further simplified to:

$$E = \pm\sqrt{(\mu B)^2 - \tau^2} \qquad \textbf{(4)}$$

Substituting the given values into Eq. [4] we obtain the interaction energy:

$$E = \pm 2.58 \times 10^{-4}\,\text{J}$$

Problem 23.11

(a) The energy Q is given by:

$$\begin{aligned} Q &= \Delta E_{parent} - \Delta E_{daughter} - \Delta E_{\alpha} \\ &= \Delta E_{\text{Pu}} - \Delta E_{\text{U}} - \Delta E_{\alpha} \\ &= (48.6 - 40.93 - 2.4248)\,\text{MeV} \\ &= 5.2452\,\text{MeV} \end{aligned}$$

(b) Using conservation of energy and conservation of momentum we find the energy of the α particle:

$$\begin{aligned} E_{\alpha} &= \frac{M_{\text{U}}Q}{M_{\text{U}} + m_{\alpha}} \\ &= \left(\frac{235 \times 5.2452}{235 + 4}\right)\text{MeV} \\ &= 5.157\,\text{MeV} \end{aligned}$$

Energy conservation can be used to find the energy of the daughter nucleus:

$$\begin{aligned} E_{\text{U}} &= Q - E_{\alpha} \\ &= (5.2452 - 5.157)\,\text{MeV} \\ &= 0.088\,\text{MeV} \end{aligned}$$

(c) We use the energy of the α particle to find its speed:

$$E_{\alpha} = \frac{1}{2}m_{\alpha}v^2 \Rightarrow v = \sqrt{\frac{2E_{\alpha}}{m_{\alpha}}}$$

After converting the energy into joules and the mass of the α particle into kilograms we find:

$$v = 1.58 \times 10^7\ \text{m/s}$$

Problem 23.13

(a) The activity A after 20 days is known to be $0.4\ A_0$, where A_0 is the initial activity. The decay constant λ can be determined through:

$$A = A_0 e^{-\lambda t} \Rightarrow \lambda = -\frac{1}{t}\ln\left(\frac{A}{A_0}\right)$$

Substituting the given values:

$$\lambda = -\frac{1}{20\,\text{days}}\ln(0.4) = 0.0458\,\text{days}^{-1}$$

(b) The half-life is defined by the equation:

$$\frac{A}{A_0} = \frac{1}{2} \Rightarrow \frac{1}{2} = e^{-\lambda T_{1/2}}$$

Solving for the half-life and using the value for the decay constant from the previous part:

$$T_{1/2} = \frac{\ln 2}{\lambda} = 15.31\,\text{days}$$

(c) The mean life is the inverse of the decay constant so that:

$$\tau = \frac{1}{\lambda} = 21.83\,\text{days}$$

Problem 23.15

(a) The Q energy in the reaction that removes one neutron is:

$$Q = \Delta E_{parent} - \Delta E_{daughter} - \Delta E_n$$
$$= \Delta E_{^{56}\text{Fe}} - \Delta E_{^{55}\text{Fe}} - \Delta E_n$$
$$= \left[-60.602 - (-57.474) - 8.0714\right]\text{MeV}$$
$$= -11.2\,\text{MeV}$$

The result is negative, which means one has to provide energy for this reaction to take place.

(b) The Q energy in the reaction that removes one proton is:

$$Q = \Delta E_{parent} - \Delta E_{daughter} - \Delta E_p$$
$$= \Delta E_{^{56}\text{Fe}} - \Delta E_{^{55}\text{Mn}} - \Delta E_p$$
$$= \left[-60.602 - (-57.705) - 7.289\right]\text{MeV}$$
$$= -10.2\,\text{MeV}$$

Again, this nuclear reaction requires energy to take place.**(c)** In order to calculate the energy necessary to break down the atom of ^{56}Fe into its fundamental constituents, we need to calculate the binding energy. The mass of all the individual elements is:

$$m = 26m_{p^+} + 30m_{n^0} + 26m_{e^-}$$
$$= 56.4651\,\text{amu}$$

From the data given the mass of ^{56}Fe is:

$$M = 55.9349\,\text{amu}$$

Therefore, the binding energy is:

$$B = m - M$$
$$= (56.4651 - 55.9349)\,\text{amu}$$
$$= 0.5302\,\text{amu}$$
$$= 494\,\text{MeV}$$

In conclusion, 494 MeV are needed to break down ^{56}Fe into its fundamental elements.

(d) For 28Al we have:

$$\Delta E_{^{28}_{13}\text{Al}} = M - A = (27.98190 - 28)\,\text{amu}$$
$$= -0.01809\,\text{amu}$$
$$= -16.815\,\text{MeV}$$

The Q energy in the fission reaction is then:

$$Q = \Delta E_{parent} - \Delta E_{daughters}$$
$$= \Delta E_{^{56}_{26}\text{Fe}} - 2\Delta E_{^{28}_{13}\text{Al}}$$
$$= -26.9\,\text{MeV}$$

CHAPTER TWENTY-FOUR

X-Rays

CONCEPTUAL QUESTIONS

Conceptual Question 24.1

Although both processes describe the scattering of photons by the electrons in an atom, they differ mainly in that during a Rayleigh scattering event the incident photon is re-emitted by the entire interacting atom with a small change in direction but no change in its energy or wavelength. In contrast, during a Compton scattering event the incident photon interacts with a valence electron in the interacting atom ejecting the electron from the atom. The incident photon changes its direction, has its energy reduced and its wavelength increased.

Conceptual Question 24.3

In the photoelectric effect, the entire energy of the incident X-ray is transferred to an electron, which is ejected from the atom. In the Compton scattering process, a photon collides with an electron and exchanges momentum and energy (the photon can have energies in the X-ray range as described in the textbook). The photon in a Compton scattering process is not completely absorbed but is deflected with a loss in energy and an increase in its wavelength.

Conceptual Question 24.5

Contrast in X-ray images is discussed in Section 24.4. The difference in compositions, density, and thickness of a tissue sample cause different yields for the incident radiation. The difference in yields generates different exposures that will then be registered lighter or darker parts on an image. The difference between these dark and bright parts is the contrast. Quantitatively, we measure contrast as a function of yield or the number of photons transmitted using Eq. [24.14].

ANALYTICAL PROBLEMS

Problem 24.1

Figure 24.7 identifies the K_α transition as a transition of an electron from the orbital with $n = 2$ to a vacancy in the orbital with $n = 1$. From the periodic system, we find $Z = 79$ for gold. In the final state after the transition, one electron screens the interaction of the electron in the K shell and the nucleus since when full, the innermost shell is occupied by two electrons. The electron/nucleus interaction before the transition is also screened by one electron for the electron undergoing the transition from the L shell. That screening electron is the single electron in the K shell since the other electron in that shell has been kicked out to allow the X–ray causing transition. Using the equation from Example 24.3, we find for the initial and final state of the transition electron:

$$\begin{aligned} E_L &= (Z-1)^2 E_2 = 78^2 \frac{(-13.6\ \text{eV})}{2^2} \\ &= -20.69\ \text{keV} \\ E_K &= (Z-1)^2 E_1 = 78^2(-13.6\ \text{eV}) \\ &= -82.74\ \text{keV} \end{aligned} \qquad \textbf{(23)}$$

in which $E_1 = -13.6$ eV and $E_2 = E_1/4$ (see Chapter 20). For the transition we find $\Delta E = E_{final} - E_{initial} = -62.05$ keV, which is a negative energy because that energy is lost by the system in form of an X–ray photon. Note that the minimum energy needed to kick the initial K shell electron out of the atom is 82.74 keV, thus, an acceleration voltage of at least 82.74 kV is required. In the actual experiment a higher voltage must be used to obtain an appreciable number of X–rays because the beam electrons slow in the material of the anode.

Problem 24.3

(a) The probability for photoelectric effect absorption is inversely proportional to the cube (third power) of the photon energy. Therefore the ratio of initial to final probabilities is:

$$\frac{\mathcal{P}_i}{\mathcal{P}_f} = \frac{E^3{}_f}{E^3{}_i}$$

Solving for the final energy we obtain:

$$E_f = E_i \sqrt[3]{\frac{\mathcal{P}_i}{\mathcal{P}_f}} = E_i \sqrt[3]{\frac{\mathcal{P}_i}{10 \cdot \mathcal{P}_i}}$$
$$= \frac{E_i}{\sqrt[3]{10}}$$

That is, the energy should be reduced by a factor of approximately 2.2 or a bit more than half the original energy.

(b) Up to energies in the range of 50 keV the probability of Compton scattering is approximately proportional to the photon energy, as illustrated in Figure 24.9. This means that a reduction in the energy by a factor of 2.2 will result in a reduction of the probability by the same factor. That is, the probability will be approximately halved.

Problem 24.5

(a) We use Beer's Law with N_0 the incident number of photons so that the fraction passing through a distance x is:

$$f(x) = \frac{N(x)}{N_0} \qquad \textbf{(1)}$$
$$= e^{-\mu x}$$

For the given linear attenuation coefficient and a thickness of 20 cm we find:

$$f = e^{-\left(0.21\,\text{cm}^{-1}\right)\left(20\,\text{cm}\right)} = 0.015$$

That is, about 1.5% of incident photons are transmitted through the body.

(b) We use Eq. [1] for bone and tissue of thickness 2 cm to find the transmitted fraction:

$$f_{\text{soft}} = e^{-\left(0.21\,\text{cm}^{-1}\right)\left(2\,\text{cm}\right)} = 0.66$$
$$f_{\text{bone}} = e^{-\left(0.57\,\text{cm}^{-1}\right)\left(2\,\text{cm}\right)} = 0.32$$

Therefore, while the soft tissue stops only 34% of incident photons, the bone stops 68% of incident photons.

Problem 24.7

(a) We use Eq. [24.13] to find the *HVL*:

$$HVL = \frac{\ln 2}{\mu} = 19.8\,\text{mm}$$

(b) We reorganize Eq. [24.13] to write the linear attenuation coefficient in terms of the *HVL* as:

$$\mu = \frac{\ln 2}{HVL} = 0.28\,\text{cm}^{-1}$$

where we have substituted the given value for the *HVL* in this part.

Problem 24.9

(a) The mechanisms by which ionizing radiation causes damage to cells of living matter are collision and charge-interaction. Both these mechanisms cause atoms in the cells to become ionized, thereby changing their chemical composition by removal of electrons from the atoms.

(b) The probable effects on a damaged cell is inhibition of cell division, abnormal cell division, changes to chromosomes as well as changes to proteins, and other molecules in the tissue cells.

(c i) The extent of cell damage depends on the type of radiation because of the different mechanisms of ionization driven by the type of radiation. For example, α-particles cause greater damage than γ-rays since α-particles cause ionization not only by collision with living cells, but also through charge interaction. γ-rays, on the other hand, are electromagnetic waves, cause ionization by collision only.

(c ii) The greater the total dose of radiation, the greater the probability of biological damage to the cells since more of the energetic photons or energetic charged particles are interacting with the atoms of the living cells resulting in more ionization.

(c iii) The greater the dose of radiation, the greater the probability of damage to living cells since the number of ionizing particles or photons per unit time allowed to interact with the atoms of living cells increases and leads to more ionization.

Problem 24.11

(a) An illustration of the spectrum should be qualitatively like Figure 24.3.

(b) The graph contains the broad Bremsstralung peak spectrum as well as the shortest wavelength λ_c found for the energy to the far right of the spectrum and with wavelength given by:

$$\lambda_c = \frac{hc}{E(\text{eV})} = \frac{1.24\times10^{-6}}{7\times10^{4}}\,\text{m}$$
$$= 1.77\times10^{-11}\,\text{m}$$

The wavelength corresponding to K_α can be calculated using Moseley's law and will correspond to the first sharp peak in the energy:

$$\frac{1}{\lambda_{K_\alpha}} = \frac{3}{4}R_H(Z-1)^2 = 4.35\times10^{9}\,\text{m}^{-1}$$

Therefore the wavelength is:

$$\lambda_{K_\alpha} = 2.3\times10^{-10}\,\text{m}$$

The wavelength corresponding to K_β can be calculated using Moseley's law once again and will be the second sharp peak in the energy.

$$\frac{1}{\lambda_{K_\beta}} = \frac{8}{3}R_H(Z-1)^2 = 1.55\times10^{10}\,\text{m}^{-1}$$

Therefore the wavelength is:

$$\lambda_{K_\beta} = 6.5\times10^{-11}\,\text{m}$$

Problem 24.13

(a) Since 1 rad corresponds to 5×10^{11} inactivating events per cubic centimeter treated, 10 millirads correspond 10×10^{-2} rad, which should lead to 5×10^{9} inactivating events per cubic centimeter.

(b) In a 1 cm^3 volume, there will be 10^{11} cells. A 10 millirad dose will inactivate 5×10^{9} cells, and therefore 5% of the tissue will be treated.

CHAPTER TWENTY-FIVE

Diagnostic Nuclear Medicine

CONCEPTUAL QUESTIONS

Conceptual Question 25.1

Nuclear medicine uses radioactive isotopes to diagnose and treat disease. In diagnostic imaging used in nuclear medicine the radiopharmaceuticals are administered into the patient's body. As the radiopharmaceuticals bond with different organs and tissues the radiation produced internally is detected and analyzed to create the images. This is different from other forms of imaging techniques that employ external radiation that passes through the body and the image is formed based on the various absorption properties of various types of tissue. The ability to create compounds that bond to very specific forms of tissue or organs allows this technique to produce images that focus on the points of interest to be imaged. In contrast, other types of imaging focus on a body region without specificity on the organs and tissue of interest. Another advantage of these techniques is that they allow for the imaging of metabolic processes as the radiopharmaceuticals pass through the organs and tissues of interest. A disadvantage of these techniques is the potential for exposure to radiation levels. Another disadvantage is the decreased resolution of the images when compared with other imaging techniques. This is particularly true in regards to the ability of the technique to be anatomically precise.

Conceptual Question 25.3

The Mo-99/Tc-99m generator is a portable and compact device that enables hospitals to have radioisotopes of appropriately short half-life for the use in nuclear imaging. It can be used a repeated number of times for production of the useful isotope Tc-99m from a source isotope of Mo-99 via a process known as milking. A further advantage is that the generator uses a fission by-product from already existing nuclear reactors.

Conceptual Question 25.5

The collimator section of Figure 25.3 is made out of parallel holes inside a heavy metal. These parallel holes will allow for the passage of gamma radiation parallel to the orientation of the holes. The metal will absorb any photons traveling in a different direction and at slanted angles. After the collimator, only parallel rays will be making it to the detector, reducing the blur and increasing the resolution and sharpness of the image.

Conceptual Question 25.7

A SPECT system uses a rotating detector designed to collect data incoming from different directions. This is done in order to produce a three-dimensional picture of the organ or tissue that is the source of the radiation. As the detector rotates, it will collect data at various set angles through a full rotation. By adding multiple cameras to the rotating device as illustrated in Figure 25.5 the collection of data at each angle is performed faster, allowing for reduced times in the image acquisition process.

Conceptual Question 25.9

Recall that each registered event in a PET detector has another event that was simultaneously generated but would be received in a detector in the opposite side of the array. This is illustrated in Figure 25.7. By determining when two events from opposite detectors originate from the same emission event we are able to trace the line that pinpoints the location of the annihilation event. Thus, the need for a collimator is avoided by the inherent collimation existing in the emission process with two simultaneous events. In other words, by establishing the line that joins the two detectors for the two events generated by the same annihilation occurrence, information on the location of the radiation is gained without the need for a collimator.

ANALYTICAL PROBLEMS

Problem 25.1

We start with Eq. [25.3] for the activity as a function of time:

$$A(t) = A_0 e^{-\lambda \cdot t}, \quad (1)$$

where A_0 is the initial activity, and λ is the decay constant. The half-life $t_{1/2}$ being defined as the time required for the activity to drop down to half of its initial value is such that:

$$A(t_{1/2}) = \frac{A_0}{2} \quad (2)$$

Substituting Eq. [2] into Eq. [1] gives:

$$\frac{\cancel{A_0}}{2} = \cancel{A_0} e^{-\lambda \cdot t_{1/2}} \quad (3)$$

Taking the natural logarithm on both sides of Eq. [3] yields:

$$\ln(1/2) = -\ln 2 = -\lambda \cdot t_{1/2} \quad (4)$$

Cancelling the signs in Eq. [4] is the last step that produces the required relationship.

Problem 25.3

Eq. [25.6] gives the time for maximum activity:

$$t_m = \frac{\ln(\lambda_B/\lambda_A)}{(\lambda_B - \lambda_A)}, \quad (1)$$

where λ_A and λ_B are the decay constants for the parent and daughter isotopes respectively. In our case, the parent is Mo-99 while the daughter is Tc-99m. Although the decay constants are not given, we can calculate them by using the result from Problem 25.1 for the relationship between the half-life and the decay constant:

$$\lambda = \frac{\ln 2}{t_{1/2}} \quad (2)$$

Given the values of $t_A = 66.7$ h for the half-life of Mo-99, and of $t_B = 6.02$ h for the half-life of Tc-99m, we can use Eq. [2] to find their respective decay constants:

$$\lambda_A = 1.04 \times 10^{-2}\ \mathrm{h^{-1}}$$
$$\lambda_B = 11.5 \times 10^{-2}\ \mathrm{h^{-1}} \quad (3)$$

Using the values from Eq. [3] into Eq. [1] we obtain:

$$t_m = \frac{\ln(11.5/1.04)}{(11.5 \times 10^{-2}\ \mathrm{h^{-1}} - 1.04 \times 10^{-2}\ \mathrm{h^{-1}})} = 23\,\mathrm{h}$$

Problem 25.5

Let the parent isotope Te-131 be the A isotope, and the daughter isotope I-131 be the B isotope.

(a) To find the time for maximum activity t_m for the daughter isotope of I-131 we need to find first the decay rates λ_A and λ_B. To do this we use the derived equation in Problem 25.1:

$$\lambda = \frac{\ln 2}{t_{1/2}} \quad (1)$$

Substituting the given half-lives from the problem in Eq. [1] we obtain:

$$\lambda_A = 6.42 \times 10^{-6}\ \mathrm{s} \quad (2)$$

and

$$\lambda_B = 1.00 \times 10^{-6}\ \mathrm{s}$$

Now, using Eq. [25.6] for t_m with the values form Eq. [2] we find:

$$t_m = \frac{\ln(\lambda_B/\lambda_A)}{(\lambda_B - \lambda_A)} = 3.97\,\mathrm{days} \quad (3)$$

(b) From Problem 25.2 we know that at t_m the activities are equal, that is:

$$A_B(t_m) = A_A(t_m) \quad \textbf{(4)}$$

Using Eq. [25.3] for isotope A with a starting activity A_0 = 1.85 × 10^5 Bq, t_m from Eq. [3], and λ_A from Eq. [2] we obtain:

$$A_A(t_m) = A_0\, e^{-\lambda_A \cdot t_m}$$
$$= 2.05 \times 10^7 \text{ Bq} \quad \textbf{(5)}$$

Given Eq. [4] we thus also know that:

$$A_B(t_m) = A_A(t_m)$$
$$= 2.05 \times 10^7 \text{ Bq} \quad \textbf{(6)}$$

(c) Since the number of atoms N is related to the activity according to:

$$A = \lambda \cdot N, \quad \textbf{(3)}$$

using Eq. [6] and Eq. [2] we obtain for Te-131:

$$N_A = \frac{A_A(t_m)}{\lambda_A}$$
$$= 3.2 \times 10^{12},$$

and for I-131:

$$N_B = \frac{A_B(t_m)}{\lambda_B} = 2.0 \times 10^{13}$$

Problem 25.7

(a) From the discussion following Eq. [25.11], the saturation activity A_{sat} is given by:

$$A_{\text{sat}} = I \cdot n \cdot \sigma$$
$$= 1.50 \times 10^9 \text{ Bq}, \quad \textbf{(1)}$$

where the proton current I, the radiological thickness n, and the cross-section σ are given by the problem.

(b) Using Eq. [25.11], the activity as a function of time is given by:

$$A(t) = A_{\text{sat}}\left(1 - e^{-\lambda t}\right) \quad \textbf{(2)}$$

In order to use Eq. [2] and Eq. [1] to find the activity after 6 h, we need the decay constant. This can be found using Problem 25.1:

$$\lambda = \frac{\ln 2}{t_{1/2}}$$
$$= 0.347 \text{ h}^{-1} \quad \textbf{(3)}$$

Combining Eq. [3] and Eq. [1] into Eq. [2] for a time of 6 h, we find:

$$A(t_{6\text{h}}) = 1.31 \times 10^9 \text{ Bq} \quad \textbf{(4)}$$

(c) The number of F-18 atoms created at time t can be computed using Eq. [25.10] since the denominator is precisely the activity at that time. Thus, using Eq. [4] and Eq. [3] we find that the number of atoms of F-18 is:

$$N_{\text{F-18}} = \frac{A(t_{6\text{h}})}{\lambda}$$
$$= 1.36 \times 10^{13} \quad \textbf{(5)}$$

Since we started with 1 g of O-18 with molecular weight 18 g/mol we have 1/18 mol, so the initial number of atoms of O-18 is:

$$N = \frac{1}{18}\text{mol} \times N_A$$
$$= 3.35 \times 10^{22} \quad \textbf{(6)}$$

The number of O-18 atoms remaining will be the difference between Eq. [6] and Eq. [5], and the required ratio is:

$$\frac{N_{\text{F-18}}}{N - N_{\text{F-18}}} \cong 4.1 \times 10^{-10}$$

Therefore, there are about 2.5 billion atoms of O-18 for each atom of F-18 after 6 h of irradiation.

Problem 25.9

The information given in the problem is precisely the activity. The number of decays per second will be the value in standard units of s^{-1} or Bq. We just need to carry out the conversion of 32 million per day into the total per second:

$$A = 32 \times 10^6 \text{ day}^{-1}$$

$$= \frac{32 \times 10^6}{24 \times 60 \times 60} \text{s}^{-1}$$

Therefore, the activity is about 370 Bq.

CHAPTER TWENTY-SIX

Radiation Therapy

CONCEPTUAL QUESTIONS

Conceptual Question 26.1

Since the exponential function in Eq. [26.1] is negative the surviving fraction will be dominated by the smaller term in linear-quadratic argument. This means that at low doses, where the linear term is large compared to the quadratic term, it is the quadratic term that dominates the value of S. Conversely, at high doses, where the quadratic term will be much larger than the linear term, it is the linear term that dominates the value of S. The exact values at which this occurs will be dependent on the tissue-specific constants α and β.

Conceptual Question 26.3

From the definition in Eq. [26.3] the PDD depends on the ratio of $D(d)$ to D_{max}. Since $D(d)$ is always less than or equal to D_{max} this ratio is less than or equal to unity and thus the PDD cannot exceed 100%.

Conceptual Question 26.5

Yes, as a matter of fact the BSF will always be greater than unity as the TAR is increasing from unity at the surface and approaching a maximum value near the depth of maximum dose.

Conceptual Question 26.7

If for instance the tumour is closer than the machine's isocentre the radiation will be delivered in an annular or ring-shaped region surrounding the tumour. This will affect normal tissue while leaving unaffected the malignant tissue. A similar problem will be encountered if the tumour is farther than the machine's isocentre. Furthermore, in both situations the very sensitive skin tissue will have a high probability of being located close to the depth where the maximum dose is deposited.

Conceptual Question 26.9

By asymmetrically weighing multiple beams it is possible to better target the location of the tumour while at the same time reducing the dose to healthy tissue. This asymmetrical weighing will then shift the dose distribution towards the desired location for treatment.

ANALYTICAL PROBLEMS

Problem 26.1

The instantaneous fractional loss of cells with respect to dose is the derivative of S with respect to D:

$$\frac{dS}{dD} = -\left(\alpha + 2\beta D\right) \cdot e^{-\left(\alpha D + \beta D^2\right)} \qquad (1)$$

The negative sign in Eq. [1] highlights the fact that this expression represents a *loss* of cells. Given that the exponential term is dimensionless, the quantity in Eq. [1] will have the units of α which are the same as the units of βD. Therefore, dS/dD has units of Gy^{-1}, which in standard SI units obeys:

$$1\,\text{Gy}^{-1} = 1\,{}^{\text{J}}\!/_{\text{kg}}$$

Problem 26.3

From the source to the collimator we have a triangle with a base of 1 cm at the source, apex at the collimator, and a height of 30 cm. This triangle must be similar to the triangle from the collimator to the penumbra. This second triangle has a base equal to the diameter of the penumbra, apex at the collimator, and a height of 70 cm. The similarity of these two triangles from the equal angle at the collimator implies:

$$\frac{d_p}{h_p} = \frac{d_s}{h_s} \qquad (1)$$

where the sub-index p represents quantities for the penumbra, while the sub-index s represents quantities for the source, and d and h are the diameter and heights, respectively. Solving for d_p in Eq. [1] with the values given we obtain:

$$d_p = d_s\left(\frac{h_p}{h_s}\right) = (1\,\text{cm})\left(\frac{70\,\text{cm}}{30\,\text{cm}}\right)$$
$$= 2.3\,\text{cm}$$

Problem 26.5

Following Example 26.2 for a given PDD the value of D_{max} is:

$$D_{\text{max}} = [10\,\text{Gy}/\text{PDD}]\times 100\% \quad \textbf{(1)}$$

We use Eq. [1] to find D_{max} for each of the given PDDs:

$$D_1 = [10\,\text{Gy}/67.0\%]\times 100\% = 14.93\,\text{Gy}$$
$$D_2 = [10\,\text{Gy}/67.9\%]\times 100\% = 14.73\,\text{Gy}$$
$$D_3 = [10\,\text{Gy}/51.6\%]\times 100\% = 19.38\,\text{Gy}$$
$$D_4 = [10\,\text{Gy}/52.5\%]\times 100\% = 19.05\,\text{Gy}$$

If we assume linearity in the field size, from D_1 and D_2 we find D_{max} for an 11 × 11 cm field at a depth of 10 cm:

$$D_{11}(10\,\text{cm}) = 14.83\,\text{Gy} \quad \textbf{(2)}$$

Also, assuming linearity in the field size, from D_3 and D_4 we find D_{max} for an 11 × 11 cm field at a depth of 15 cm:

$$D_{11}(15\,\text{cm}) = 19.22\,\text{Gy} \quad \textbf{(3)}$$

Now we assume linearity in the depth between the results of Eq. [2] and Eq. [3] to find D_{max} for an 11 × 11 cm field at a depth of 12 cm:

$$D_{\text{max}} = 16.59\,\text{Gy}$$

This last result represents the maximum dose received at any location within the patient's anatomy when 10 Gy is to be delivered to a tumour at a depth of 12 cm with a 6 MeV beam in an 11 × 11 cm field.

Problem 26.7

We want to deliver a dose 3 Gy at a depth of 0.5 cm. Since for a typical Co-60 unit at this depth the maximum dose D_{max} is achieved, the TAR is precisely the BSF. We use Eq. [26.4] with BSF instead of TAR to find the dose that would be required in air:

$$D_{\text{air}} = D(d)/\text{TAR} = 3\,\text{Gy}/1.015$$
$$= 2.956\,\text{Gy}$$

Given that the machine output in air at isocentre is 1.5 Gy/min, the treatment time is:

$$t_{\text{treat}} = \frac{D_{\text{air}}}{1.5\,\text{Gy}/\text{min}} = 1.97\,\text{min}$$
$$= 118\,\text{s}$$

CHAPTER TWENTY-SEVEN

Nuclear Magnetic Resonance

CONCEPTUAL QUESTIONS

Conceptual Question 27.1

(a) NMR relies on the resonant absorption at high-frequencies between an applied external magnetic field and the difference in the energies of the two-state system represented by the nuclear spins. Without the presence of these spins there will be no effective absorption.

(b) The active nuclei used in NMR must have a non-zero spin to interact with the external magnetic field. Nuclei with even number of protons and even number of neutrons have zero spin and thus are not useful for NMR. Nuclei with odd number of neutrons and odd number of protons have integer spins and can be used in NMR. All other nuclei with odd atomic masses have half-integer spins that can also be used in an NMR.

Conceptual Question 27.3

The frequency shift with respect to the isocentre gives the RF pulse used by the student. We have:

$$\Delta f = f - f_0 = \gamma G_z z$$

Therefore:

$$f = f_0 + \gamma G_z z$$

Substituting the given values:

$$\begin{aligned} f &= 63.85 + 42.58 \times 0.0003 \times (-6.5) \\ &= 63.85 - 0.083 = 63.77\,\text{MHz} \end{aligned}$$

Conceptual Question 27.5

The time constant T_2 is a measure of the spin-spin dephasing that occurs as neighbouring spins interact with each other and out of phase with the external field as their precession frequencies differ from the Larmor frequency. This process assumes an external a homogeneous magnetic field which in practice does not exist. The inhomogeneities present in a real magnet will generate an accelerated dephasing with time constant $T_2{}^* < T_2$.

Conceptual Question 27.7

Section 27.5 discusses the use of gradients. A gradient introduces a magnetic field that is not uniform across the sample, that is, a field with components that vary as a function of one of the coordinate components. This gradient causes different magnetic fields at different positions and thus different Larmor frequencies. The frequency variation can be used to pinpoint the location.

ANALYTICAL PROBLEMS

Problem 27.1

(a) We look at Section 27.4.1 and Section 27.4.2 along with Table 27.2. For a T_1-weighted image shorter T_1 yields brighter images and thus white matter is brighter than gray matter. However, for a T_2-weighted image shorter T_2 yields darker images and thus white matter is darker than gray matter. From Section 27.4.3 the smaller proton density will yield a darker image and thus the white matter will be darker than the gray matter in a spin density-weighed image.

(b) The weighing should be a T_1 since it is not true that $TR >> T_1$ as it would be required for a T_2 weighing and a spin density-weighing. Furthermore, $TE << T_2$ which is required for T_1 weighing. The contrast is then the ratio of the magnetizations:

$$\Delta = \frac{\left[\frac{N}{V}\left(1 - e^{-TR/T_1}\right)\right]_{\text{white}}}{\left[\frac{N}{V}\left(1 - e^{-TR/T_1}\right)\right]_{\text{gray}}} \qquad \textbf{(1)}$$

Substituting in Eq. [1] the values from Table 27.2 and the TE and TR provided in the problem we find a contrast:

$$\Delta = \frac{0.452}{0.438} = 1.0311$$

(c) In this case, the weighing should be a T_2 since it is not true that $TE << T_2$ as it would be required for a T_1 weighing and a spin density-weighing. Furthermore, $TR >> T_1$ which is required for T_2 weighing. The contrast is once more the ratio of the magnetizations:

$$\Delta = \frac{\left[\frac{N}{v}\left(e^{-TE/T_2}\right)\right]_{\text{gray}}}{\left[\frac{N}{v}\left(e^{-TE/T_2}\right)\right]_{\text{white}}} \qquad \textbf{(2)}$$

Substituting in Eq. [2] the values from Table 27.2 and the *TE* and *TR* provided in the problem we find a contrast:

$$\Delta = \frac{0.366}{0.313} = 1.1702$$

Problem 27.3

The z-component of magnetization at any time t is given by:

$$M_z(t) = M_0\left(1 - e^{-t/T_1}\right)$$

where M_0 is the equilibrium magnetization. At time T the magnetization would have recovered 95% of its equilibrium value:

$$0.95 = \frac{M_z(T)}{M_0} = 1 - e^{-T/T_1}$$

Solving for T we find:

$$1 - 0.95 = 0.05 = e^{-T/T_1}$$

Therefore:

$$T = -T_1 \ln 0.05 = 6.0\,\text{s}$$

Problem 27.5

The amplitude of the RF pulse is given by:

$$B_1 = \frac{\theta}{\gamma t_p} = \frac{\theta}{100} \qquad \textbf{(1)}$$

Furthermore, from the given ratio we find that at $t = 0^+$:

$$\frac{M_{xy}(0^+)}{M_z(0^+)} = 0.8 = \tan\theta$$

We can now solve for the angle and substitute it back into Eq. [1]:

$$B_1 = \frac{\arctan 0.8}{100} = 6.75\,\text{mT}$$

Problem 27.7

The direction of the magnetization is given by:

$$\theta = \gamma B_1 \tau \qquad \textbf{(1)}$$

where τ is the pulse duration, B_1 is the amplitude of the RF field, and γ is the gyromagnetic ratio. Since for protons:

$$\gamma = 2\pi \cdot 42.58\,\text{MHz}/\text{T}$$

we can substitute the remaining given values into Eq. [1] and find:

$$\theta = 2.51\,\text{rad}$$

Problem 27.9

(a) The signal amplitude is fixed by the transverse component:

$$M_z = M_0 \cos(\pi/3) = (1/2) M_0$$
$$M_{xy} = M_0 \sin(\pi/3) = \left(\sqrt{3}/2\right) M_0$$

Prior to θ_2:

$$M_z(TR_<) = M_z(0) e^{-1/5} + M_0\left(1 - e^{-1/5}\right) = 0.591\, M_0$$
$$M_{xy} = 0$$

After θ_2:

$$M_z = M_z(TR_<) \cos(\pi/3) = 0.295\, M_0$$
$$M_{xy} = M_z(TR_<) \sin(\pi/3) = 0.512\, M_0$$

(b) For the second signal to have zero amplitude we need $M_Z(TR_<) = 0$ so that:

$$M_z(TR_<) = M_0 \cos\theta_1 e^{-TR/T_1} + M_0\left(1 - e^{-TR/T_1}\right) = 0$$

Reorganizing and solving for the angle:

$$\cos\theta_1 = -\left(1 - e^{-TR/T_1}\right) e^{TR/T1}$$

And thus $\theta_1 = 102.8°$.

(c) We now require $M_{xy}(0_>) = M_{xy}(TR_>)$. For $\theta_1 = 25°$, we calculate $M_{xy}(0_>) = 0.423\ M_0$. Consequently:

$$M_z(TR_<) = M_0 \cos 25^\circ e^{-1/5} + M_0\left(1 - e^{-1/5}\right) = 0.923\, M_0$$

and since:

$$M_{xy}(TR_>) = M_z(TR_<) \sin\theta_2 = M_{xy}(0_>)$$

we can solve for the angle $\theta_2 = 27.3°$.

(d) If one ignores the T_1 effects, then $M_{xy}(0_>) = \sin\theta_1$ and $M_{xy}(TR_>) = \cos\theta_1 \sin\theta_2$. The object is to equate these amplitudes and optimize them. One solution is (θ_1=45°, θ_2=90°).

Problem 27.11

(a) The ratio of anti-parallel to parallel spins at temperature T is n_d/n_u given by:

$$\frac{n_d}{n_u} = \exp\left(-\frac{h\gamma B}{k_B T}\right)$$

(b) and **(c)** Using the values for room temperature T in Kelvin, k_B as Boltzman's constant, h as Planck's constant, and the respective gyromagnetic ratios γ, we fill the following table:

Magnetic Field	Ratio for Protons	Ratio for C^{13}
7.0 T	0.99995	0.99999
3.0 T	0.99998	0.999995
1.5 T	0.99999	0.999997

Problem 27.13

The frequency offset from the isocentre is:

$$\Delta f = \gamma G_y y$$

Solving for y:

$$y = \frac{\Delta f}{\gamma G_y} \quad \textbf{(1)}$$

We substitute into Eq. [1] the given frequencies and the frequency-encoding gradient after converting it from Gauss to Tesla to obtain the locations:

$$y_1 = 0.117\,\text{cm}$$
$$y_2 = 0.059\,\text{cm}$$

